Snapshots

Literature for Young Adults

EDITORIAL DIRECTOR   Julie A. Schumacher
SENIOR EDITOR   Gay Russell-Dempsey
SENIOR WRITER   Sheri Reda
EDITORIAL ASSISTANT   Suzanne Foggia
PERMISSIONS   Meghan Schumacher
DESIGN   Mary Ann Lea Design
PRODUCTION   H&S Graphics

TEACHER REVIEWERS   Mary Gershon, Platteville Middle School, Platteville, Wisconsin
Vikki Proctor, Martin Luther King Experimental Laboratory School, Evanston, Illinois

STUDENT REVIEWERS   Students from Ms. Proctor's 7th- and 8th-grade classes, Martin Luther King Experimental Laboratory School, Evanston, Illinois
Nicole Portela, W. C. Young Middle School, Pembroke Pines, Florida

The Editors and Designer would also like to thank Kathleen Fischer and the students of Morton East High School in Cicero, IL; Lawrence Ware and the students of Evanston Township High School in Evanston, IL; Deborah Zaire and the students of Lake Forest High School in Lake Forest, IL; Michael Baruch and the students of Barat College, Lake Forest, IL; and the young people from Mumbai, India; Mexico City, Mexico; Cape Town, South Africa; and Los Angeles, California; whose work was commissioned by the Getty Conservation Institute; for the photographs that so skillfully enhance the selections in this anthology.

7 8 9 10 11 12 RRD 13 12 11 10 09 08
Paperback ISBN 13: 978-0-7891-5939-7
Paperback ISBN 10: 0-7891-5939-2
Hardback ISBN 13: 978-0-7569-9952-0
Hardback ISBN 10: 0-7569-9952-9

MANY VOICES LITERATURE SERIES

Snapshots
Literature for Young Adults

PERFECTION LEARNING

Table of Contents

UNIT SIX
Postcards from Beyond

Life in the Middle

■■■■

Adults sometimes think that kids have it easy—no job to get to, no debts, and no major responsibilities. But you know that's not the real picture. You have a job all right—to attend school and learn all you can. You may not have the same concerns that adults have, but you do have concerns, and many young people today feel an overwhelming sense of responsibility to their friends, their schools, and their families.

They also worry about what the future holds—never mind getting through one more day in the present. Most students your age feel lost and confused now and again. "Who am I and where am I going?" you may ask. Finding out is an important part of growing up.

We have gathered the selections in this book with your life in mind—your hopes, your dreams, your fears, your interests, your happy times, and your sad times, too. We have chosen stories and poems written by the finest authors of our time—people who understand the human condition and delight in sharing their interesting perspectives with readers your age. They know that becoming an adult is not an easy journey. You will encounter dead ends, rough roads, and washed out bridges. But you will also experience the exhilaration of the wind in your hair and the sun in your face.

Your life right now may not always be what you'd like it to be, but at least on a good day, it should be exciting, challenging, and educational. It should offer you the chance to be creative and adventurous—and to get to know yourself a little better, too. We hope you enjoy what you read in the pages to come, and that your reading helps you better understand your "life in the middle."

Active Reading
What Is It and Why Is It Important?

■■■■

Reading is a lot like sports. Both require practice and a good understanding of the rules. In both you have a goal, either to reach the finish line or to finish the last line. And both demand active participation. Of course reading does not leave you sweaty and exhausted like a good game of soccer, but it does require lots of activity—mind activity. Like a good athlete, a good reader must be on his or her toes, ready at all times to spring into action.

That is what Active Reading is all about: Jumping into your reading with both feet, getting involved, being a part of the action, and relating to the characters. The chart below will help you understand, remember, and use the Active Reading strategies. If you train yourself to use these strategies every time you read, they will become second nature to you. Soon, you will be using them without being aware of them. You will become a skilled reader who learns efficiently and enjoys reading.

The Six Active Reading Strategies

■ **Questioning**   Ask questions that come to mind as you read.
   Example: *The first little pig built his house of straw, what will the second little pig use?*

■ **Predicting**   Use what has happened to guess what will happen next.
   Example: *The Big Bad Wolf is going to huff and puff and blow the stick house down, just as he did the straw house.*

■ **Clarifying**   Clear up confusion and answer any questions you may have.
   Example: *The wolf blew down two houses, but does he really think he can also blow down a brick house? Yes. He tries, but fails.*

■ **Connecting**   Compare the text with something in your own experience or with other things you have read or seen.
   Example: *I think that the wolf has met his match. If I were the wolf, I would leave this third pig alone.*

■ **Summarizing**   Review what has happened so far.
   Example: *The wolf has been able to blow down a straw and a stick house, but not the brick house of the third little pig. He is now going to climb down the third little pig's chimney.*

■ **Evaluating**   Use evidence in the selection as well as your common sense to form opinions and arrive at conclusions.
   Example: *The story of the wolf and the three little pigs is a good example of using the right materials to combat disaster.*

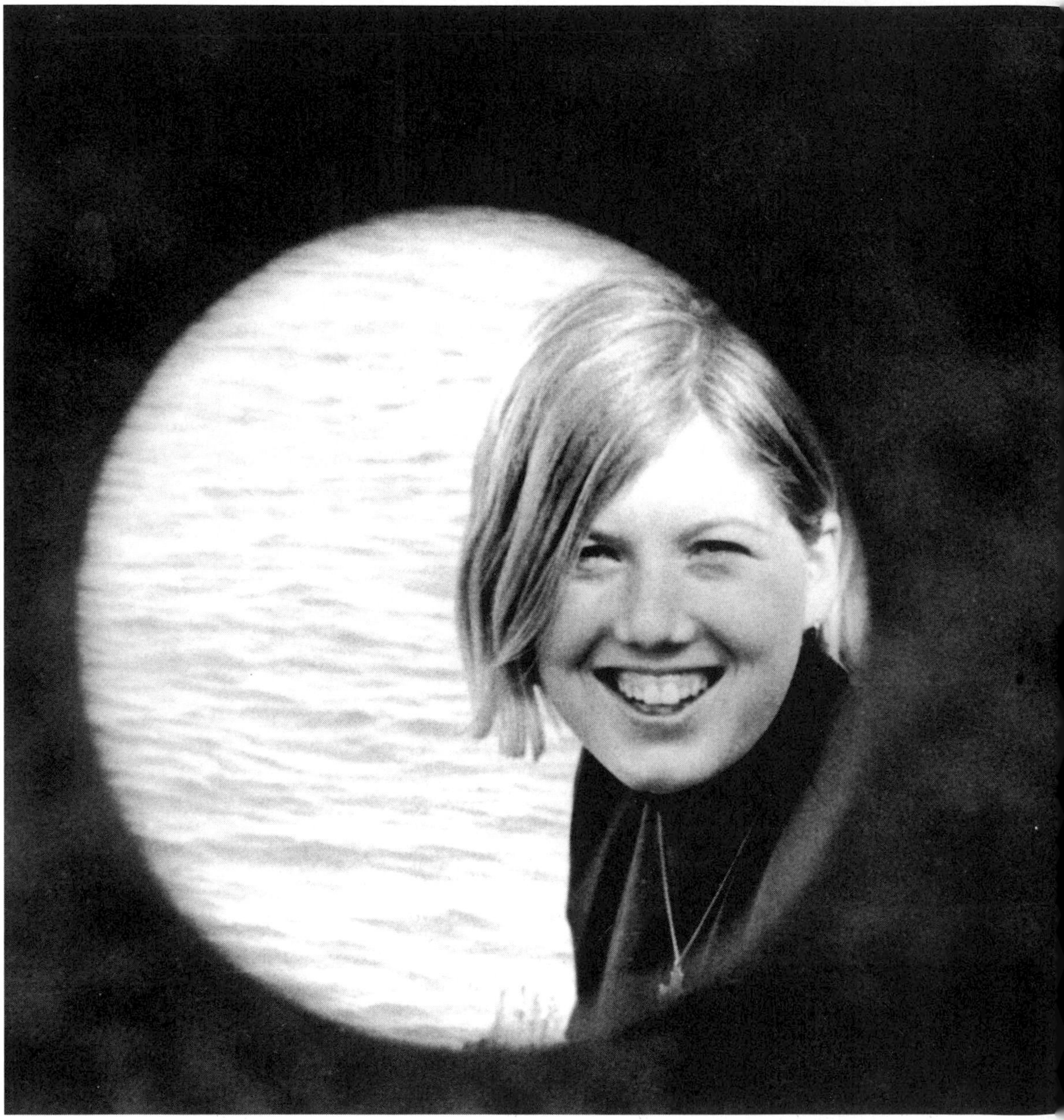

Self Portrait

*. . . I have to start trying to figure out who
I am and where I want to go . . .*

from "The One Who Watches"
by Judith Ortiz Cofer

Active Reading Alert!

QUESTIONING

Ask yourself questions as you read the selections
in this unit. Questioning helps you stay alert to
your reading. As your initial questions are
answered, new ones will arise, and you will
become increasingly involved in the
unfolding events.

Dear Marsha

Judie Angell

Dear Anne Marie,

I guess this letter is probably a big surprise to you... I mean, you probably looked at the return address and sign-off and all and saw that it's from nobody you ever heard of, right? Well, here's the reason I'm writing.

Maybe you remember this assignment that the kids in our English class got back in February. Our teacher (Ms. Bernardi, maybe that rings a bell) wrote to your English teacher and she asked him if he'd like to do this experiment: He would send a list of all the kids in your class with their names and addresses and we would pick those names out of a hat and write a letter to the name we picked. See, you all lived far away and the idea was to see if we could form a "relationship" (Ms. Bernardi grew up in the sixties) with a perfect stranger, using only pen and paper. (Or typewriter, I mean, YOU know.) Anyway, Ms. Bernardi said she wasn't going to grade the assignment, or even see it or anything because this assignment was personal, just for ourselves. You know, to "express ourselves" with a perfect stranger. Whatever. So naturally, if it didn't mean a grade or anything, I didn't do it.

But the thing is—I picked your name out of the hat and I just sort of kept it, you know, and now it's summer and hot and practically all of my friends are away, so... Here's a letter. You're a stranger even if you may not be perfect (or maybe you are perfect, I don't know), but here I am, trying to form this "relationship" using only two fingers on the typewriter (please excuse the mistakes, I'm taking Business Typing next semester) and you're the one I'm supposed to try it with.

Well, I'm not going to say anything more until I hear back from you—Hope you turn out to be cool.

Your new pen pal (maybe)
Marsha

LITERARY LENS

Judie Angell once wrote that growing up is so hard "some of us never get there." Remember this quote as you read the following story and poem.

July 18

Dear Marsha,

Your letter was great! It really picked up a slow summer for me.

I remember that assignment. Some of the kids really got into it when they got letters from your class and they're still writing back and forth. The friendships are terrific because everybody feels safe with them, you know? I mean, because we're so far away no one knows anyone the pen pal knows. And since you never have to meet, you feel freer to say whatever you want with no one coming down on you or whatever, you know.

So I'm glad you wrote and I'm also glad it's now instead of then, because back in Feb. I was really WIPED, I mean really. See, my dad died, it wasn't sudden or anything, he was sick a long time, but still it was very hard on everybody as you can probably figure out. So now it's just my mom and my sister and me and . . . we miss Dad, so sometimes we get on each other's nerves.

I guess if you wanted me to be the first one to give out personal stuff I guess there's that. Plus . . . let's see. . . . If you're thinking about "m-e-n," I don't go out a whole lot, but there's one guy I like at school. The thing is, he's YOUNGER than I am and I get embarrassed about that and since he doesn't even know I like him . . . I guess you can't count it as a "relationship." (That word bugs me too.)

I hope this is enough for you to think that maybe we could be friends, and I like the idea of a pen pal.

From
Anne Marie

July 21

Dear Ann Marie,

You are DEFINITELY the coolest person! I couldn't wait to hear back from you, so I'm writing you the same day I got your letter.

I'm sorry about your dad. That must be tough to deal with. I mean, I have both of my parents and it never occurred to me that one of them could die. I know that sounds stupid, but I just never thought about it. They're okay most of the time, but really, I guess I just take them for granted, to be honest about it.

So now I'll tell you more about myself.

I'm a senior in high school, or at least I will be starting September. Which is okay, because the sooner I graduate the sooner I can start My Life. My dad says I could go to college if I want. (HE'S the one who really wants me to go), but I'm not sure I could stand all that much school. I'm thinking about it more this summer, though, because I have this job at our local five-and-ten as a checkout girl and if anything is bor-ing, that is IT! Here's what you get: "Mar-sha, last week you had green grosgrain[1] in the sewing department and now it isn't there, why NOT?" And—"Mar-sha, you took ten minutes extra for lunch yesterday and it came off MY time, so you better come back ten minutes early today." That kind of stuff. Borrrr-ing.

Okay, well—I'm five feet five inches tall, which is about average, I guess, and I have black hair which in this weather I wear either in a chignon[2] (sp.?) or in a ponytail. It's pretty long and straight and I guess it's my nicest feature. I'm a cheerleader and I think my hair looks good flopping up and down when I jump. (I'm not really as **conceited** as that sounds!) Also I have brown eyes and no more BRACES. I'm pretty thin, which isn't too great when you wear a bathing suit. What do you look like? I picture Anne Marie as a blonde.

I don't have a boyfriend right now, although there's a very nice guy who works in the stockroom at the five-and-ten. Hmmm . . . maybe. . . .

Most of my friends got jobs at resorts and hotels in the mountains. I should have applied to one of them but as usual I was late and lazy, so here I am, bored at the five-and-ten. Write soon.

Your friend,
Marsha

conceited
having too high an opinion of yourself

---

1 **grosgrain:** [grō′grān] a closely woven silk or rayon cloth, often used for ribbons
2 **chignon:** [shēn′ yan] a knot of hair worn at the back of the head

Dear Marsha,

Boy, do I know what you mean about boredom! I'm working part time at my school—office stuff, and the rest of the time I'm at home because my mom and sister really need for us all to be together. Your town sounds like the same kind of hick burg mine is. You have one movie house and it's just got around to showing talkies, right? And: one Laundromat, a drugstore (NO BARE FEET, THIS MEANS YOU), a post office, and if you're real lucky, one of those no-alcohol bars for kids to hang out in on weekends.

One nice thing here, though—there is a lake we can go to. In fact, our family has always had a cabin there. It's called Lake Michigan, which was someone's idea of a joke because it's more of a pond than a lake and it has a lot more brambly woods than pond. But this summer no one in my house seems to have the energy for going up there a lot.

I'm a little shorter than you—five two exactly—and I do have blondish-brownish hair that's short and curly. I always wanted long black hair like yours. You sound really pretty and I bet that guy in the stockroom notices you pretty soon! I used to wear glasses but I got contacts finally and I think I look better now. Wish I had more to write but I don't, so let's hope things start to get more exciting for both of us!

Love,
Anne Marie

Dear Anne Marie,

It took me a while before I could write again. It's not that I didn't want to, but some stuff happened and I've been kind of scared and depressed ever since.

What happened was, this girl at work—she's the one I was kidding about in my last letter, the one who whines about my coming back late from lunch. Her name is Claudia and we **alternate** shifts. Anyway, when I realized she was actually counting every one of my lunchtime minutes, I started coming back really on time, you know? Sometimes, even early. Well, last week when I relieved her, I counted up the **receipts** and the money in the register and stuff and it seemed to me that I was coming up short. The receipts and the money didn't check out, you know? But I figured it was me, I must've done something wrong. I mean, my math is hardly the greatest. So I let it go and when Claudia came back at four o'clock, I told her to check it out. So she did and said I was wrong and dumb and everything was okay and blah, blah, blah. But the next thing I know, Mrs. Handy, the manager, started checking everything between shifts because she said we were losing some money.

Listen, I won't drag this on, but **accusations** were thrown around and Claudia accused me of stealing. That was when I caught on that she was the one who was stealing and I knew that one time I got back too early for her to be able to hide it.

Well, of course she said I was the one and since it was her word against mine and she's a full-time worker and I'm only part time and no one noticed any shortage before I got there—naturally I got blamed. I wasn't arrested or anything because no one could prove I did it, but I did get fired. And as you put it so well, this IS a hick burg, and I stand about as much chance of getting another job as I have of spreading wings and flying away. Which I'd sure like to do. I really didn't steal, Anne Marie. I hope you believe me. The cute boy in the stockroom sure doesn't. You should have seen the look he gave me.

So . . . things got exciting for a while, anyway.

Love,
Marsha

alternate
to take turns

receipts
written account of money taken in from sales

accusations
charges made of wrongdoing

August 5

Dear Marsha,

I got your letter and broke into tears, I swear I did. Of course I believe you didn't steal anything. But they will find out eventually. Claudia won't stop stealing and I bet she does the same thing with the next person they hire and they will all catch on.

I feel so bad for you, I don't know what to say. After I read your letter I told my mom and sister that I just had to get away for a while, so I took the bus up to our cabin and that's where I am now. I'm sitting on the porch and looking out at (ha-ha) Lake Michigan and thinking about you. People can be so mean. But I bet there are lots of people in the town who know you well enough to know it was all a lie and will be glad to hire you.

It's so peaceful up here, really. Just about an hour and fifteen minutes north of my house, but it feels like another world. Wait a minute, Marsha. . . .

You won't believe it! I'm back now, but I had to go inside and close the windows and doors and spray everything with Lysol! While I was sitting there describing all the peace and quiet, this SKUNK marches right up on the porch and lets me have some of what skunks do best! YUUUUCH! This is just AWFUL, did you ever get a whiff of skunk? They say tomato juice takes the smell away, but I don't have any and what are you supposed to do, bathe in it or what? PEEEEW!

So I'm sitting here in this locked cabin wondering which smells worse, the Lysol or the skunk or the mixture of both, and thinking of you.

Love,
Anne Marie

August 10

Dear Anne Marie,

Your letter gave me the first good laugh I've had in a while! I'm still laughing because I think I can smell that combination of stuff you mentioned on the pages of the letter! You can't even imagine how much I wish I had a place to go like Lake Michigan (without the skunk!) but we're pretty far from any quiet place with water and woods. I mean, there's a pool at the town recreation center, but that's not exactly what I had in mind. The closest I can get to coolness and peace and quiet is my basement, but THAT smells of cat litter and Clorox, ALMOST as bad as your place!

Well, my mom and dad believe I didn't take any money or anything else, but it's hard for them because everyone they know heard about what happened. And so when people say, "Oh, Marsha, wasn't that awful, we just KNOW you'd never" and all that, I somehow get the feeling they're really thinking Maybe she did, you know these kids today. . . .

Anyway, tell me something good to cheer me up. Your letters are the only nice thing to happen this whole stinking summer—NO PUN INTENDED!

Love,
Marsha

August 16

Dear Marsha,

I hope by the time this gets to you that you're feeling better. I want you to know I really do think about you all the time.

Maybe this will cheer you up a little. . . . Did you ever have a carnival come to your town? Our firehouse sits on a tract of land of about twelve acres and every year they put on a really terrific carnival. Picture this: There's a high booth on wheels with a glass window where you can watch a boy spin pink cotton candy around and around. Close your eyes now, and you can smell it, all sickly sweet and gorgeous, and you can make mustaches and beards and eyebrows and earrings all over your face with it, you know? And they also have this huge plastic bubble, all different colors, with a foam bottom and you can go in there and jump your heart out. You fall over a lot, of course, but you don't get hurt even if you fall on your face because it's so soft. And there are these booths where you can throw baseballs at little Indian teepees and win neat stuff like plush polar bear dolls and clock radios and blow-dryers with three speeds and makeup mirrors and everything. And best of all is the Ferris wheel, because they stop it for a few minutes when you get to the top, and it's like you really are on top of the world. So picture yourself on top of the world and that's where you'll be.

That's where I was last night. And when I got to the top I thought about you and made a wish, so I know things will get better soon for you.

And also, guess what? At the shooting gallery, guess who I met? That younger guy I told you about. And we went on the Whip together. And I'm going back tonight, so . . . who knows?

Love,
Anne Marie

Judie Angell

August 20

Dear Anne Marie,

I have read your letter about eight hundred times. Where you live sounds so great. I pictured the carnival. I really tasted the cotton candy. I won a stuffed bear. I rode on the Ferris wheel with you and I think the "younger man" is cute. I liked being on top of the world, even if it was only for a few minutes.

Things here only seem to be getting worse. One of my girlfriends is back from her hotel job and you wouldn't believe how she sounded on the phone when I called her up. I feel like everyone's looking at me whenever I walk down the street.

Now I'm seriously starting to think about college, if only to get away from here. My dad says he's sorry it took something like this to get me thinking about it, but he's glad I am, he says. A blessing in disguise, he says. Ha, some blessing! But even if I do go to college, I still have a year of high school left and I honestly don't know how I'm going to stand it.

Tell me something else to smell and taste and ride on.

Love,
Marsha

August 25

Dear Marsha,

I think it's neat you're thinking about college. If you're lucky enough to be able to go, I really think that's what you should do. It's just my opinion, but that's what I think.

Marsha, did you ever see kittens being born? You have NEVER seen anything so incredible in your whole life! My Y-M (younger man) works at his dad's carpentry shop in the summer and they have this mama cat who was about to give birth and he asked me if I'd like to watch. Well, it took from six o'clock to around ten. The mama had a litter of seven kittens, and they came out two, two, one, and two, over all those four hours. They each came out wrapped in a shiny silver cover, which the mama licked up and ate. I know it sounds really gross, but it was honestly beautiful. Their teeny eyes were shut tight and they made these little squeaky noises and they looked at first as if they had no fur, but they do. Y-M says I can have one.

Keep thinking about college and you'll see how quickly the year will go.

Love,
Anne Marie

September 1

Dear Anne Marie,

It's Labor Day weekend and I'm spending it crying. The cheerleading squad is meeting Tuesday, the day before school starts, and I'm "not welcome" on it anymore. I got the word straight from the captain herself. "Oh, I don't believe any of it, Marsha," she says, "but you know how people think of cheerleaders, they're supposed to represent the school's highest standards" and blah, blah, blah! "I know you'll sacrifice," she says, "for the good of the school." Right. Can you BELIEVE it? Anne Marie, it's SO not fair!

Well, I can't handle it, Anne Marie, I really can't. I just can't spend an entire year at school like this. So I've made this decision, and I just know being the kind of person you are and with the kind of family you say you have, that you might be happy about it. This decision, I mean.

I know my mom and dad are on my side, but they're not, you know, the same as a FRIEND or anything. And this summer, I guess you know that you became my very best friend.

I want to be where I can sit on top of the world on a Ferris wheel and watch little kittens being born and chase skunks away from a cabin porch. And spend all my time with a true friend, who's sensitive and caring and growing up with the same kinds of feelings I have. That stupid school assignment was the best thing that ever happened to me, Anne Marie, and I know I'm dragging this out, but here's my idea:

Could I spend the year with you? I swear on my own life I won't be any trouble, in fact, I'll be a help. With your dad gone, I can help make up for the work he did around the house. I'm very handy, I really am, I can do all kinds of things.

And best of all, we could go to school together, and do our homework together, and sit up nights and talk, and bake stuff and double date and go to the prom and make Senior Year everything it's supposed to be! And I'll bring my tapes—I bet I have the best rock and roll tape collection you ever heard!

Don't you think it would be great? Don't you? School's starting next week, Ann Marie. . . . Please let me know. . . .

Love,
Marsha

WESTERN UNION

Received at : **NIGHT LETTER TUES SEPT 5**

DEAR MARSHA—YOU MUST STAY IN SCHOOL, RIGHT THERE IN YOUR OWN TOWN—IT WILL BE HARD, VERY HARD, BUT YOU MUST DO IT—REMEMBER, YOU DIDN'T DO ANYTHING WRONG AND THEREFORE YOU MUST NOT RUN AWAY—YOU MUST NEVER LET STUPID AND CRUEL PEOPLE GET THE BEST OF YOU—I AM SURE YOUR MOM AND DAD HAVE TOLD YOU THE SAME—HOLD YOUR HEAD UP AS HIGH AS YOU CAN AND GIVE THAT CHEERLEADING SQUAD A GOOD RASPBERRY—

MARSHA, I CANNOT TELL YOU HOW SORRY I AM FOR THIS—MY NAME WAS NOT SUPPOSED TO BE INCLUDED IN THAT LIST YOUR TEACHER RECEIVED FROM OUR TEACHER—SOMEONE MUST HAVE PUT IT IN AS A JOKE—BUT I DIDN'T MIND BECAUSE YOUR FIRST LETTERS WERE SUCH A JOY THAT I SIMPLY HAD TO ANSWER THEM IN KIND—THEN WHEN YOUR TROUBLE BEGAN, ALL I WANTED WAS TO MAKE YOU FEEL BETTER—MARSHA, I HOPE YOU WON'T MIND THIS—I HOPE IT DOESN'T MAKE ANY DIFFERENCE TO YOU—I HOPE WE CAN CONTINUE TO WRITE AND BE FRIENDS—

DEAR MARSHA, MY DAD DID DIE LAST WINTER AND I DO LIVE WITH MY MOTHER AND SISTER—THEY ARE EIGHTY-THREE AND SIXTY-THREE, **RESPECTIVELY** — I'M THE PRINCIPAL OF OUR SCHOOL AND I'M SIXTY-ONE YEARS OLD—

ALL MY BEST LOVE, ANNE MARIE

respectively
each in the order mentioned

Hanging Fire

Audre Lorde

I am fourteen
and my skin has betrayed me
the boy I cannot live without
still sucks his thumb
in secret
how come my knees are
always so ashy
what if I die
before morning
and momma's in the bedroom
with the door closed.

I have to learn how to dance
in time for the next party
my room is too small for me
suppose I die before graduation
they will sing sad melodies
but finally
tell the truth about me
There is nothing I want to do
and too much
that has to be done
and momma's in the bedroom
with the door closed.

Nobody even stops to think
about my side of it
I should have been on Math Team
my marks were better than his
why do I have to be
the one
wearing braces
I have nothing to wear tomorrow
will I live long enough
to grow up
and momma's in the bedroom
with the door closed.

LITERARY LENS

*What images from the
story and the poem help
you visualize some of the
difficulties in growing up?*

Golden Glass

Alma Villanueva

*I*t was his fourteenth summer. He was thinning out, becoming angular and clumsy, but the cautiousness, the old-man seriousness he'd had as a baby, kept him contained, ageless and safe. His humor, always dry and to the bone since a small child, let you know he was watching everything.

He seemed always to be at the center of his own universe, so it was no surprise to his mother to hear Ted say: "I'm building a fort and sleeping out in it all summer, and I won't come in for anything, not even food. Okay?"

This had been their silent **communion**, the steady presence of love that flowed regularly, daily—food. The presence of his mother preparing it, his great appetite and obvious enjoyment of it—his nose smelling everything, seeing his mother more vividly than with his eyes.

He watched her now for signs of offense, alarm, and only saw interest. "Where will you put the fort?" Vida asked.

She trusted him to build well and not ruin things, but of course she had to know where. She looked at his dark, contained face and her eyes turned in and saw him when he was small, with curly golden hair, when he wrapped his arms around her neck. Their quiet times—undemanding—he could be let down, and a small toy could delight him for hours. She thought of the year he began kissing her elbow in passing, the way he preferred. Vida would touch his hair, his forehead, his shoulders—the body breathing out at the touch, his stillness. Then the explosion out the door told her he needed her touch, still.

"I'll build it by the redwoods, in the cypress trees. Okay?"

"Make sure you keep your nails together and don't dig into the trees. I'll be checking. If the trees get damaged, it'll have to come down."

"Jason already said he'd bring my food and stuff."

"Where do you plan to shower and go to the bathroom?" Vida wondered.

"With the hose when it's hot and I'll dig holes behind the barn," Ted said so quietly as to seem unspoken. He knew how to slither under her, smoothly, like silk.

"Sounds interesting, but it better stay clean—this place isn't that big. Also, on your dinner night, you can cook outdoors."

communion
exchange of thoughts and feelings

LITERARY LENS

As you read the story, note how Ted and his mother relate to one another.

His eyes flashed, but he said, "Okay."

He began to gather wood from various stacks, drying it patiently from the long rains. He kept in his room one of the hammers and a supply of nails that he'd bought. It was early June and the seasonal creek was still running. It was pretty dark out there and she wondered if he'd meant what he'd said.

Ted hadn't seen his father in nearly four years, and he didn't miss him like you should a regular father, he thought. His father's image blurred with the memory of a football hitting him too hard, pointed (a bullet), right in the stomach, and the punishment for the penny candies—a test his father had set up for him to fail. His stomach hardened at the thought of his father, and he found he didn't miss him at all.

He began to look at the shapes of the trees, where the limbs were solid, where a space was provided (he knew his mother really would make him tear down the fort if he hurt the trees). The cypress was right next to the redwoods, making it seem very **remote**. Redwoods do that—they suck up sound and time and smell like another place. So he counted the footsteps, when no one was looking, from the fort to the house. He couldn't believe it was so close; it seemed so separate, alone—especially in the dark, when the only safe way of travel seemed flight (invisible at best).

Ted had seen his mother walk out to the bridge at night with a glass of wine, looking into the water, listening to it. He knew she loved to see the moon's reflection in the water. She'd pointed it out to him once by a river where they camped, her face full of longing—too naked somehow, he thought. Then, she swam out into the water, at night, as though trying to touch the moon. He wouldn't look at her. He sat and glared at the fire and roasted another marshmallow the way he liked it: bubbly, soft, and brown (maybe six if he could get away with it). Then she'd be back, chilled and bright, and he was glad she went. Maybe I like the moon too, he thought, involuntarily, as though the thought weren't his own—but it was.

He built the ground floor directly on the earth, with a cover of old plywood, then scattered remnant rugs that he'd asked Vida to get for him. He **concocted** a latch and a door, with his hand ax over it, just in case. He brought his sleeping bag, some pillows, a transistor radio, some clothes, and moved in for the summer. The first week he

remote
far away; distant

concocted
made; invented

slept with his buck knife open in his hand and his pellet gun loaded on the same side, his right. The second week Ted sheathed the knife and put it under his head, but kept the pellet gun loaded at all times. He missed no one in the house but the dog, so he brought him into the cramped little space, enduring dog breath and farts because he missed *someone*.

Ted thought of when his father left, when they lived in the city, with forty kids on one side of the block and forty on the other. He remembered that one little kid with the funny sores on his body who chose an apple over candy every time. He worried they would starve or something worse. That time he woke up screaming in his room (he forgot why), and his sister began crying at the same time, "Someone's in here," as though they were having the same terrible dream. Vida ran in with a chair in one hand and a kitchen knife in the other, which frightened them even more. But when their mother realized it was only their **hysteria**, she became angry and left. Later they all laughed about this till they cried, including Vida, and things felt safer.

He began to build the top floor now but he had to prune some limbs out of the way. Well, that was okay as long as he was careful. So he stacked them to one side for kindling and began to brace things in place. It felt weird going up into the tree, not as safe as his small, contained place on the ground. He began to build it, thinking of light. He could bring his comic books, new ones, sit up straight, and eat snacks in the daytime. He would put in a side window facing the house to watch them, if he wanted, and a tunnel from the bottom floor to the top. Also, a ladder he'd found and repaired—he could pull it up and place it on hooks, out of reach. A hatch at the top of the ceiling for leaving or entering, tied down inside with a rope. He began to sleep up here, without the dog, with the tunnel closed off.

Vida noticed Ted had become cheerful and would stand next to her, to her left side, talking sometimes. But she realized she mustn't face him or he'd become silent and wander away. So she stood listening, in the same even breath and heartbeat she kept when she spotted the wild pheasants with their long, lush tails trailing the grape arbor, picking delicately and greedily at the unpicked grapes in the early autumn light. So sharp, so perfect, so rare to see a wild thing at peace.

She knew he ate well—his brother brought out a half gallon of milk that never came back, waiting to be asked to join him, but never daring to ask. His sister made him an extra piece of ham for his four eggs; most always he ate cold cereal and fruit or got a hot chocolate on his way to summer school. They treated Ted somewhat like a stranger, because he was.

Ted was taking a makeup course and one in stained glass. There, he talked and acted relaxed, like a boy; no one expected any more or less. The colors of the stained glass were deep and beautiful, and special—you couldn't waste this glass. The sides were sharp, the cuts were slow and **meticulous** with a steady pressure. The design's plan had to be absolutely followed or the beautiful glass would go to waste, and he'd curse himself.

It was late August and Ted hadn't gone inside the house once. He liked waking up, hearing nothing but birds—not his mother's voice or his sister's or his brother's. He could tell the various bird calls and liked the soft brown quail call the best. He imagined their taste and wondered if their flesh was as soft as their song. Quail would've been okay to kill, as long as he ate it, his mother said.

Instead, he killed jays because they irritated him so much with their shrill cries. Besides, a neighbor paid Ted per bird because he didn't want them in his garden. But that was last summer and he didn't do that anymore, and the quail were proud and plump and swift, and Ted was glad.

LITERARY LENS

How does Ted's relationship with his mother change after he decides to build and live in the fort?

The stained glass was finished and he decided to place it in his fort facing the back fields. In fact, it looked like the back fields—trees and the sun in a dark sky. During the day the glass sun shimmered a beautiful yellow, the blue a much better color than the sky outside: deeper, like night.

He was so used to sleeping outside now he didn't wake up during the night, just like in the house. One night, toward the end when he'd have to move back with everyone (school was starting, frost was coming and the rains), Ted woke up to see the stained glass full of light. The little sun was a golden moon and the inside glass sky and the outside sky matched.

In a few days he'd be inside, and he wouldn't mind at all.

Tiffany

as told to Rebecca Carroll

presume
suppose something is true without proof

LITERARY LENS

As you read, think about how Tiffany sees herself in her school setting. Compare her feelings to those of the speaker in the poem.

hat I'd like to say to black girls in America is that it's okay to be who they are and to express what they want to express. And what I'd like to say to white people in America is that I am not offended by their prejudices; if they want to **presume** that I am offended, then I'm going to presume that it is not my responsibility to educate them in any sort of detail.

My neighborhood is black. I've lived in white neighborhoods, too, and I've been the only black girl in a crowd of white kids. But I've never seen any reason to feel bad about it. There's nothing to feel bad about. In fact, I feel kind of special when I'm the only one. I feel like it's me against the world. I think it's silly to try and look for an experience that has made me feel different or has made me think that my struggle is harder than white people's struggle. You just gotta know who you are, and if you don't know, you can't look anywhere else but inside yourself.

For me, it is very important to have black friends. I have one good, close black friend at school. I also have white friends, but the fact is, if we are talking about something that might be considered "black," like a certain rap group or the language a rap group might use, my white friends are not going to understand, which is fine; they don't have to. Everyone is so upset that black people and white people don't all eat, sleep, and breathe the same everything, but if we did, we'd be in big trouble. I don't feel like I have to explain something like rap music to my white friends. If they want to listen to it, too, that's all right, but I don't know why they would think that I need to or can explain what it's like to listen to rap music or how I feel about it. And you know they'll ask, too. They'll say, "What is rap music all about?" What am I gonna tell them? Well, it has good beats.

defensive
resisting attack; protective

I'm not **defensive** about the music I listen to and I don't really have a theory about it. But I have seen some videos on television that make me wonder about some of the music I listen to, like Snoop Doggy Dogg.[1] I think he's crazy offensive and I really don't understand why any woman would actually agree to be in his videos knowing that they're going to be **exploited** like they are. I don't want or need those women to be role models for me, but they do need to

exploited
selfishly used for profit or gain

---

1 **Snoop Doggy Dogg:** a rap artist popular in the 1990s, later called Snoop Dogg

Rebecca Carroll

think about what they're doing to themselves and the message they are sending to young people. It's a shame, but if you are black in this society and you have the opportunity to be in front of millions of people, you need to pay attention to what you're doing and how you're doing it, especially if you are a female. It's bad enough that everything on the news talks about black females always being pregnant and on welfare. What's the difference between that and the black females actin' a fool in Snoop Doggy Dogg's videos?

The school I'm at now is good. I went to a much bigger and more diverse school before starting at this one. It hasn't been the easiest transition, but I'm doing all right. I know it's a good opportunity for me. I like my classes and have some good teachers. I like science the best, partly because I have a good teacher who takes the time to explain something if I don't understand and partly because I love that science is all about discovery. We do fun and exciting things in class, like go on scavenger hunts where we have to find and identify certain kinds of plants and stuff. I haven't decided what I want to be when I grow up. It's too early, I think, but I know I want to do something that involves discovering ideas and inventing things.

There are no black teachers at my school. The only black adults are the custodians. And that does have an impact on the students, I think. It would be nice to have even one black teacher at the school so that students, both black and white, could see that black people can be teachers, too and not just custodians. And also I think it would be important for the black students to be taught from the perspective of a black adult, not necessarily because there is a "black" way of teaching, but I know that it would be nice to feel like a teacher is talking to me and in some way understanding how I feel about certain things.

I'm not as concerned with black history as I am with black present. I think about black history sometimes, but I feel like it's more important to have the present be good for us. I don't have to think about black history to feel proud. I am *proud* today. I have a really solid family, which I feel lucky about. My mom is the kind of woman who cares a lot about people but doesn't ever go so far as to lose sight of herself. My dad and I are really close. He's a fireman. I haven't gone with him to any fires yet, but I think I will one day. I worry about him sometimes, but then I'll sit down and have a talk with him and feel better. We can talk about anything. He's always there for me. I think his most admirable quality is that he's weird. You know, he's not afraid to do anything at all—I mean anything. He is really fearless.

I have one older brother and he goes to a larger, more diverse school than the school I go to. I think being black means something different for boys than it does for girls, I think for boys everything rides on being tough and being cool. And being cool doesn't include hanging out with white people at all, as in the thought doesn't even fit into the picture. Somehow it seems like black girls can be more comfortable around white people. I don't know why, although I'm sure there's a reason. I just know that there are real serious pressures for black boys in society today and I try not to mess with it too much.

I have close white girlfriends at school. They're close, but not *real* close. There is a fine line between close and real close, but I guess what it really comes down to is trust. And see, it's the same with the way I feel about being black; I don't think about it; I just know. With my white friends, I don't think about being close or real close, I just know that there is a difference between being close and real close. For example, I take karate, and I am the only black girl in the class. See, I don't feel like an outcast because I'm pretty good at karate. But then again, one time I was at a karate tournament and I scored the highest on my team as well as against the other team who was white. But the first-place trophy was given to another girl on my team who was white. I was mad, but it's almost like I know things like this are going to happen and it takes a lot of courage to keep getting up and moving on. When you just know things, there isn't a whole lot of time or really much use in trying to figure out why they are what they are.

I claim the right to be Tiffany and Tiffany is many things. I claim the right to play basketball, study science, do karate, listen to rap music, love my parents, be as loud as I please, and have an attitude that separates me from everyone else. My attitude can be all that or real chill, but whatever it is, it's mine. And if anyone has a problem with that, they can speak to me directly.

Rebecca Carroll

Time Somebody Told Me

Quantedius Hall, "Son of Reality," age 12

Time Somebody Told Me
That I am lovely, good and real
That I am beautiful inside
If they only knew
How that would make me feel.

Time Somebody Told Me
That my mind is quick, sharp
and full of wit
That I should keep on trying
and never quit.

Time Somebody Told Me
How they loved and needed me
How my smile is filled with hope
and my spirit sets them free
How my eyes shine, full of light
How good they feel when they hug
me tight.

Time Somebody Told Me

So, I had a talk with myself
Just me, nobody else
'cause it was time
Somebody Told Me.

LITERARY LENS

*What do Tiffany and the
speaker in the poem have
in common? How are they
different?*

Jared

David Gifaldi

$\mathcal{E}$arly for his appointment, Jared walked the paved trail beside the converted house that was the clinic. Normally the parklike setting with its bank of alders and tiny creek below helped him to relax before going in. But today even the playful antics of a pair of ducks couldn't take his mind off the slip of paper in his pocket. He wished Ryan hadn't given him the paper . . . hadn't clapped him on the back and said, "She's all yours," with that knowing wink. Ryan was supposed to be his friend. You'd think the big jerk would know better. Know that the mere thought of meeting girls made Jared feel as if he were hanging from some window ledge—forty stories up—fingers already starting their slide.

"Ryan," he breathed, his face beginning to throb with the pain that was always just below the surface now. Reaching up, he doffed[1] the floppy-brimmed felt hat that had become his protection from the eyes of the world and wiped the wet from his forehead. He was at the place where the path became dirt, curving to the footbridge that led to the apartments across the way. He didn't hear the woman and the little girl who rounded the curve together. His eyes met the woman's for only an instant before **veering** down to the girl's. He could see the girl's lips . . . how they'd already begun to shape themselves into a *Hello*. Then stopped. He turned as abruptly, jamming the hat back on and looking to where the ducks were spinning and bobbing like well-oiled wind-up toys. Behind him he could hear the woman's soft hushing. Footsteps moving away with increased speed. The little girl's voice was all the louder for the quiet of the trees.

"But, Mommy, what happened to that boy's face?"

■■■■

The waiting room was set up to be calming. Framed landscapes on the walls, classical music . . . a thick, cushiony, blue carpet. The receptionist's name was Beth, an older college student with a ready smile who always looked at Jared straight on.

"Hi, kid," Beth said, looking up from a textbook. "How's it going? Don will be a few minutes yet. Need a cup of java?"

"Naw. I think I'll go it alone this time."

LITERARY LENS

Consider what Jared is afraid of as you read, and evaluate how he deals with his fear.

veering
swerving; changing direction

---

1 **doffed:** removed

He hadn't meant to be funny, but Beth cracked up. Jared had to admit it felt good to hear her snorty laugh. He took a seat in the corner near a plant that was almost a tree and picked up a *New Yorker*. Thumbing the pages, he was aware of the paper still stuffed in his pocket, wondering if he would share it with Don or chicken out.

He'd gotten through a half-dozen cartoons, none of which were that great, when the fat woman who preceded him every Tuesday suddenly sailed in from the hall. Usually the woman came out red-eyed and clutching a fistful of tissues. But today she was tissueless and beaming. Sometimes it was that way for Jared, too. When a session went particularly well, he'd come out feeling light as a fluff ball . . . like one of those dandelion things you chased as a kid. The feeling would last for as long as he could keep from looking into a window or seeing his reflection in a mirror. Two or three days if he was extra careful.

"Hi, Jared," Don called from the doorway. "Be just a sec. Go ahead back."

Soft murmurs issued from the closed doors along the hall. Jared walked to the end, entered Don's office, and threw himself into the overstuffed chair by the window. Don came in a moment later, tall and gray-haired—a cup of coffee in hand—and closed the door behind him before taking the leather chair opposite. Setting the coffee on the side table, he checked his calendar book, folded his glasses into their case, eyed the little clock only he could see, and leaned back, giving Jared the look that said, *Ready when you are.*

This was the hard part . . . starting. Sometimes whole clumps of time would go by with Jared staring out the window or tracing the intricate designs of the Oriental rug with his eyes. Don never began the sessions. It must be what he learned in Shrink School . . . something about letting the patient make the first move. Jared thought it was a bunch of bull. He hated that initial silence during which he felt like a laboratory specimen, severed and laid out, his every move and expression open for study.

"I've never seen you without your hat."

Jared jerked alert, thinking it impossible that Don had spoken first. "What?"

"I said, you've been coming here twice a week for almost three months now, and I've never seen you without your hat."

Jared tugged the hat even lower over the right side of his face. He knew he could leave. Get up, say good-bye, and be gone. Don had always said there were no rules. He could hop the bus and get home early . . . throw something together for dinner before his mom got home. Or walk. He liked walking now that it was getting darker earlier. Liked the dark.

"There's this girl," he said suddenly, surprised to hear the urgency in his voice. His gaze swept the room, leaping over Don, before skidding to a stop on the rug. He had his right thumb hooked in the pocket of his jeans, fingers moving over the paper within.

"I don't know her or anything. I mean, I know her name and I've seen her once, but I don't know her. Ryan met her at the mall. She was with some friends . . . girls. They all go to Franklin, the next school over. And Ryan and Jeff and Mark introduced themselves. I was—around. You know . . . I didn't want to blow their chances. So I stayed out of sight and watched to see if the guys scored."

"Scored?"

"Not in that way. To see if the girls would give them the time of day . . . if they were interested."

"And were they?"

"Yeah. They did a lot of gabbing and got on real good. Even had Cokes together at Friendly's. You could tell they were having a good time—" His voice cracked, so he cut it off.

"And how did that make you feel?"

Don's standard line. Jared pictured a building collapsing and Don being the first on the scene, moving from corpse to corpse: *How did that make you feel? . . . How did that make you feel?*

"I felt awful. I mean, I felt okay at first, seeing as how Ryan and the guys were scoring. Then I felt awful."

Jared's left eye had already learned to compensate for the right, which had been narrowed and pulled askew by the last surgery. His left now traced the bars of color in the rug, following the staircase design . . . down, over, down, over. There were shapes and patterns in everything, he thought. Even the spaces between shapes were shapes if you looked hard enough. He'd found a whole zoo of animals in the hospital ceiling after the accident. It was a textured ceiling. Textured, bumpy surfaces were best for finding things. Surfaces discolored and scarred and sewn together. Just that morning he'd found the Big Dipper in the mirror while brushing his teeth. Each star a white blotch on a raw, pink picket sky. He wondered if the doctors played the shape game during the skin grafts. Using his face for a game board.

Don's eyes remained steady and expressionless. Jared squirmed, slouching lower and flinging his leg over the chair's armrest.

"You see, this one girl . . . Megan . . . the one Ryan hit it off with . . . She was beautiful. Not in the magazine way or anything. But really sharp." He shook his head. "It's hard to explain . . . the way she . . . you know . . . walked, moved. She smiled a lot, too. Only the smiles were real, not like some girls. I could just tell she was nice. Really nice. Not just cute-and-cool nice. But *really* nice. And afterward Ryan said she was. Said I'd really like her. And—"

He stopped, knowing he'd reached that familiar place of self-pity. He could feel the warm, black ooze trying to suck him under.

"Why weren't you with the boys?" Don said. "They're your friends, aren't they?"

Jared set his jaw. "You know why I wasn't with them. They were trying to impress girls. To score. They didn't need someone tagging along who would scare the girls away or make them sick."

"So you decided you'd only be a negative in this affair."

"Not just a negative. I'd blow the whole thing."

"I see. So you let the others introduce themselves and they had a good time and you stayed off by yourself, mad as hell. And that's it?"

"What do you mean, is that it?"

"Well, it doesn't sound much different from how you usually react to meeting new people."

"It's different! Because—" He yanked the paper from his pocket. "Because later on they all traded phone numbers, and today Ryan said it was too bad in a way that he and Stephanie were getting back together because he had that phone number of the girl at the mall. Megan. The nice one. The one I'd asked him about. And he gave it to me. Gave me the number."

He felt like an idiot holding his fist up in the air like that, his heart racing and his breath coming hard, as if he were about to lead some troops into battle. Lowering his hand, he shoved the paper back in his pocket.

David Gifaldi

"Are you gonna call?"

Sometimes Jared thought he could make a better therapist than Don. Don could be so thick. "What kind of a question is that?" he asked.

"Just a question. Are you?"

"Am I *what*?"

"Gonna call this girl . . . this Megan?"

"No!"

"Because you're afraid she might . . . what?"

"Because if I call and say you don't know me but I think you're nice and could we go out sometime and she says yes—what then?"

"You could go out?"

"And scare her to death when she opens the door?"

"How many people have died from looking at you?"

It wasn't even worth answering. Died? . . . None. Sure. But how many had been repulsed? How many had looked away or stared with wrinkled faces like it was painful to see? One little boy had even screamed. Screamed right there in the library where he'd been playing under Jared's table. The kid had popped up, giggling, his little teeth suddenly slicing into his lip before letting go with a scream that brought half a dozen people racing over.

"I'm a creature feature," Jared spat. "A regular Phantom of the Opera. An elephant man."

"You're nothing of the sort," Don said. "You're scarred. From an accident. You were burned. And the marks are there. But it's getting better. You'll have more surgery. You'll . . ."

But of course Jared had heard it all before, and he closed himself off. Sealed himself into a box of silence. The same box he closed around himself in school or at home when his mind threw up the white flag of surrender, pleading for **respite** from the hell of mirrors and murmurs and pitying expressions. Inside the box the walls were smooth and dark and comforting—the air warm and fluid and only slightly **fetid**. He stayed there in the safe and the dark and the quiet. Until Don's voice came through like a shoulder-nudging wake-up call: "I'm afraid our time is up for today. We'll see you next time."

■ ■ ■ ■

respite
a period of temporary delay or relief

fetid
stinking; foul; smelly

It was one of those hurried dinners—toasted cheese sandwiches and canned lentil soup. Picking up on Jared's mood, his mother waited till they were finished before asking about the session.

"I'm tired of going," Jared said. "Twice a week for how long? It's a waste of money. You could save yourself a bundle. I want to quit anyway." He cleared off their plates and slid them noisily into the sink.

"You can't quit," she said. "You promised you'd give it six months. It was part of the deal."

Jared **scoffed**, but he knew it was true. It had been his idea to move. His mother's company had an office in Salem, and she had agreed to apply for a transfer only if Jared promised to enter therapy. At the time he was sick of his old classmates and friends offering their gloomy expressions of pity while keeping a safe distance away, as if he had some contagious disease. He thought a clean break would be good. He was sorry now. It was even worse being both a freak and a stranger. Having no history. He wanted to put a sign around his neck. *Hi, my name is Jared Wheatley. I wasn't born this way. I even thought I was someone once. Liked baseball and girls and even school sometimes . . . believed I was slick and smart and the rest of it. But that was before the nightmare. Before a ball of fire ate up half my face.*

If a person was still interested, he could turn the sign over, sweeten their curiosity with some real gore: *How, you want to know? Excuse me for smiling. It was a barbecue. That's right. A good old-fashioned barbecue. A cookout. Ever hear of a sixteen-year-old knocking over a can of gas into a fire? . . . Trying to save a plate of stupid hot dogs from tipping and elbowing over a can of gas he should never have been using anyway? Ever smelled your own skin burning? Felt your face sliding from side to side? But I go on. Here, give me your hand. Glad to meet you.*

His hand moved outward and he brought it back quickly, embarrassed that his daydreams were becoming so real. It would be something to discuss with Don. Right up his alley. Fantasy versus reality. Jared saw the look of sadness in his mother's eyes, the look that said, *I know how it is.* But she couldn't. How could she? "I'm going upstairs," he said, hurrying past her.

In his room the music, the homework, nothing could take his mind off the paper with Megan's number. On the bus ride home he'd taken the paper from his pocket and smoothed it some before slipping it into his geometry book. Now he took it out, placing it on

David Gifaldi

the desk before him, intrigued by the bold letters, the purple ink, the way the sevens in the number were crossed European style so that they looked like *7*s.

The phone was in plain sight. On the dresser across from him. A sleek, black number with a green-lit dial pad. His mother had bought it for him after the move to encourage him to be more social. The phone was another waste of money as far as Jared was concerned. The only person he ever called was Ryan, and him hardly at all since they lived so close. Not that there was a whole lot to talk about even with Ryan. The two hadn't even a single class together at school. Ryan had befriended Jared because they were neighbors. One of Jared's worst fears was that Ryan had been instructed by his parents to be nice to the new freak down the street.

He left the desk lamp on low and flicked off the overhead so the room would be darker. The dresser's mirror was mostly covered with posters and magazine pics—action shots of cars, baseball players, skiers, and board sailors. A small square of mirror had been left uncovered—too high to see into without standing on your toes. A bit of insurance against accidentally scaring himself.

"Megan."

He let the name drop off his lips, watching his mouth move, his tongue curl. He stood on tiptoes, his left side facing the glass, amazed at how perfect that side was. He said the name again, trying for just the right stress. The music coming from the radio had suddenly softened. A ballad of some sort. Soft and intimate, like he imagined Megan's voice would be.

The ringing drummed deep in his ear. He wondered when he had picked up the phone. How he had pressed the numbers so quickly. Was he nuts? Put the damned thing down before—

"Hello."

And again. "Hello."

A girl's voice. He cleared his throat. "Megan?"

"Yes, who's calling, please?"

He paced to the center of the room and had to dive back to catch the phone before it toppled off the dresser.

"This is Jared . . . Jared Wheatley . . . You don't know me."

There was a pause. Then, "Hey, is this a prank call? Or one of those obscene things?"

"NO . . . This is a good call . . . I mean, I'm a friend of Ryan's."

"Do I know a Ryan?" She said it almost to herself and Jared could see her brow furrowing beneath her thick bangs, a finger poised at her lips.

"You met him at the mall in front of Friendly's the other day... Saturday."

"Oh, yeah . . . How come this isn't him then?"

The heat shot from his neck to his face, needle points of pain flashing on and off. "Because Ryan isn't available," he said. "I mean, see, he's going steady with somebody and—"

"And you're his friend and he gave you my number, thinking I was up for grabs by whoever happened to have the ability to dial? Get a life, Jared whatever-your-name-is . . . I'm not for sale *or* hire."

"Don't! Don't hang up! It's not like that. I mean, Ryan's a good guy. He wouldn't think of anyone like that."

"But you would."

"No, I just saw you with him and—"

"You were one of the other guys?"

"No, I was . . ." *Hiding.* "Working . . . working at the restaurant . . . behind the counter."

"Do you lie often?"

"Huh?"

"I wasn't born yesterday. You've got lie written all over your voice."

"Listen," he said, pressing now, scared. "I just called to say hi and to say I think you're . . ." *Neat—no, that's sick.* "I mean, I thought you were . . ." *Beautiful?—too much.*

He felt like a four-year-old on the verge of tears. "Megan, I'm sorry. It was all a mistake. Good-bye."

Crumpling the paper, he flung it hard against the wall. *You're a dork*, he told himself. *A first-class freak of a dork.*

■■■

The box of silence stayed tight and tamperproof throughout the next day. He was a **nonentity**, a ghost floating to and from classes. After school he walked until the cold November night settled in, forcing him home. It was the hanging up that upset him the most. Such a coward's way.

nonentity
nobody; someone or something of no importance

44   David Gifaldi

After dinner he retreated to his room. Made a stab at completing some homework. Actually got halfway through a play that had been assigned for English before realizing he had no idea what the play was about. Frantic, he searched until he found the paper wrapped in dust, stuck behind the leg of his desk. Tearing the ball open, he lunged for the dresser, finger flying over the green-lit pad before his mind had a chance to say no.

"Megan?"

"Are you the same kid from last night?"

His tongue refused to move.

"I thought you might call back."

"You did?"

"Yeah, you sounded desperate."

"Oh, I'm not desperate . . . Just wanted to be friends."

"With a perfect stranger?"

"I'm sorry for last night . . . I mean, for hanging up. I don't usually act—"

"Let's hope not," she cut in. "It's Jared, right?"

"Yes."

"You wanna talk? Is that why you called again?"

"Please." It sounded **wheedling** and he wanted to take it back, but she gave him no time.

"Might not be a bad idea," she said. "My parents are glued to the tube and I'm bored stiff since they never let me out midterm week. I guess even if you are an ax murderer, you can't do much damage over the phone. Go ahead, shoot."

■■■■

"We talked for over an hour!" Jared told Don the next day.

"I still can't believe it. School, parents, likes, hates, sports . . . you name it. It was so easy!

"It's perfect, don't you see," he added. "We can be friends over the phone. She said to call again tonight. She likes to take things real slow when it comes to boy-girl stuff. I told her I was the same. It's perfect."

"You should be proud of yourself," Don said. "For taking the plunge. Look at what you would have missed."

It was true, Jared thought. For the first time in so long he felt

wheedling
coaxing in a whining way

free. Wondrously, gloriously free. Later over dinner his mother asked who he'd been talking to the previous night. "It was past eleven when I turned off the light and you were still yapping away."

"Mom, I can't talk about it yet. I mean, it's good. But I'm a little nervous about it. You won't feel bad if I play this one close to my chest for a while, will you?"

"Play it however you like. I'm just glad to see you so happy. You seem like a new person. Like the person—

"No," she said. "That's not what I mean. You're just fine with me, up or down . . . any old way. I just want the best for you." Her eyes were moist. "You've been through a lot."

Jared turned away, afraid that he might get teary, too. His mother had stuck with him through all of it. He knew it was joy she was feeling now, but tears were tears and he didn't want to start blubbering. You start crying, and you never know where it might lead . . . might lead right back to the unanswerable. Questions like *Why me?* and *How could such a thing happen?*

"Your hair is growing out some," she said.

Jared's hand swung up to touch the stubs over his right ear. The doctors had said it was still too early to tell if the follicles there had been overly damaged by the fire. He thought he'd noticed the bristles moving out some, but was afraid it might just be wishful thinking.

"You really think so?"

"I know so," she said. "Here, let me see."

But he couldn't bring himself to let her touch him. He felt naked enough having to reveal his ugliness to her every day from a distance. He couldn't stomach the thought of having her really look, up close like that. It wasn't only his vanity. It was also that he knew how much she hurt for him, and he didn't want her to hurt. So he made a face, crinkling up his nose, and asked if she was wearing a new perfume.

"Same old stuff," she said, smiling.

He nodded. "Always liked that one."

■ ■ ■

Friday night. Saturday night. Sunday. Monday. Tuesday. Wednesday. Jared called each night at ten. He and Megan were so good together. There was never a lack of things to talk about. The only subject off limits for Jared was the accident. And anything to do with his looks.

Megan tried to press him on the looks issue only once, but it was clear from the way he suddenly clammed up that he didn't want to talk about it, and she let it go. "It's even better this way," she said. "I can picture you any way I want."

"So when are you going to ask her out?" Don asked on Thursday.

"We haven't talked about it. She seems to like it this way, too. She likes to take things slow. She's shy. I told you that." There was a tremor in his voice and his stomach went queasy. "I mean, sooner or later, sure, we'll have to meet. But she doesn't appear to be in a hurry and—"

"And you still haven't discussed the accident?"

"Why do you have to ruin everything?" Jared shot.

"Am I ruining everything?"

"What if I don't want to meet her? What if we're both happy just the way it is? I think you should just stay out of it."

"Even if I think you might be making a mistake?"

"You always said there are no mistakes. Just opportunities for learning and all that. Now you're telling me I'm making a mistake."

"I just think it's best to be honest."

"Yeah, well, you don't know everything. Things are fine, okay? Just fine."

And they were, Jared's nightly phone calls sometimes stretching until midnight. The two of them . . . exploring, discovering, teasing, flirting, laughing. Until week three. Friday. A note of impishness to Megan's voice. "What size shoe do you wear?"

"What?"

She giggled. "What's your shoe size?"

He couldn't help a giggle himself. Her sunny way was always infectious with him. "Eight and a half, I guess. Why?"

"'Cause I'm putting together a composite."[2]

"A what?"

"A composite . . . of you. I figure if you give me your shoe size, waist and inseam measurements, neck and pecs and head . . . then I'll be able to figure out what you look like."

"Forget the numbers," he said. "I can describe it all in three words—tall, dark, handsome."

---

2 **composite:** a combination of essential characteristics

"Mmmm," she said. "But my reception must be off. I can't tell if you're fibbing or not."

"Mom always said I was cute as a button," he said. "Does that help?"

"Nope, moms don't count. Godzilla thought her baby was cute, too."

He felt suddenly nauseous, his gaze pitching from desk to bed to floor, desperate to locate a new topic.

"If you must know, I'm dying with curiosity over the whole thing," Megan said. "I mean, I probably know you better than any boy I've known in a long time. But my mental image keeps fuzzing up... changing. Won't it be exciting to meet?"

"Sure."

"Sure." She mimicked the **lackluster** tone of his voice. "You don't sound excited at all."

lackluster
dull; commonplace

"No, I am. I mean, it'd be great to really meet you. It's just that I thought we could maybe hold off for a while longer."

"Why?"

"Because—"

"See. No reason whatsoever. That settles it then. We can meet tomorrow. At the mall. Afternoon would be best, then it wouldn't be like a heavy thing . . . you know, no pressure-filled Saturday-night thing. We could just meet in front of Friendly's and have a Coke or something. Sound good?"

"Yeah . . . sure . . . except I think tomorrow is when Mom wanted me to—"

"Uh-uh," she said. "My antennae are working loud and clear now. I told you I could spot a lie a mile off. Your social calendar is about as full as mine for tomorrow. Which translates to *free*. Nope. It's tomorrow, all right. How's two sound to you?"

His insides felt raked.

"Good," she said when he didn't answer.

They talked some more. Or rather, Megan did. Jared had to hang on the best he could. He hadn't planned on this. Hadn't planned on it at all. He wished now he'd taken the possibility more seriously with Don. Don would tell him everything would be all right. It was another of Don's standard lines. He could use a standard line right then. Something familiar. Something known—like that TV jingle he liked so much. The one he'd sung to himself in the hospital when the pain tore at him. No words. Just a tune. On TV the music was accompanied by pictures of trees and mountain trails. *La-la-laaa . . . la-laa-la.*

"I guess you're just not in a talkative mood tonight," Megan said, finally.

"Not really."

"Well, we'll have plenty of time tomorrow. See you then, my mysterious friend."

■■■■

He lay in bed, humming the *la-la* tune, trying to stop his stomach from whirling. His face was hot, the heat pricking its way down to his neck and chest. When the sweat came, he tore off the covers and lay naked except for his shorts. He couldn't figure out why he was thinking of his dad. His dad who had left so suddenly when Jared was only ten. Even years later, Jared had had a hard time bringing himself to go down to the basement of the old house alone. The basement had been his dad's **domain**. It was where they had built things together. Where they'd set up Jared's train set . . . an American Flyer with forty feet of figure-eight track complete with tunnels, bridges, and a water tower that stood over a foot high. He wondered now if he had ever really forgiven his dad for dropping dead like that. Dead at the age of thirty-seven. People said it was unheard of. Didn't happen to a healthy young man with a wife and a son and everything to live for.

domain
an area owned or controlled by someone; territory

Wearily, he got up, stumbled out to the hall . . . made his way to the bathroom, where he fell to his knees over the toilet and purged the snakes from his stomach.

"Jared?"

"It's okay, Mom. Go back to bed."

"Are you sick?"

"No. Go back to bed."

"Take a pain pill if you need it."

"I'm all right."

He rinsed his mouth and swallowed a capful of Listerine, letting his eyes focus on the face in the mirror. On the three rectangular slabs of skin sewn one below the other. They looked like farm fields seen from a plane far above—fields tied together with barbed wire and cut by irrigation streams flashing gray and purple and white.

Slamming the light switch, he returned to bed. The wringing in his stomach had stopped. And he slept, dreaming of himself as a young boy. Seeing himself running and laughing and calling out to his cousins behind his grandmother's barn. "Ready or not," he could hear himself saying. And he went out looking for them, only to discover they were running away . . . farther and farther from him. They weren't hiding at all. Just running. Looking back with frightened faces. He ran till he could run no longer, then dropped to the ground, crying out for them to stop, crying for his father to stop them from running, yelling how unfair it was as the dream took a turn . . . The young boy suddenly transformed to that of one older. Himself at sixteen. Shrieking. Stumbling. Arms flailing. His mother sobbing as she cradles his toweled head in her hands. The hurt like nothing he has ever experienced. So that he must hum. Hum the *la-la* jingle. Wonder where his father is as his mother rocks him in the pulsing, stench-filled dark of the towel.

■■■■

It was past eleven the next morning when he woke. After showering from the neck down, he washed his hair in the sink and daubed at his face with the special towelettes that smelled of menthol. Pulling on a clean pair of jeans, he spent a good ten minutes deciding on a shirt, choosing in the end his light blue pinstripe, freshly pressed. Gently, he fingered some cream onto his face, a cosmetic that dulled the streaks of color and paled the lumpy ridges. Or was supposed to. He didn't check long enough to make an assessment . . . just looked to see he hadn't left any gobs.

Downstairs he poured himself a cup of coffee, slurping it quickly while telling his mother he needed to pick up a few things at the mall.

"I'll be leaving soon, myself," she said. "I've got a million little errands to run . . . I could drop you off if you want."

"No," he replied much too loudly. "I mean, thanks, but I want to walk."

On the way the wind stung coldly and he turned up his jacket collar and lowered the brim of his hat, quickening his pace even though he knew he was early. He wondered if Megan was as nervous as he . . . if she'd taken extra care in deciding what to wear... if her parents knew about their meeting . . . if she'd swallowed that tall, dark, and handsome line. It didn't matter. He probably wouldn't go through with it anyway. Didn't have to. He could back out anytime. Breeze right past her. A stranger. Cool and anonymous.

Once inside the mall he headed to the sunken area of benches down from Friendly's. It was from here that he had watched Ryan and Megan and the others the first time. The benches were laid out to look like a maze. About eight benches in all, with vinyl cushions and tiled backs. He chose the bench in the middle, farthest from the walkways on either side. Here he sat, hunkered into his jacket, his hat angled low over his face, eyeing the currents of shoppers, his gaze darting regularly to the restaurant.

He gasped audibly when he saw her exit one of the smaller boutiques. Stopping to check the time, she slung the colorful canvas carryall higher over her shoulder before crossing to the restaurant with the somewhat embarrassed look of one who knows she may be being watched. Still, she looked confident. And beautiful. More beautiful than he had remembered. He got a kick over the fact that she was wearing her dad's Chicago Cubs jacket, the one she'd talked about. The jacket swung open as she walked, revealing a classy Western shirt with silver tips on the collar and big silver buttons. Reaching Friendly's she turned, eyes sweeping the mallway in either direction.

Jared froze up. He was a block of ice sitting there on the bench, only his mind working. He had no right, he thought. No right to put her in this kind of a situation. Don was right. He should have been honest with her from the beginning. It wasn't fair to have someone get to know you . . . for you to draw someone into liking you without telling them your biggest flaw. His mind swerved back to Don. What was it Don had told him so often? To go with his gut? But his gut said to run. Was that it? Was that what he was feeling? Yes. Scared. Scared, pure and simple.

He saw Megan check the hanging clock above. Watched her smile when she saw a little girl try to play hopscotch on the large marble floor tiles . . . the smile giving way to a look of disapproval when the girl's mother yelled and yanked the child back, causing the girl to break into a soft cry.

Reined in, Jared thought. Whenever something good happens, there's always someone or some god-awful thing that happens that pulls you back. Snuffing out what was good. Leaving sadness and resentment and pain. So that you have to find a way to go on. Find a place where there are no surprises . . . no more hurts. He wondered if the little girl was finding a way even then. Her crying had stopped, her tiny face suddenly hard as stone as her mother whisked her past the benches. Was she building a box? Making a place where the yanks and the scorn and the put-downs could never enter?

Abruptly, he got up. Megan would have to discover for herself what a creep he was. Someone who would make a date and then cop out. A creep. Better a creep, he thought, than to be discovered with his face put together with slabs of skin from his nether parts. *Forget it,* he said to himself.

He was a fish swimming upstream against the rush of incoming shoppers, taking one last look at her before reaching the door. In the vestibule beyond the inner doors was a crowd of young people, laughing and talking. Jared felt their stares when he pushed open one of the doors. Heard their conversation **dwindle** to almost nothing. It wasn't just the smoky air and the closed-in feeling that make him retch[3] . . . made him turn and throw his shoulder into the glass, the door bursting open so that he was back inside, nearly bowling over a group of exiting shoppers in his rush for the wall. It was his gut. Speaking so loud it almost picked him off his feet. Saying, *No, no, no!*—the same as it had when the fireball hit. Spinning on his heels, he ran into two women loaded down with shopping bags . . . mumbled an excuse . . . went quickly on, his stomach in knots, heart fluttering like some chained bird under his shirt. He knew it now. How it was the box that his gut was crying out against. The box . . . with its sour air and aloneness and dark. His gut like a prisoner wrongly accused, saying *no* to the silence . . . the shame . . . the invisible **oblivion** of the box.

Megan was looking the other way when he came up to her. Looking for him. For Jared. The voice over the phone. The child running and laughing and playing. The boy. The almost man. The kernel that was Jared and would always be.

Pulling off his hat with one hand, he flicked his hair with the other.

---

3 **retch:** gag as if to vomit

dwindle
shrink; gradually decrease

oblivion
the state of being forgotten; obscurity

"Megan?"

She turned quickly.

The initial look of delight and anticipation would be forever engraved in his mind.

"It's me," he said, leading with his gut. "Jared."

 THE POET'S PERSPECTIVE

Almost Ready:

Arnold Adoff

I	as
am	this
going	cool
to	and
her	in-
birth-	control
day	young
party	dude:

as	as	as	as
soon	soon	soon	soon
as	as	as	as
I	I	I	I
find	find	find	find
my	my	my	my
new	hip	deep	right
shirt,	shoes,	voice,	mask.

LITERARY LENS

What do you think is Jared's biggest fear? Does the speaker in the poem have a similar fear?

The One Who Watches

Judith Ortiz Cofer

"*M*ira! Mira!"[1] my friend Yolanda yells out. She's always telling me to look at something. And I always do. I look, she does. That's the way it's always been. Yolanda just turned sixteen, I'm six months younger. I was born to follow the leader, that's what my mother says when she sees us together, and it's true.

It's like the world is a deli full of pricey treats to Yolanda, and she wants the most expensive ones in fancy boxes, the ones she can't afford. We spend hours shopping downtown. Sometimes when Yolanda gets excited about an outfit, we go into the store and she tries it on. But the salespeople are getting to know us. They know we don't have any money. So we get chased out of places a lot. Yolanda always yells at the security man, "I've been thrown out of better places than this!" And we have.

LITERARY LENS

As you read the following story, pay attention to Doris's feelings about Yolanda.

One time Yolanda and I skipped school and took a bus into the city—just because Yolanda wanted to look around the big store on Thirty-fourth Street. They were having a teen fashion show that day, for all the rich girls in New York and their overdressed mothers. And guess what? Yolanda sneaked into one of the dressing rooms, with me following her, and she actually got in line for one of the dresses being handed out by all these busy-looking women with tape measures around their necks who called all the girls "honey" and measured their chest, waist, and hips in about thirty seconds flat. Then this guy in a purple skintight body suit screeches out, "Hey, you!" and I nearly pass out, thinking we had gotten caught.

"Those earrings are monstrous!" he screams at Yolanda, who's wearing pink rubber fish earrings to match her pink-and-black-striped minidress.

"Here, try these!" He hands her a set of gold hoops in a very fancy black velvet box; then he screams at another model. I go into a dressing stall to hide and Yolanda runs in and sits on my lap, laughing her head off.

"Mira, Doris, mira." She shows me the earrings, which look like real gold. I hug Yolanda—I just love this girl. She's crazy and will try anything for fun.

I help Yolanda put on the dress she says she's going to model. The price tag inside says $350.00. It's my turn to say "Mira" to

---

1 **Mira!**: Spanish for "Look!"

Yolanda. She shrugs.

"I ain't gonna steal it, Doris," she says. "I'm just gonna walk down that runway, like this." She walks out of the dressing room with one hand on a hip, looking like a real model in a green velvet dress, gold earrings, and her white sneakers. The man in the body suit runs up to her, screaming, "No, no! What do you think you're doing? Those shoes are monstrous!" He waves over one of the women with measuring tapes around their necks and has her take down Yolanda's shoe size. Soon I'm helping her try on shoes from a stack as tall as I am. She decides on black patent leather pumps.[2]

There's such confusion back there that Yolanda doesn't get caught until the girls are lined up for the show to begin. Then nobody can find Yolanda on the list. She really does a good job of acting offended at all the trouble. I think it's her New Jersey Puerto Rican accent that gives her away. The others talk with their noses way up in the air, sounding like they have a little **congestion**.

"Whaddaya mean my name ain't there?" Yolanda demands, sticking her nose up there in orbit too.

I just stand to the side and watch everything, pretending that it's a play and Yolanda is the star. I promise myself that if it gets too dangerous, I'll just slip out. See, I'm not flashy like Yolanda. I'm practically invisible. My hair is kinky, so I keep it greased down, and I'm short and plain. Not ugly, not beautiful. Just a nothing. If it wasn't for Yolanda, nobody would know I'm around. She's great, but she scares me, like the modeling thing at the store. I have enough problems without getting arrested. So I tell myself that if the police come, I'll just make myself invisible and walk away. Then I'd be really alone. If Yolanda knew how scared I really am, she'd leave me anyway. Yolanda always says that nothing scares her except scared people. She says she hates a snitch worse than anything, and that's what scared people do, she tells me. They blame others for their troubles. That's why she dumped her last best friend, Connie Colón. Connie got scared when her mother found out she'd been skipping school with Yolanda, and told. Yolanda gets a cold look in her eyes when she talks about Connie, like she wants her dead. I don't want Yolanda to ever look at me that way.

Anyway, a big bossy woman came to lead us to her office on the

congestion
too much mucus in the nasal passages or chest

---

2 **patent leather pumps:** woman's dress shoes with heels, made of glossy leather

Judith Ortiz Cofer

top floor. It was bigger than my bedroom and her desk was at least the size of my bed. There was a rug under our feet that was as thick as a fur coat. From her window you could see most of New York. She looked at Yolanda with an expression on her face like I see on people walking by street people. It's like they want to ask them, "What are you doing on *my* sidewalk?" The lady didn't even look at me, so I glued myself to the gray wall.

"Young lady, do you realize that what you did today could be considered a crime?" She spoke very slowly, sounding out each word. I guess she knew by now that we were Puerto Rican and wanted to make sure we understood.

Yolanda didn't answer. They had made her take off the velvet dress, the shoes, and the earrings. The woman who carried them out with her fingertips put them in a plastic bag before handing them to this woman in front of us now.

Holding up the plastic bag in front of Yolanda, she asked another question: "Do you know how much money the things you took are worth?"

I watched Yolanda get up slowly from tying her shoestrings. She put on her pink fish earrings next without any hurry. Then she straightened out her tight skirt. She still looked offended. And maybe like she wanted a fight.

"I wasn't stealing your *theengs*," she said, imitating the woman's uptown accent.

"Then what were you doing in our dressing room, trying to disrupt the fashion show?"

"No. I was going to model the dress." Yolanda put her hands on her hips as if daring the woman to argue with her.

"Model? You wanted to model clothes *here*?" The woman laughed. "Young lady—"

"My name is Yolanda." Yolanda was getting angry, I could tell by the way she made her eyes flash at the woman, like a cat getting ready to pounce. It was strange to watch Yolanda, who is barely five feet tall, facing off with this big woman in a gray suit and high heels.

"All right, Yolanda. Let me tell you something. You can't just decide to be a model, sneak into a dressing room, and go on a runway. These girls have been to modeling school. They have been practicing for weeks. Did you really think you could get away with this?" She was sounding angry now. I edged toward the door. "I'll tell you what. I'm not going to turn you in. I'm going to have our security guard escort you outside. And I never want to see you in this store again. Look." She pointed to a camera practically invisible on the ceiling.

"We have pictures of you now, Yolanda." She finally looked over at me. "And of your partner there. If you come back, all I have to do is show them to the judge."

We were shown the way out to Thirty-fourth Street by the security guard, who looked just like any rich shopper in his wool sweater and expensive jeans. You never know who's watching you.

So Yolanda is telling the truth when she tells the store people that we've been thrown out of better places. She's always looking for a better place to get thrown out of. But the Thirty-fourth Street store may be hard to beat.

That same day we went up to the eighty-sixth floor of the Empire State Building—it's just down the street from the store. Yolanda went all around the viewing deck like a child, yelling out, "Mira! Mira!" from every corner. She was feeling good.

■■■

At home there is always salsa music[3] playing, but it's not because anyone is happy or feels like dancing. To my parents music is a job. They're both in a Latino music band called ¡Caliente![4] He plays the drums and she sings, so they're always listening to tapes. They play at the same barrio[5] club every night, the Caribbean Moon, and the regular customers want to hear new songs every week. So Mami sings along with the tapes, but she looks bored while she's doing it. Most of my life she stopped singing only to tell me to do something or to yell at me. My father doesn't say much. He's hardly ever around during the day; either he sleeps until the afternoon, since they play sets until three in the morning, or he goes down to the basement to practice his drums. The super of our building, Tito, is his best friend and lets Papi keep his drums in a storage room near the washers and dryers. Our apartment has walls thin and crumbly as old cardboard, and if he

---

3 **salsa music:** Latin American music that combines elements of rhythm and blues, jazz, and rock

4 **¡Caliente!:** Spanish for "Hot!"

5 **barrio:** a neighborhood where mostly Spanish-speaking people live

tried to play drums in it they'd probably crash around our heads.

My mother is singing along with Celia Cruz, the old Cuban *salsera*,[6] when I come in. She's at the stove, sautéing some codfish. I can smell the olive oil simmering, but I'm not hungry. Yolanda and I ate a whole bagful of butterscotch candy. She wouldn't tell me where she got it and I never saw her buy it, although I spent the whole day with her.

"*Hola*,[7] Doris, how's school?" my mother asks. But she doesn't look at me and she doesn't wait for me to answer. She just keeps on singing something about leaving the cold American city and going home to a lover in the sun. I stand there watching her; I'm feeling invisible again. The tape ends and she asks me where I've been, since school let out hours ago.

"New York."

She finally looks at me and smiles as if she doesn't believe me. "I bet you've been following that Yolanda around again. Niña,[8] I'm telling you that señorita[9] is trouble. She's trying to grow up too fast, sabes?[10] Mira…" Mami takes my chin into her hand that smells like oregano and garlic and other Island spices. She looks really tired. She's short like me and we look a lot alike, but I don't think she's noticed. "Doris, tonight is not a school night, why don't you come to the club with us and listen to some music?" She's asked me to do that once a week for years, but I'm not interested in hanging out at a cheap nightclub with a bunch of drunks. Besides, I'd have to sit in the back the whole time because I'm a minor. In case the police do a check—I can slip out the kitchen door. When I was little, I had to go with them a lot, and it wasn't fun. I'd rather stay home by myself.

I shake my head and go into my room. I put a pillow over my face so I won't hear the music and my mother singing about people in love and islands with beaches and sun.

I spend all day Saturday at Yolanda's. We have the place to ourselves because her mother works weekends. She believes in spiritism,[11] so there are candles everywhere with things written on

---

6 *salsera:* Spanish for "singer of salsa music"

7 *Hola:* Spanish for "Hello"

8 **niña:** Spanish for "girl"

9 **señorita:** Spanish for "young lady"

10 **sabes?:** Spanish for "do you know?"

11 **spiritism:** the view that spirits have the power to guide events in people's lives

altar
place used in religious worship

the glass jars like "For money and luck," and "For protection against your enemies," and "To bring your loved one home." She's got a little table set up as an **altar** with statues of *santos*[12] and the Virgin Mary, and a picture of her dead husband, Yolanda's father, who was killed during a robbery. Yolanda says she doesn't remember him that well anymore, even though it's only a couple of years since he died.

The place is stuffy with incense smells, and Yolanda tells me we are going shopping today.

"You got money?" I notice that she's wearing a big raincoat of her mother's. It's made of shiny bright green plastic and it has huge pockets. I start feeling a little sick to my stomach and almost tell her I'm going home to bed.

"I got what it takes, honey." Yolanda models the ugly raincoat for me by turning around and around in the small room.

We have to pass my apartment on our way out, and I can hear my mother singing an old song without the usual music tape accompanying her in the background. I stop to listen. It's "Cielito Lindo"— a sort of lullaby that she used to sing to me when I was little. Her voice sounds sweet, like she is really into the song for once. Yolanda is standing in front of me with her hands on her hips, giving me a funny look like she thinks I'm a **sentimental** baby. Before she says something **sarcastic**, I run down the stairs.

sentimental
having or showing much tender feeling

sarcastic
said in a bitter or sneering way

Yolanda is not just window-shopping today. She tells me that she's seen something she really wants. When we get to the store— one of the most expensive ones downtown—she shows me. It's a black beaded evening bag with a long strap. She puts it on over her shoulder.

"It's cute," I tell her, feeling sicker by the minute. I want to get out of the store fast, but I'm too weak to move.

"You really like it, Doris?" Yolanda unlatches the flap on the purse and takes out the crumpled paper in it. She reaches into her pocket for a fistful of candy. "Want some?" In one motion she has stuffed the little bag into her coat pocket.

"Yolanda . . ." I finally begin to feel my legs under me. I am moving back, away from the scene that starts happening really fast in front of me, as if someone had yelled "Action!" on a movie set. Yolanda is standing there eating candy. I am moving backward even

---

12 *santos:* Spanish for "saints"

Judith Ortiz Cofer

as she tries to hand me some. A man in a gray suit is moving toward her. I am now behind a rack of purses. I smell the leather. It reminds me of my father's drums that he used to let me play when I was little. Yolanda looks around, but she can't see me. I'm still moving back toward the light of the door. I know that I can't act scared, that I shouldn't run. People look at me. I know they can see me. I know where my arms are, where my legs are, where my head is. I am out on the street in the sun. A woman with a baby carriage bumps into me and says, "Excuse me!" She can see me! I hear a police car siren getting louder as I hurry across the street. I walk faster and faster until I am running and the world is going by so fast that I can't tell what anyone else is doing. I only hear my heart pounding in my chest.

When I crash through the door at home, Mami comes out of the bedroom looking like she just woke up from a deep sleep. I lie down on the sofa. I am sweating and shaking; a sick feeling in my stomach makes me want to curl up. Mami takes my head into her hands. Her fingers are warm and soft. "Are you sick, hija?"[13] I nod my head. Yes. I am sick. I am sick of following Yolanda into trouble. She has problems that make her act crazy. Maybe someday she'll work them out, but I have to start trying to figure out who I am and where I want to go before I can help anybody else. I don't tell my mother any of this. It's better if I just let her take care of me for a little while.

Even as she feels my forehead for fever, my mother can't help humming a tune. It's one I used to know. It's a song about being lonely, even in a crowd, and how that's the way life is for most people. But you have to keep watching out for love because it's out there waiting for you. That's the chorus, I mean. I keep my eyes closed until the words come back to me, until I know it by heart. And I know that I will keep watching but not just watching. Sometimes you have to run fast to catch love because it's hard to see, even when it's right in front of you. I say this to Mami, who laughs and starts really singing. She is really into it now, singing like she was standing in front of hundreds of people in Carnegie Hall,[14] even though I'm the only one here to hear her. The song is for me.

LITERARY LENS

How do Doris's feelings about Yolanda change? What does Doris come to realize about herself in the process?

---

13 **hija:** Spanish for "daughter"
14 **Carnegie Hall:** a famous recital hall in New York City

RESPONDING TO UNIT ONE
Self Portrait

REFLECTING

1. Which character in this unit do you think faces the greatest struggle in finding his or her true "self." Why?

2. Think about Marsha's problem in "Dear Marsha." If you were her classmate, how would you behave toward her, knowing what she was accused of?

3. Ted is eager to test his independence in the story "Golden Glass." In what way or ways can you assert your independence?

4. Tiffany states that she is not that concerned with black history. Do you agree with her? Explain.

ANALYZING

5. Each selection in this unit centers on at least one challenge a young person faces in developing a self-image. In a chart like the one below, identify some of the challenges. After you have completed the chart, write a few sentences telling how these challenges might prepare a young person for adulthood.

Selection	Character	Challenge faced
Dear Marsha	Marsha	
Golden Glass	Ted	*becoming independent*
Tiffany	Tiffany	
Jared	Jared	
The One Who Watches	Doris	

6. Many of the characters in this unit make personal discoveries that lead to self-awareness. Choose at least three characters and rate their self-awareness on a scale of one to five (one being lowest and five being highest). Explain why you ranked them as you did.

7. When Jared finally meets Megan, she turns to him with "a look of delight and anticipation." Then he says, "It's me, Jared." Does the author give you any clues as to how Megan will respond? Explain your reasoning.

8. Compare and contrast the language used in the poems "Hanging Fire," "Time Somebody Told Me," and "Almost Ready:." What words in each poem alert you to the age of the narrator?

9. **Active Reading** List three questions you asked while reading pages 51 to 53 of "Jared." How often did you remember to use this **questioning** strategy while reading other selections in this unit?

DISCUSSING

Imagine that a friend of yours did something that you consider wrong. Before confessing to the deed, the friend has made you promise not to tell anyone. Talk about what you would do once you learn the details.

WRITING

Sincerely Yours Marsha and her pen pal gained two kinds of benefits from writing to each other. They were able to think through events as they wrote them, and they were also able to hear a friend's point of view. Write your own letter to a friend, relative, or even someone you haven't met. Use the letter to think through a real or imaginary problem, develop an opinion, describe a frustration, or celebrate good news.

Journal Journey You can also gain insight into your own way of seeing things by keeping a journal or diary. The object of a journal is to write down the things you observe, hear, smell, touch, or taste, and what you make of it all. Start by jotting down the things you see while walking to school or the conversations you hear on the bus. Be sure to write something every day.

WORK IN PROGRESS

Here I Am Use both words and images to make a three-dimensional representation of yourself. Create a collage that tells the world what makes you who you are. When you are satisfied with your work, share it with your classmates.

The Once and Future Me What do you think you will be doing twenty years from today? What will you look like? Where will you be living? Create a drawing, sculpture, or piece of writing that represents you twenty years in the future.

Ready? Rap! Because it uses rhythm and repetition, "Almost Ready:" lends itself to performance as a song or rap. Develop a performance of this poem with your classmates in small groups or pairs.

Family Album

Our own talk at dinner was loud with belly laughs and marked by our pointing forks at one another.

from *"Looking for Work"*
by Gary Soto

Active Reading Alert!

PREDICTING

As you read the selections in this unit, keep guessing as to what will happen next. Predicting keeps you thinking about the plot, what the characters are up to, and where the author may take you next. As your predictions come true (or do not), you can make new predictions—right up until the end of the story.

Looking for Work

Gary Soto

One July, while killing ants on the kitchen sink with a rolled newspaper, I had a nine-year-old's vision of wealth that would save us from ourselves. For weeks I had drunk Kool-Aid and watched morning reruns of *Father Knows Best*,[1] whose family was so uncomplicated in its routine that I very much wanted to imitate it. The first step was to get my brother and sister to wear shoes at dinner.

"Come on, Rick—come on, Deb," I whined. But Rick **mimicked** me and the same day that I asked him to wear shoes he came to the dinner table in only his swim trunks. My mother didn't notice, nor did my sister, as we sat to eat our beans and tortillas in the stifling heat of our kitchen. We all gleamed like cellophane, wiping the sweat from our brows with the backs of our hands as we talked about the day: Frankie our neighbor was beat up by Faustino; the swimming pool at the playground would be closed for a day because the pump was broken.

Such was our life. So that morning, while doing in the train of ants which arrived each day, I decided to become wealthy, and right away! After downing a bowl of cereal, I took a rake from the garage and started up the block to look for work.

We lived on an ordinary block of mostly working-class people: warehousemen, egg candlers,[2] welders, mechanics, and a union plumber. And there were many retired people who kept their lawns green and the gutters uncluttered of the chewing gum wrappers we dropped as we rode by on our bikes. They bent down to gather our litter, muttering at our evilness.

At the corner house I rapped the screen door and a very large woman in a muu-muu[3] answered. She sized me up and then asked what I could do.

"Rake leaves," I answered, smiling.

"It's summer, and there ain't no leaves," she countered. Her face was pinched with lines; fat jiggled under her chin. She pointed to the lawn, then the flower bed, and said: "You see any leaves there— or there?" I followed her pointing arm, stupidly. But she had a job

mimicked
made fun of by imitating

LITERARY LENS

As you read, compare and contrast the family in the story with families you know.

---

1 *Father Knows Best*: a television show that aired from 1954 to 1962, depicting a picture-perfect family with a mother, a father, and three children

2 **egg candlers**: people who test eggs for quality

3 **muu–muu**: a long, loose dress with bright colors and patterns

for me and that was to get her a Coke at the liquor store. She gave me twenty cents, and after ditching my rake in a bush, off I ran. I returned with an unbagged Pepsi, for which she thanked me and gave me a nickel from her apron.

I skipped off her porch, fetched my rake, and crossed the street to the next block where Mrs. Moore, mother of Earl the retarded man, let me weed a flower bed. She handed me a trowel[4] and for a good part of the morning my fingers dipped into the moist dirt, ripping up runners of Bermuda grass. Worms surfaced in my search for deep roots, and I cut them in halves, tossing them to Mrs. Moore's cat who pawed them playfully as they dried in the sun. I made out Earl whose face was pressed to the back window of the house, and although he was calling to me I couldn't understand what he was trying to say. Embarrassed, I worked without looking up, but I imagined his **contorted** mouth and the ring of keys attached to his belt—keys that jingled with each palsied step. He scared me and I worked quickly to finish the flower bed. When I did finish Mrs. Moore gave me a quarter and two peaches from her tree, which I washed there but ate in the alley behind my house.

contorted
twisted and strained

I was sucking on the second one, a bit of juice staining the front of my T-shirt, when Little John, my best friend, came walking down the alley with a baseball bat over his shoulder, knocking over trash cans as he made his way toward me.

Little John and I went to St. John's Catholic School, where we sat among the "stupids." Miss Marino, our teacher, alternated the rows of good students with the bad, hoping that by sitting side-by-side with the bright students the stupids might become more intelligent, as though intelligence were **contagious**. But we didn't progress as she had hoped. She grew frustrated when one day, while dismissing class for recess, Little John couldn't get up because his arms were stuck in the slats of the chair's backrest. She scolded us when we knocked over the globe, denting the already troubled Africa. She muttered curses when Leroy White, a real stupid but a great softball player with the gift to hit to all fields, openly chewed his host when he made his First Communion; his hands swung at his sides as he returned to the pew looking around with a big smile.

contagious
spread from one person to another; catching

---

4 **trowel:** a garden tool used to smooth, shape, or dig

Gary Soto

Little John asked what I was doing, and I told him that I was taking a break from work, as I sat comfortably among high weeds. He wanted to join me, but I reminded him that the last time he'd gone door-to-door asking for work his mother had whipped him. I was with him when his mother, a New Jersey Italian who could rise up in anger one moment and love the next, told me in a polite but matter-of-fact voice that I had to leave because she was going to beat her son. She gave me a homemade popsicle, ushered me to the door, and said that I could see Little John the next day. But it was sooner than that. I went around to his bedroom window to suck my popsicle and watch Little John dodge his mother's blows, a few hitting their mark but many whirring air.

It was midday when Little John and I converged in the alley, the sun blazing in the high nineties, and he suggested that we go to Roosevelt High School to swim. He needed five cents to make fifteen, the cost of admission, and I lent him a nickel. We ran home for my bike and when my sister found out that we were going swimming, she started to cry because she didn't have the fifteen cents but only an empty Coke bottle. I waved for her to come and three of us mounted the bike—Debra on the crossbar, Little John on the handlebars and holding the Coke bottle which we would cash for a nickel and make up the difference that would allow all of us to get in, and me pumping up the crooked streets, dodging cars and pot holes. We spent the day swimming under the afternoon sun, so that when we got home our mom asked us what was darker, the floor or us? She **feigned** a stern posture, her hands on her hips and her mouth puckered. We played along. Looking down, Debbie and I said in unison, "Us."

feigned
pretended

That evening at dinner we all sat down in our bathing suits to eat our beans, laughing and chewing loudly. Our mom was in a good mood, so I took a risk and asked her if sometime we could have turtle soup. A few days before I had watched a television program in which a Polynesian tribe killed a large turtle, gutted it, and then stewed it over an open fire. The turtle, basted in a sugary sauce, looked delicious as I ate an afternoon bowl of cereal, but my sister, who was watching the program with a glass of Kool-Aid between her knees, said, "Caca."

My mother looked at me in **bewilderment**. "Boy, are you a crazy Mexican. Where did you get the idea that people eat turtles?"

"On television," I said, explaining the program. Then I took it a step further. "Mom, do you think we could get dressed up for dinner one of these days? David King does."

"*Ay, Dios*,"[5] my mother laughed. She started collecting the dinner plates, but my brother wouldn't let go of his. He was still drawing a picture in the bean sauce. Giggling, he said it was me, but I didn't want to listen because I wanted an answer from Mom. This was the summer when I spent the mornings in front of the television that showed the comfortable lives of white kids. There were no beatings, no **rifts** in the family. They wore bright clothes; toys tumbled from their closets. They hopped into bed with kisses and woke to glasses of fresh orange juice, and to a father sitting before his morning coffee while the mother buttered his toast. They hurried through the day making friends and gobs of money, returning home to a warmly lit living room, and then dinner. *Leave It to Beaver*[6] was the program I replayed in my mind:

"May I have the mashed potatoes?" asks Beaver with a smile.

"Sure, Beav," replies Wally as he taps the corners of his mouth with a starched napkin.

The father looks on in his suit. The mother, decked out in earrings and a pearl necklace, cuts into her steak and blushes. Their conversation is politely clipped.

"Swell," says Beaver, his cheeks puffed with food.

Our own talk at dinner was loud with belly laughs and marked by our pointing forks at one another. The subjects were commonplace.

"Gary, let's go to the ditch tomorrow," my brother suggests. He explains that he has made a life preserver out of four empty detergent bottles strung together with twine and that he will make me one if I can find more bottles. "No way are we going to drown."

"Yeah, then we could have a dirt clod fight," I reply, so happy to be alive.

Whereas the Beaver's family enjoyed dessert in dishes at the table, our mom sent us outside, and more often than not I went into the alley to peek over the neighbor's fences and spy out fruit, apricot or peaches.

---

5 *Ay, Dios:* Spanish for "Oh, God"
6 *Leave It to Beaver:* a sitcom that aired from 1957 to 1963 on which the characters Wally and Beaver were brothers

Gary Soto

I had asked my mom and again she laughed that I was a crazy *chavalo*[7] as she stood in front of the sink, her arms rising and falling with suds, face glistening from the heat. She sent me outside where my brother and sister were sitting in the shade that the fence threw out like a blanket. They were talking about me when I plopped down next to them. They looked at one another and then Debbie, my eight-year-old sister, started in.

"What's this crap about getting dressed up?"

She had entered her **profanity** stage. A year later she would give up such words and slip into her Catholic uniform, and into squealing on my brother and me when we "cussed this" and "cussed that."

profanity
using bad words; swearing

I tried to convince them that if we improved the way we looked we might get along better in life. White people would like us more. They might invite us places, like their homes or front yards. They might not hate us so much.

My sister called me a "craphead," and got up to leave with a stalk of grass dangling from her mouth. "They'll never like us."

---

7 *chavalo*: Spanish for "young person"
8 **Armenian:** from Armenia, a country in southeast Europe

My brother's mood lightened as he talked about the ditch—the white water, the broken pieces of glass, and the rusted car fenders that awaited our knees. There would be toads, and rocks to smash them.

David King, the only person we knew who resembled the middle class, called from over the fence. David was Catholic, of Armenian[8] and French **descent**, and his closet was filled with toys. A bear-shaped cookie jar, like the ones on television, sat on the kitchen counter. His mother was remarkably kind while she put up with the racket we made on the street. Evenings, she often watered the front yard and it must have upset her to see us—my brother and I and others—jump from trees laughing, the unkillable kids of the very poor, who got up unshaken, brushed off, and climbed into another one to try again.

David called again. Rick got up and slapped grass from his pants. When I asked if I could come along he said no. David said no. They were two years older so their affairs were different from mine. They greeted one another with foul names and took off down the alley to look for trouble.

I went inside the house, turned on the television, and was about to sit down with a glass of Kool-Aid when Mom shooed me outside.

"It's still light," she said. "Later you'll bug me to let you stay out longer. So go on."

I downed my Kool-Aid and went outside to the front yard. No one was around. The day had cooled and a breeze rustled the trees. Mr. Jackson, the plumber, was watering his lawn and when he saw me he turned away to wash off his front steps. There was more than an hour of light left, so I took advantage of it and decided to look for work. I felt suddenly alive as I skipped down the block in search of an overgrown flower bed and the dime that would end the day right.

descent
heritage; birth

LITERARY LENS

How is the narrator's family like your family? How is it different?

Gary Soto

A Plate of Peas

Rick Beyer

*M*y grandfather died when I was a small boy, and my grandmother started staying with us for about six months every year. She lived in a room that doubled as my father's office, which we referred to as "the back room." She carried with her a powerful aroma. I don't know what kind of perfume she used, but it was the double-barrel, ninety-proof, knock-down, rend-the-victim-unconscious, moose-killing variety. She kept it in a huge atomizer[1] and applied it frequently and liberally. It was almost impossible to go into her room and remain breathing for any length of time. When she would leave the house to go spend six months with my Aunt Lillian, my mother and sisters would throw open all the windows, strip the bed, and take out the curtains and rugs. Then they would spend several days washing and airing things out, trying frantically to make the **pungent** odor go away.

LITERARY LENS

In this story, the narrator's grandmother carries "a powerful aroma." Be aware of her other powers as you read.

pungent
sharp; stinging; biting

This, then, was my grandmother at the time of the infamous pea incident.

It took place at the Biltmore Hotel, which, to my eight-year-old mind, was just about the fanciest place to eat in all of Providence. My grandmother, my mother, and I were having lunch after a morning spent shopping. I grandly ordered a salisbury steak, confident in the knowledge that beneath that fancy name was a good old hamburger with gravy. When brought to the table, it was accompanied by a plate of peas.

I do not like peas now. I did not like peas then. I have always hated peas. It is a complete mystery to me why anyone would voluntarily eat peas. I did not eat them at home. I did not eat them at restaurants. And I certainly was not about to eat them now.

"Eat your peas," my grandmother said.

"Mother," said my mother in her warning voice. "He doesn't like peas. Leave him alone."

My grandmother did not reply, but there was a glint in her eye and a grim set to her jaw that signaled she was not going to be **thwarted**. She leaned in my direction, looked me in the eye, and uttered the fateful words that changed my life:

"I'll pay you five dollars if you eat those peas."

I had absolutely no idea of the **impending** doom that was heading

thwarted
opposed; defeated

impending
threatening; approaching

---

1 **atomizer:** a container that reduces liquid to a fine spray or mist

Rick Beyer

my way like a giant wrecking ball. I only knew that five dollars was an *enormous*, nearly *unimaginable* amount of money, and as awful as peas were, only one plate of them stood between me and the possession of that five dollars. I began to force the wretched things down my throat.

My mother was livid.[2] My grandmother had that self-satisfied look of someone who has thrown down an unbeatable trump card. "I can do what I want, Ellen, and you can't stop me." My mother glared at her mother. She glared at me. No one can glare like my mother. If there were a glaring Olympics, she would undoubtedly win the gold medal.

I, of course, kept shoving peas down my throat. The glares made me nervous, and every single pea made me want to throw up, but the magical image of that five dollars floated before me, and I finally gagged down every last one of them. My grandmother handed me the five dollars with a flourish. My mother continued to glare in silence. And the episode ended. Or so I thought.

My grandmother left for Aunt Lillian's a few weeks later. That night, at dinner, my mother served two of my all-time favorite foods, meatloaf and mashed potatoes. Along with them came a big, steaming bowl of peas. She offered me some peas, and I, in the very last moments of my innocent youth, declined. My mother fixed me with a cold eye as she heaped a huge pile of peas onto my plate. Then came the words that were to haunt me for years.

"You ate them for money," she said. "You can eat them for love."

Oh, despair! Oh, devastation! Now, too late, came the dawning realization that I had unwittingly damned myself to a hell from which there was no escape.

"You ate them for money. You can eat them for love."

What possible argument could I muster[3] against that? There was none. Did I eat the peas? You bet I did. I ate them that day and every other time they were served thereafter. The five dollars were quickly spent. My grandmother passed away a few years later. But the legacy of the peas lived on, as it lives on to this day. If I so much as curl my lip when they are served (because, after all, I still hate the horrid little things), my mother repeats the dreaded words one more time:

"You ate them for money," she says. "You can eat them for love."

LITERARY LENS

Why do you think the grandmother offered the boy money?

---

2 **livid:** very angry

3 **muster:** bring together

Ashes

Susan Beth Pfeffer

*T*hat winter, it felt like every time I saw my father, the sun cast off just a little more warmth than it had the day before. I don't remember a gray day when I saw him. Once it had snowed the night before, and getting to his apartment took longer than normal, as the buses inched their ways past snowbanks and awkwardly parked cars. But the sun made everything glisten, and the snow still had a pure look to it, which I knew would be gone by the following morning.

I saw him Tuesdays. I'd been seeing him Tuesdays for almost two years at that point. Before then, it had been Tuesdays and alternate weekends, but as my life got busier, weekends got harder, and Dad didn't complain when we fell instead into a Tuesday-evening ritual. Mom, who was still working on completing her degree, took Tuesday and Thursday evening classes, so I'd go straight to Dad's from school, wait for him to show, and then we'd have supper together and talk. It helped that he didn't live a hundred miles away. Just the other end of town, a two-bus-trip ride.

LITERARY LENS

Notice how the fathers are characterized in both this short story and the poem that follows it.

Dad drove me home Tuesday nights, and the moon always shone as brightly as the sun had and the winter stars looked joyful and beckoning. When I was little, Dad used to promise me the stars for a necklace, but like most of his promises, that one never quite happened.

"I'm a dreamer," he said to me more than once, which really wasn't all that different from what Mom said. "He's an irresponsible bum" was her way of wording it. I knew he was both, but I also knew that winter that the sun and the moon dreamed with him.

Sometimes when I haven't seen Dad for a few days, on a Saturday or a Sunday, I'll try to figure out why Mom ever married him. She's the most practical person I know, always putting aside for a rainy day. With Mom, there are a lot of rainy days and she takes a grim sort of pleasure in being ready for them. The flashlight with working batteries for a blackout. The extra quarters when the laundry isn't quite dry. The gift-wrapped bottle of wine for the unexpected and undesired Christmas guest. Her pocketbook overflows with tissues for anyone who might need them.

Dad gets by on a grin and a willingness to help. He's always there if you need him. Well, not always. He's unexpectedly there, like a warm day in January. He's a rescuer. "I saw a woman stranded on the road," he'd say. "So I changed her tire for her." Or he took the box of kittens to the Humane Society, or he found the wallet with the ID intact, and returned it in person to its owner (and, of course, turned down a reward). He helps blind people cross the street and lost people find their way.

"I go to bed at night, and ask myself, 'Is the world a better place because I exist?'" he told me once. "If I've done one thing, no matter how small, that made the world a better place, I'm satisfied."

Of course no one ever got rich helping blind people cross the street. The world might be a better place, but child support checks don't always show up on time, and I never did get that necklace made of stars. Both Mom and Dad see to it I know his limitations.

"All I can give you is dreams, Ashes," he said to me once. "But one good dream is worth a thousand flashlight batteries."

Ashes. I can still hear the fight. It was just a couple of months before the final breakup. I was in bed, **allegedly** asleep, when they went at it.

allegedly
supposedly; thought to be true

"Her name is Ashleigh!" Mom shouted. "A name you insisted on. So why do you call her 'Ashes'?"

"That's just my nickname for her," Dad replied. He was always harder to hear when they fought. The angrier Mom got, the lower his voice dropped. For some reason, that made her shout even louder.

"But ashes are cold, gray, dead things," Mom yelled. "You're calling your daughter something dead!"

"It's just a nickname," Dad repeated, a little quieter.

"You call her that just to annoy me!" Mom yelled, but Dad's reply was so soft, I could no longer hear him.

A couple of days later, when Dad forgot to pick me up at school, or didn't have the money for the class trip, or got all his favorite kinds of Chinese and none of Mom's and mine, I thought maybe Mom was right, and Dad did call me Ashes just to annoy her. I made a list that evening of all the words that rhymed with ashes—smashes and crashes, trashes and bashes, clashes and mashes—and it didn't seem quite so nice anymore, having a special nickname. But then Dad gave me roses or sang a song he'd written for me. Or maybe he moved two buses away. And I realized he still called me Ashes, where Mom couldn't hear him to be annoyed. And that made me feel special all over again. Mom might never be caught without batteries or tissues, but she just called me Ashleigh—a name she didn't even like—and never promised me anything.

"Mom, can I have an extra five dollars to go to the movies this weekend?"

"I can't promise you that."

What could Dad have promised her to get her to love him? And what could Mom have offered to make Dad love her back? Whatever it was, it was dying by the time I was born, and dead before I turned six. Dad could make everyone in the world smile, except Mom. And Mom was always prepared, except for what Dad did to her.

It was toward the end of February that winter, and the sun was shining and the air was crisp and clean. I sat waiting for Dad, who I knew would show up eventually. I probably did my homework, or maybe I looked out the window for his car to show. The room he was renting didn't have a TV. Maybe there was a library book to read. Maybe I folded his laundry.

When he got in, he was full of smiles and kisses and I no longer resented the waiting, if I had resented it at all. "Ashes!" he cried, as though it had been years since we'd last seen each other, and not a simple week of overcast skies and bone-chilling weather. "Have you ever seen such a day!"

I had, seven days before. But I smiled at Dad, who always seemed to discover the weather each time we visited.

"You look radiant," he said. "You get more and more beautiful. Turn around. Let me admire every single inch."

So I turned around. I was wearing jeans and a bulky brown sweater Mom had given me for Christmas.

"You could be a model," Dad said. "Have you thought about that, Ashes. Modeling? Some of those supermodels make a fortune."

"Dad," I said. "I could never be a supermodel."

"Don't sell yourself short," he replied. "I've read interviews where they say they never thought they were pretty. Not in high school. Just tall and skinny. And you don't have to worry about being tall or skinny."

"I know, Dad," I said. "Which is why I'll never be a supermodel."

He looked at me and then he grinned. "All right," he said. "You're too smart for that kind of work anyway. Be a photographer instead, or a dress designer. You have flair, Ashes. Style. You do something like that, you're sure to make your mark."

Last week he'd told me to be an astronaut. The week before that, the CEO of a Fortune 500 corporation.[1] And the week before that, he'd been stunned by my spirituality.

"Oh, Ashes," he said, taking off his winter coat and dropping it on the sofa bed. "I wish I deserved you."

"I wouldn't have any other dad," I told him. "My friends' fathers, they just tell my friends to study more. They never tell them they have flair or style."

"Maybe they don't," Dad said. "You're the special one, Ashes. You're the one-in-a-million girl."

"Am I really?" I asked, not needing the reassurance. I knew I wasn't a one-in-a-million girl, no matter how often Dad told me I was. But no matter how often he told me, I still loved hearing him say it.

"One in a million," he said. "And don't let anyone ever tell you otherwise, Ashes. They will, you know. They'll try to tear you down. They'll laugh at your dreams. Even your mother—and she's a saint to have put up with me all those years—even she will discourage you from being all you can be. I hate to speak against her, but she's not a dreamer, Ashes. She's the most levelheaded woman I know. As straight as a yardstick. But I was the only dream she ever believed in and once I failed her, she never let herself dream again."

"Mom's all right," I said.

"She certainly is," Dad said. "She's a fine woman."

pondered
thought seriously about

We were both silent as we **pondered** Mom. Then Dad laughed. "She'd never let you go hungry," he said. "What do you want for supper, Ashes? I can offer you pizza, Chinese, or fast."

"Anything," I said.

"No, no," he said, and he clapped his hands. "I remember. There's a new diner, opened right around the block. Let's treat ourselves, Ashes, and go out on the town."

"Can you afford it?" I asked, after doing the mental arithmetic of diner versus pizza.

"For a special date with my daughter?" he replied. "Of course I can afford it. Besides, I have something to celebrate."

---

1 **CEO of a Fortune 500 corporation:** chief executive officer, or top boss, of a company ranked as one of the 500 largest in the United States

Susan Beth Pfeffer

"What?" I asked.

"I have a chance at something really big," he said. "All I need to do is put together a little financing, and I'll be set for life."

"For life?" I said, and I must have sounded like Mom because he stopped smiling.

"All right, not for life," he said. "But it'll be the start of something really big, Ashes. I can feel it. Just a couple hundred bucks, and then all the pieces will fall into place."

I had no idea where Dad thought he could get two hundred dollars. But he looked so happy I had to smile, too.

"Then diner it is," I said, and I got my coat. Dad picked his up from the sofa and put it back on. "Rice pudding for dessert," he said as we walked out the door. "You can always tell the quality of a diner by its rice pudding."

The diner might have been brand new, but already it had a shabby run down quality that made it fit right in with the neighborhood. It was two-thirds empty when we got there, and we had our choice of booths. Dad took one that faced the door, and sat in the seat where he could check who was coming in. He hadn't done that with me in a long time, and my stomach hurt in an old familiar way.

"Waiting for someone?" I asked him. I stared at the menu, so I wouldn't have to look at him not looking at me.

"Of course not," he said. "Not when I'm with you. Take your pick, Ashes. Hamburger, triple-decker, chicken salad platter. Whatever you want."

I ordered the burger and fries, hoping that by the time it came I'd feel like eating. Dad took a quick look at the menu, closed it, and ordered coffee.

"You'll share my fries," I said to him.

He nodded as though we'd just completed a difficult **negotiation**. "I'll even eat your pickle," he said. But then he looked back at the door.

negotiation
process of coming to an agreement

"What is it?" I asked him.

"It's nothing," he said. "Oh hell, Ashes, you can always see right through me."

He was the one who'd been looking right through me toward the door, but I didn't say anything.

"That money," he said. "The two hundred dollars?"

I nodded.

"Well it isn't so much for a deal as to help pay off one I already made," Dad said. "But I've got to tell you, honey, once that money is paid, I'm on my way to easy street. Just a little setback. But you know how those guys are. They get itchy when you owe them money. And it's not always comfortable to be where they can scratch you."

"You owe them two hundred dollars?" I asked, trying to keep the panic out of my voice.

"Give or take," Dad said. "But don't worry about it, honey. I'll work it out. I always do."

My burger and fries came then. Dad took a long sip of his coffee, while I poured ketchup on my plate and twirled a fry in it. "Can I help?" I asked.

Dad smiled like I'd offered him the key to the mint.[2] "I love you so much," he said. "You're ten thousand times better than I deserve, Ashes."

"Have a fry," I said, pushing my plate toward him. Dad took one. He seemed to have more of an appetite than I did.

"I had a thought," he said as he reached for my pickle. "Your mother keeps a couple hundred in cash at her place."

I didn't think either of us was supposed to know that.

"In that pretty teapot her mother gave her," Dad said. "Unless she's changed her hiding place. I know she changed the locks when I moved out, so maybe she changed her hiding place as well."

Sometimes, when Mom wasn't home, I'd take the lid off the teapot and stare into it, imagining what I could do with two hundred dollars. I looked at Dad and realized he'd had those same fantasies. Well, why not. I was his daughter, after all.

"The money's still in the teapot," I said.

Dad grinned. "She's a wonderful woman," he said. "But she gets one idea and she never wants to change it."

"What do you want to do, Dad?" I asked. "Come into the apartment with me and take the money?"

"Oh no," he said, and he looked really shocked. "That would be robbery, Ashes. I would never steal from your mother. I've caused her pain enough."

---

2 **key to the mint:** expression meaning "access to unlimited money"

I took a bite of burger. Dad ate some more fries.

"No, I just thought maybe you could borrow the money," he said. "Just for a day or two, until I straighten out all my finances. Your mother would never know the difference. Unless there's an earthquake or the Martians invade. I think we can gamble neither of those things will happen before Friday."

"You'll be able to pay her back by Friday?" I asked.

"You," Dad said. "I'd be borrowing the money from you. And I swear to you, Ashes, I'd have the money in your hands by Friday at the latest." He wiped his hand on his napkin and offered it to me as though to shake on the deal.

"Dad, I don't know," I said. "That's a lot of money. What if Mom finds out?"

"It's me she'd be angry at," Dad said. "Which is why she'll never find out. I wouldn't **jeopardize** our time together, honey. You let me have the money tonight, I'll straighten out my little difficulty, and Thursday night, when your mom is out, I'll give you back what I owe you. No earthquakes, no Martians, no problem."

jeopardize
expose to danger

I looked at the clock on the wall behind Dad. "Mom'll be home soon," I said.

"You all through?" he asked.

I nodded.

"Let's go, then," he said, the rice-pudding test long forgotten.

We went back to his place so I could pick up my books. Then we walked down to his car. "Why don't you sell your car?" I asked him. If he did that, I'd keep my hands clean, and Mom would never know. "You could get the money you need that way."

"You're your mother's daughter," he said. "Good head on your shoulders. Problem is, I'd never be able to find another car this cheap to replace it. No, Ashes, the teapot's the way to go."

We drove back to Mom's in silence. Usually we talked. Sometimes Dad sang one of his songs to me. For a moment, a cloud drifted past the moon and the sky turned greenish gray.

"Snow tomorrow," Dad said. "Maybe you'll get a snow day."

"Maybe," I said.

Dad parked the car a block away from Mom's. "Just in case she gets home early," he said. "I don't want her to see me waiting."

"Okay," I said.

"You go up to the apartment," he said. "Take the money, and come right down. Then I'll drop you off in front of her place, like always, and she'll never know the difference."

"What do I do if Mom's already there?" I asked.

"Just stay where you are," he said. "If you're not back here in ten minutes, I'll go home."

"All right," I said, and reached to unlock the door.

Dad touched me on my shoulder, gloved hand on winter coat. "You're one in a million," he said to me. "The best daughter a man could dream of."

I got out of the car and ran over to the apartment. I took the elevator to the tenth floor and unlocked the door. The apartment was quiet. It always felt a little colder when Mom wasn't there. Even with the lights turned on, it seemed a little darker.

I walked into the kitchen and turned on the light. The teapot was right where it belonged. I lifted its lid and stared at her emergency money. It was shaped like a little house, with a curtained window and a flowerpot on the windowsill. It was the sort of house I'd never lived in, probably never would with the amount of time it was taking Mom to finish her degree.

I stood over the teapot and stared at the money. Mom's emergency money. Her earthquake money. Her Martian money. Ten Andrew Jacksons[3] stared right back at me. They offered me no advice on what I should do.

I looked out the window and saw only ash gray sky. In the cold stillness of the night, I could hear my father's car keening[4] in the distance. "You're one in a million," it cried.

---

3 **Andrew Jacksons:** slang for twenty-dollar bills, which have Andrew Jackson's picture on them

4 **keening:** making a loud, wailing sound

Susan Beth Pfeffer

✳ THE POET'S PERSPECTIVE

After the Divorce

Jewel Kilcher

After the divorce
we moved to Homer
to live in a one bedroom apartment
behind Uncle Otto's machine shop.

My brothers slept in the water closet
after my dad painted it any color
they wanted. The pipes looked like
silver trees sprouting up through
the frames of their bunk beds.

For me, we took the door
off the coat closet
and built a narrow bed
four feet off the ground
with a ladder of rough wood
to climb up that hurt my bare feet.
My dad tried hard
to keep us all together
and work at the same time,
but things just weren't the same.
He pulled my hair when he brushed it
and didn't sing to us at night
before we went to sleep.

I was eight and started cooking.
Shane grocery shopped
and Atz, well, he was a kid.
By 7 A.M. every morning
we walked ourselves out to the road
and waited for the school bus
with all the other kids.
Looking for signs
of when life might strike **random**
again and scatter us like seeds
on the unknowable winds
of chance.

random
*without purpose;
meaningless*

✳ LITERARY LENS

*How would you compare
the father in the short story
to the father in the poem?*

Atomic Blue Pieces

Angela Johnson

Somebody told me once you can't die from pain, even if you want to.

You can make your world what you want it to be sometimes.

So there wasn't any pain for me, for a while.

While I was lying there all I could think about was how I was supposed to take out the garbage at home. No pain. I had a dental appointment on Friday—Mama would have to write me an excuse to get out of school. No pain. And I was never letting my best friend, Cougar, use my notes from American history again. He must have lived his whole life on pizza, and my notes proved it.

No pain. No busted leg. No pain.

If you count between thunderclaps during a storm you'll know whether the storm is coming or going during the next count. Lower number—it's coming at you. Higher number—it's leaving.

I can count during a storm.

■■■■

The day my brother Leon left I broke my leg falling down the steps of an old deserted building that Mama had told me not to go in. I lay there half a day.

I remember Cougar picking me up and running down the broken steps two at a time. I remember how it hurt so much just before we got out of the place I saw a flash of white light and passed out.

No more pain.

The morning before Leon left he shared half his toast with me and most of his bacon. We didn't get bacon that much, either. He'd sat there smiling at me while I picked out of his plate and babbled about nothing.

Mama had already told me to shut up, twice. Leon had shot her dirty looks, though, and smiled back at me.

I'd eaten one more piece of Leon's bacon and had run my bare feet underneath the chair. The linoleum was gritty and cold. Leon kept on smiling.

When I found out that night after I'd gotten back from the emergency room that Leon was gone I stared out the kitchen window until Mama yelled at me that I was just like that "damned Leon." When she stomped out the room I took an Atomic Blue Magic Marker and wrote my brother's name all over my cast.

The day my brother Leon left was mostly white light and pain. But it also was atomic blue, bacon, and his face. Atomic blue and Leon's smiling face all around.

■■■■

wedged
pressed into a narrow space

Chalky's Trailer Park is **wedged** up against Route 82 and Cave Man Woods. So everybody who grows up there spends most of their lives listening to grown people yelling at them to stay off the highway and not to go into the swamp woods.

That meant until you are sixteen or have a friend who can drive you're stuck at Chalky's. My days stuck around here were coming to an end. I'd steal a car and drive to hell if I had to, 'cause even though I'd been stuck, I'd had Leon and Cougar. We'd all hung out in the swamp like all the kids who lived at Chalky's.

It was all something else then. Something I could live with.

I'd walked down Route 82 with anybody who was sure their parents weren't going to be coming down the road and waving us back to Chalky's.

Didn't they know that they couldn't keep us locked up and away from everything that we were looking for? Didn't they know that sooner or later . . .

Sooner or later . . .

Maybe Mama knew about sooner or later. Maybe she knew it as she stood processing turkeys at Bil-Mars.

Maybe she knew it when she'd go out with her girlfriends and drink beers at Star Lanes Bowling while smiling at men who worked at Bil-Mars and were out with their friends.

Maybe she even knew about sooner or later when she'd sit in the front window of our trailer all night long listening to Sam Cooke records and playing solitaire. Sometimes getting me up to drink a cup of hot chocolate with her in winter and lemon iced tea in the summer, always at 3:00 A.M. She called this time the hour of souls and she didn't want to be alone when the clock chimed to three.

I only remember Mama at these times because of extremes. Extreme cold. Extreme heat.

Angela Johnson

Leon says Mama is intense. And I wondered out loud once if that was the reason our dad left. Leon got mad when he heard me say it. He turned away from me and whispered, "She got intense after he left us."

■■■■

If I'd known Leon would leave us for good I would have paid him back the ten dollars I owed him for fronting me movie tickets and nachos last month. For the last few days it's all I can think about. I figure he could probably use that ten. He could buy a lot of nachos with it.

He could buy bottled water. He drank it all the time.

I still dream that he'll come back for the money. Ten dollars is a lot of money when you have nothing. Did he have anything? Was he warm and safe?

Did he think about us?

Me and Mama walking around like ghosts at Chalky's. Mama wanting to stay home and go looking for him but knowing she couldn't afford to lose her job. Me waking up in the middle of history class calling out his name.

Was he thinking about us?

■■■■

In the end Leon had to go because no one but me would believe him. And that was funny 'cause Leon is the most honest person in the world. So honest that sometimes I didn't think he belonged in this century.

Leon talked about honor and loyalty. Not the stupid kind where people don't tell when they see their friends hurt or kill somebody.

Leon has honor and **morality** that Mama always used to be proud of until it brought the cops and social services to our trailer.

morality
good actions, virtue

Honor and loyalty is just fine I guess as long as it doesn't visit you when you least expect it and get in the way of your life.

Was Leon thinking about us?

■■■■

He'd play the African drums on the top of Selby's drugstore, well, what used to be Selby's. Leon said he loved to watch everybody from above—six stories above. He wanted to play the drums for everybody.

He did.

Sweet, faraway drumming all over the town.

Leon would drum on top of Selby's in the morning and just as the sun was going down. He'd drum everybody in Springhill awake and asleep. Sweet, faraway drumming like he was calling to people he never met in a country he'd never been to.

Leon's drumming made me sad. 'Cause I knew. I knew what I didn't want to know. Leon was not one of us. Even the us everybody our age in Springhill would probably become whether we wanted to or not.

He wouldn't work at the turkey farm or go to Star Lanes on Friday night. He wouldn't stand along the fence watching high school football and talking about how he could have been.

He'd never put on a pig roast and stand around a bonfire passing a paper bag full of whisky that stung you all the way down, like a lot did years after they couldn't run fast anymore and the weather channel was more important to them than the world news.

I know if Leon had stayed in the county and went to football games, the boy who drummed for us would be gone forever.

The boy who used to let me sit beside him and draw while he drummed would just vanish in the mist like people did in scary books. The boy who let me draw him drumming in blue as the sun set would disappear. And he did.

■■■

Mama cries all the time now, but I don't really think she's crying for Leon. I think she's crying for all the ones who have left her. Not for their sake, but her own.

She keeps saying, "Just like his damned daddy."

And I'm just like that "damned Leon."

Daddy, Leon, and me are all damned in Mama's eyes. A whole trailer full of the damned.

■■■

Leon used to go to day camp with T-Boy James. They learned to swim together. But T-Boy had stuff happen to him. He changed from the kid who used to share his pudding with my brother. He turned nasty and dangerous. His grandma cried when they dragged him away.

When T-Boy James got out of **juvenile** it didn't take him long to start messing with everybody that he thought put him there. That was a lot of people 'cause T-Boy did everything but kill before they finally locked him up. He'd spent two years in Holcomb and some people say he'd had a bad time there 'cause there is always somebody badder in the world.

Cougar got on the bus twice in two weeks with a bloody nose.

Somebody had broken every window out of the science lab and keyed[1] all the police cars parked by the courthouse. There was other stuff, but the night the block of apartments across from Selby's went up in flames was one of the worst nights of my life.

An old lady didn't make it out.

And a couple of hours later men were looking under our trailer and knocking the door in and dragging Leon off.

■ ■ ■ ■

Mama went and picked Leon up from the police station that night. Both her and the legal aid lawyer she brought with her looked overworked and nervous.

Leon came home sleepy and quiet. He hugged me hard just before he crawled into bed with all his clothes on. I didn't know it then, but I only had a week to be in the company of my brother.

■ ■ ■ ■

I used to wonder what would happen to me when Leon went away. I used to think that I'd probably miss him so bad, it would hurt. But I thought away meant college or a job in another state, so he'd come back to me and my loneliness . . .

I do not know the woman who calls herself my mother.

She doesn't really know me.

Leon knows both of us, though.

But now he's gone.

■ ■ ■ ■

juvenile
short for juvenile detention, a place for convicts under 18

---

1 **keyed:** scratched the paint with the tip of a key

In the end it didn't matter that T-Boy heard Leon drumming on Selby's roof when he poured the first drops of gasoline or that he hid the gas can under our trailer. It doesn't even matter that everybody would have found out the truth about Leon in the end.

It's about pain.

T-Boy's pain, Leon's pain, everybody's pain. The pains might never even have had to come together for my brother to leave this town. But he did. He did in broad daylight with a backpack and his drum under one arm. A man getting to the turkey farm late for work saw him get in a semi off Route 44.

He said he was smiling when he got in.

I can't believe that though, 'cause I heard Leon on the roof way after that man says he got in the truck. I can still smell the smoke of the gutted building across the street as I climbed the steps to the roof.

Sweet drumming.

Sweet Leon playing . . .

I even thought I heard him as I fell and **visions** of atomic blue drawings and pain shot through me.

visions
things seen in a dream

■■■■

I always count during the pain, now.

Two thousand one, two thousand two . . .

Higher numbers it's coming—lower numbers it's going away. My leg has healed and they knocked Selby's to the ground so no more accidents would happen there and no more boys who thought about somewhere else would sit on its roof.

Somebody told me once that you can't die from pain, but I don't remember who.

LITERARY LENS

Do you agree or disagree with the narrator's thoughts about honor, loyalty, and family?

The Night the Bear Ate Goombaw

Patrick F. McManus

*t*here was so much confusion over the incident anyway that I don't want to add to it by getting the **sequences** mixed up. First of all—and I remember this clearly—it was the summer after Crazy Eddie Muldoon and I had been sprung from third grade at Delmore Blight Grade School. The Muldoons' only good milk cow died that summer, shortly after the weasel got in their chicken house and killed most of the laying hens. This was just before the fertilizer company Mr. Muldoon worked for went bankrupt, and he lost his job. The engine on his tractor blew up a week later, so he couldn't harvest his crops, which were all pretty much dried up from the drought anyway.

LITERARY LENS

There is an object in this story that will become very significant before the story ends. Try to figure out what that object is.

Then Mr. Muldoon fell in the pit trap that Crazy Eddie and I had dug to capture wild animals. Our plan was to train the wild animals and then put on shows to earn a little extra money for the family. But Mr. Muldoon fell in the trap, and afterwards made us shovel all the dirt back into it. The only wild animal we had trapped was a skunk, and when Mr. Muldoon fell in on top of it, he terrified the poor creature practically to death. Neither Mr. Muldoon nor the skunk was hurt much, but the skunk managed to escape during all the excitement. So there went our wild-animal show. This occurred about midsummer, as I recall, about the time Mr. Muldoon's nerves got so bad that old Doc Hix told him to stop drinking coffee, which apparently was what had brought on his nervous condition.

For the rest of the summer, Mr. Muldoon gave off a faint, gradually fading odor of skunk. Unless he got wet. Then the odor reconstituted[1] itself to approximately its original power, which placed a major **restraint** on the Muldoons' social life, meager as that was. Fortunately, Mr. Muldoon didn't get wet that often, mainly because of the drought that had killed off his crops. As Mrs. Muldoon was fond of saying, every cloud has a silver lining.

So far it had been a fairly typical summer for Mr. Muldoon, but he claimed to be worried about a premonition[2] that his luck was about to turn bad. Then Eddie's grandmother, Mrs. Muldoon's mother, showed up for a visit.

---

1 **reconstituted:** restored
2 **premonition:** forewarning

Patrick F. McManus

"I knew it!" Mr. Muldoon told a neighbor. "I knew something like this was about to happen! I must be physic."[3]

After I got to know Eddie's grandmother a little better, I could see why Mr. Muldoon regarded her visit as a stroke of bad luck. She immediately assumed command of the family and began to boss everyone around, including me. Nevertheless, I doubted that Mr. Muldoon was actually physic, because otherwise he would never have come up with the idea of the camping trip.

"I'm worried about Pa," Eddie said one morning as we sat on his back porch. "He's not been hisself lately."

"Who's he been?" I asked, somewhat startled, although I regarded Mr. Muldoon as one of the oddest persons I knew.

"Pa's just started acting weird, that's all. You know what crazy idea he came up with this morning? He says we all gotta go on a camping trip up in the mountains and pick huckleberries. He says we can sell any extra huckleberries we get for cash. But Pa don't know anything about camping. We don't even have any camping stuff. Ain't that strange?"

"Yeah," I said. "Say, Eddie, you don't suppose your pa . . . uh . . . your pa . . ." I tried to think of a delicate way to phrase it.

"What?" Eddie said.

"Uh, you don't suppose your pa . . . uh . . . would let me go on the camping trip too, do you?"

When Eddie put the question to his father, Mr. Muldoon tried to conceal his affection for me beneath a **malevolent** frown. "Oh, all right," he growled at me. "But no mischief. That means no knives, no hatchets, no matches, no slingshots, and *no shovels*! Understood?"

Eddie and I laughed. It was good to see his father in a humorous mood once again.

I rushed home and asked my mother if I could go camping with the Muldoons. "You'd be away from home a whole week?" she said. "I'll have to think about that. Okay, you can go."

I quickly packed my hatchet, knife, and slingshot, along with edibles Mom gave me to contribute to the Muldoon grub box. The one major item I lacked was a sleeping bag. "I'll just make a bedroll out of some blankets off my bed," I informed my mother.

"You most certainly won't," she informed me. "You'll use the coat."

malevolent
showing ill will or evil

---

3 **physic:** Mr. Muldoon has used the wrong word, *physic*, meaning the practice of healing diseases, for the word *psychic*, meaning able to employ supernatural forces; in other words, he thinks he can see into the future.

"Ah, gee, Ma, the coat's so stupid. Mr. Muldoon will tease me all during the trip if I have to use that stupid coat for a sleeping bag."

The coat in question was a tattered, dog-chewed old fur of **indeterminate** species that my grandmother had acquired during a brief period of family wealth in the previous century. It had been given to me as a "sleeping bag" for my frequent but always aborted[4] attempts at sleeping out alone in the yard. For all its hideous appearance, it was warm and cozy, and covered my nine-year-old body nicely from end to end. Still, I knew the Muldoons would laugh themselves silly when they saw me bed down in a woman's fur coat. My only hope of retaining a shred of dignity, not to mention my carefully nursed macho image, was to slip into it after they had all gone to sleep. I stuffed the coat into a gunnysack,[5] concealing it under the one threadbare blanket my mother reluctantly issued me.

The day of the big camping trip dawned bright and clear, a common ruse[6] of Mother Nature to lure unsuspecting souls out into the wilds. The five of us piled into the ancient Muldoon sedan and set off for the mountains. Most of our camping gear, such as it was, balanced precariously atop the car. It was wrapped in a huge hay tarp, which was to serve as our tent. "Ain't had a drop of rain in three months," Mr. Muldoon had said. "Probably won't need the tarp." This statement would later be recalled and admitted as evidence in the case against Mr. Muldoon's being physic.

"How you doin' back there, Goombaw?" Mr. Muldoon said to Eddie's grandmother. For some reason, everyone called her Goombaw.

"How you think I'm doin?" Goombaw snapped back. "Wedged in between these two sweaty young-uns! I'm boilin' in my own juice! This camping trip is the stupidest dang fool idear you ever come up with, Herbert! We'll probably all get et by bears. Tell me, what about bears, Herbert?"

Yeah, I thought. What about bears?

"Ha ha ha ha," Mr. Muldoon laughed. "You don't have to worry about bears. They're more afraid of humans than we are of them."

Well, I thought, that's certainly not true of all humans, particularly one that I know personally. It's probably not true of bears either. But

---

4 **aborted:** cancelled
5 **gunnysack:** a sack made of a heavy fabric, such as burlap
6 **ruse:** trick

Patrick F. McManus

I kept these thoughts to myself, since Goombaw was doing a thorough job of grilling Mr. Muldoon on the subject. I could tell that the talk of bears was making Mrs. Muldoon nervous, not that she was the only one.

"Let's change the subject, Goombaw," she said.

"Oh, all right. How about mountain lions, Herbert?"

For the rest of the long, hot, dusty ride up to the huckleberry patches, Goombaw harangued[7] Mr. Muldoon about every possible threat to our well-being, from bears to crazed woodcutters. By the time we reached our campsite, she had everyone in such a nervous state that we were almost afraid to get out of the car. Mr. Muldoon stepped out, swiveled his head about as though expecting an attack from any quarter, and then ordered us to help set up camp.

No level area for our tent was immediately apparent, but Crazy Eddie and I finally located one. It was down a steep bank and on the far side of a little creek. Mr. Muldoon, Eddie, and I dragged the bundle of camp gear down the bank and across a log to the little clearing in the brush and trees. In no time at all Mr. Muldoon had constructed a fine shelter out of the tarp. Eddie and I built a fire ring of rocks, and Mrs. Muldoon and Goombaw got a fire going and put coffee on to boil, apparently forgetting that the doctor had told Mr. Muldoon to cut down on his coffee drinking because of his nerves. Eddie and I sampled the fishing in the creek. All in all, the camping trip showed signs of becoming a pleasant experience. Then it got dark.

"I say keep a fire goin' all night," Goombaw advised. "It might help keep the bears off of us."

"There ain't no bears," Mr. Muldoon said. "Now stop worrying about bears. Ha! Bears are more afraid of us than we are of them. Now, everybody get a good night's sleep. We got a lot of huckleberries to pick tomorrow." He stripped down to his long underwear and burrowed into the pile of quilts and blankets Mrs. Muldoon had arranged on the ground. I pulled my threadbare blanket out of the gunnysack and spread it out in the dirt next to Goombaw.

"Good heavens, Patrick!" Mrs. Muldoon said. "Is that all you have to sleep in, that one little blanket? The night can get pretty chilly up here in the mountains."

"Oh, I've got more blankets in my sack," I lied. "If it turns cold,

---

7 **harangued:** lectured

I'll just put some more on. But I sleep warm."

As the night dragged on into its full depth, I lay there shivering in my blanket, studying with considerable interest the looming dark shapes the full moon revealed around our camp. Finally, Goombaw and the Muldoons ceased their thrashing about on the hard ground and began to emit the sounds of sleep. I jerked the fur coat out of the gunnysack and buttoned myself into its comforting warmth. I set a mental alarm to awaken me before the Muldoons, so I could conceal the coat before they caught sight of the hideous thing. Then I drifted off into fitful sleep.

"Wazzat?" Goombaw shouted in my ear.

Later, she claimed only to be having a nightmare, but, fortunately for us, she sounded the alarm just in time. In the silence that followed Goombaw's shout, you could almost hear four pairs of eyelids popping open in the dark.

"A bear!" Goombaw shouted. "A bear's got me!"

Since I was lying right next to Goombaw, this announcement aroused my curiosity no end. I tried to leap to my feet but, wrapped in the fur coat, could only manage to make it to all fours.

"Bear!" screamed Crazy Eddie. "Bear's got Gooooo—!"

"Bear!" shrieked Mrs. Muldoon. "There it is!"

Goombaw made a horrible sound. I could make out the big round whites of her eyes fixed on me in the darkness, no doubt pleading wordlessly with me for help, but what could a small boy do against a bear?

"Holy bleep!" roared Mr. Muldoon. He lunged to his feet, knocking over the ridgepole[8] and dropping the tarp on us and the bear. Figuring Goombaw already for a goner and myself next on the bear's menu, I tore out from under the tarp just in time to see Mr. Muldoon trying to unstick an ax from the stump in which he had embedded it the night before. Even in the shadowy dimness of moonlight, I could see the look of surprise and horror wash over Mr. Muldoon's face as I rushed toward him for protection. He emitted a strangled cry and rushed off through the woods on legs so wobbly it looked as if his knees had come unhinged. Under the circumstances, I could only surmise that the bear was close on my heels, and I raced off after Mr. Muldoon, unable to think of anything better to do.

---

8 **ridgepole:** the highest horizontal bar on a tent where the peak comes together

Patrick F. McManus

With his **abrupt** departure, Mr. Muldoon had clearly let it be known that now it was every man for himself.

Bounding over a log with the effortless ease that accompanies total panic, I came upon Mr. Muldoon peeling bark and limbs off a small tree. Since he was only four feet up the tree, I debated briefly whether to wait for him to gain altitude or to find my own tree. Then Mr. Muldoon caught sight of the bear closing fast on us. He sprang out of the tree and took off again, with me so close behind that I could have reached out and grabbed the snapping flap of his long underwear. The thought did occur to me to do so, because I was nearing exhaustion, and Mr. Muldoon could have towed me along with his underwear flap. Upon later reflection, however, I think it is well that I didn't grab the flap, for it probably would have been a source of considerable embarrassment to both of us.

When I could run no more, I dropped to the ground, deciding I might as well let the bear eat me as run me to death. But the bear was gone. Perhaps he had taken a shortcut through the woods, hoping to cut me and Mr. Muldoon off at a pass. In any case, I never did get to see the bear, narrow as my escape had been. **Sweltering** in the fur coat, I took the thing off and stuffed it down a hollow stump, glad to be rid of the thing.

When I got back to camp, everyone was gone. I climbed up to the car, inside of which I found Eddie, his mother, and Goombaw, each more or less in one piece.

"Thank heavens," cried Mrs. Muldoon. "We thought the bear had got you! Have you seen Mr. Muldoon?"

I said yes I had, not mentioning that I had seen even more of him than I cared to. Half an hour later, Mr. Muldoon scrambled up the bank to the car. Upon learning that everyone was intact, he explained how he had led the bear away from camp, at considerable risk to himself. I was surprised that he neglected to mention my role in leading the bear off, but didn't think it my place to mention it.

"You got to keep a cool head during a bear attack," Mr. Muldoon explained. "Panic and you're done for."

"Wheweee!" Goombaw said. "I smell skunk! Somebody step on a skunk in the dark?"

Then it started to rain. Hard.

abrupt
sudden

sweltering
very hot

LITERARY LENS

The fur coat plays an important role in this story. Explain how it creates a misunderstanding.

Saying Good-bye to the Tall Man

Rick Book

*T*he weather-beaten door rolled open with the usual protest—rusty metal wheels screeching on the metal track. I stepped over the worn wooden sill and into the dark coolness of the barn. A long sigh. It felt safe here. Maybe the darkness would erase things, maybe even the day itself.

I slid the door shut. To my right an enclosed wooden stairway led up to the loft. The steps were covered with dust and straw. I sat down on one. The big trapdoor above was closed. There was a light switch by my head on the wall, but the quiet of the dark was better. In this gloomy cave I inhaled the comforting smells of old dust, harness, ropes, hay and cows. On the wall beside me there was faded writing in pencil. I couldn't see it in the dark but traced my fingers over the boards, reading the silvered grain like Braille. Grandpa had shown it to me years ago. I knew it by heart.

LITERARY LENS

While reading both the short story and the poem, think about the setting.

> *Barn erected July 16, 1914*
> *Sunny, hot, 17 people here*
> *Ted*

Ted was my Grandpa, my dad's dad. He was tall and thin, straight as a telephone pole. Swallows could build nests under the big bushy eaves of his eyebrows. He had blue eyes that glistened like stones in a riverbank pool. And thick white hair that always looked like he'd combed it with a rake. Mom called it "touseldy."[1] But mostly Grandpa wore a white Stetson with a flat brim, and when he walked toward me, with his big white hat and his big white teeth, I knew he was happy to see me. Not like today.

I couldn't breathe. A noose tightened around my neck. Standing up I yanked on the knot of my tie, tore open the top of my Sunday shirt. I felt the button release, heard the tiny sound of it landing. But it was gone—disappeared into some secret dusty place. I wiped off the seat of my good pants and walked into the shop, in a converted stall right next to the stairs.

Dad's shop was in a new machine shed. This place, with its old tools and old cobwebs, was always Grandpa's. I just stood there. Everything was covered with a velvety mouse-brown layer of dust, including the window above the bench. A few rays of light struggled through; specks of dust hung in the beams like stars.

---

1 **touseldy:** from *tousled*, meaning "a tangled mass"

bristled
full of or covered with stiff hairs

Everything looked strange, like I'd never seen it before. The walls **bristled** with stuff hanging on nails: old truck fan belts, Swedish crosscut saws, braces and bits, pieces of metal chain, harness buckles, a horse bridle, draw knife, hacksaws, rusty handsaws, tin dust goggles with cracked yellow glass lenses, hand-carved wooden airplane propellers and a faded picture from a 1952 calendar of a green Ford driving down a treelined lane.

Grandpa had built shelves between the upright two-by-fours on the walls. Every shelf was jammed with old cardboard boxes and tin cans half-full of cotter keys and cotter pins, screws of all sizes, shiny ball bearings wrapped in oily paper, washers, connecting links for chains. He'd built the wooden workbench of heavy planks, now black with oil and dirt. In the middle was a big iron vice, nicked and dimpled from years of hammering. I'd made many of the marks myself. To the right a hand-operated grinding wheel for sharpening knives and chisels. It whined like a jet engine when we kids wound it up to a hundred miles an hour.

I stood in front of the hand-operated drill press mounted on the wall. Its wooden handle glowed with years of oil from oily hands. Its gears purred as they turned slowly. I'd drilled a lot of holes here—making boats or slingshots or wooden guns. I imagined Grandpa standing on this spot, hunched over some broken piece of machinery, anxious to get back out to the field, back to the horses and the hired men, and back to his work. I leaned my forehead against the cold steel adjusting wheel at the top of the drill. My body heaved like a dog trying to hork up breakfast. But nothing happened. I wasn't very good at crying.

Grandpa's dead! I kicked a wooden box; black bolts skittered across the floor like mice. He'd had a heart attack last week. Two days later he was gone. Grandma had died three years ago. They'd never come out from town for visits again. They'd never drive up our lane slowly in their old blue Chev. Grandpa used to get out, stretch his arms, turn to me and say, "Let's go have a look around." Grandma would go into the house or down to the garden with Mom, and Grandpa and I'd walk around the farm so he could see what Dad was up to. How the buildings and machinery looked. The fences Dad had fixed. The mowing I'd done. We'd check out the chickens, the new litter of pigs. And sample the rhubarb growing in the hollow by the pasture fence.

We always ended up in the barn, out of the heat and the wind. He'd sit on an old milk stool—a section of tree with a leather handle nailed to it; the top polished smooth by farmers' butts—and he'd tell me stories. He'd talk about coming to Saskatchewan from the States with his brother in 1903.

"The only thing here was a stake in the ground, a survey stake with a number on it." He'd chew on a soft green stem of crested wheat grass. "It marked the corner of our 160 acres. Nothing else around for miles but grass and wild flowers. Maybe a meadowlark sitting on the odd stick of a tree. On the horizon you could see one or two of our neighbors' new barns rising up like ships at sea."

Grandpa and his brother had been sodbusters;[2] they'd started their farms side by side and both got married. Grandpa'd married Katarina, who'd come from Austria. They'd called their homestead Bonnieview Farm and painted the name on the barn's big hay door with two crossed Union Jacks[3] underneath. The name and the flags are still there. Sometimes, when the sun was setting and it lit up the barn with an orange light, Grandpa and I would sit on the steps of the house and look at those flags.

We keep only a handful of cows now, but Grandpa talked about when the barn had been full of milk cows, full of their low moo's and soft chewing sounds. "I can still hear the kerosene lantern sliding along the wire in the barn," he said one time. I thought it strange that such a little sound seemed so important to him. He talked about the shadows, too, the way they swayed as the lantern slowly swung while the boys—Dad and my uncles—milked and talked and sang songs to the cows.

"Not one of them could carry a note. With all that awful crooning and warbling going on, I'm surprised those cows didn't produce cottage cheese." Grandpa's eyes would crinkle up and he'd laugh in that quiet way of his.

Grandpa had kept the horses in the barn's lean-to, one team in each stall. Their harness hung on the barn posts beside them. In winter, when it was forty below, there'd be hoarfrost bristling like sugary icicles on the harness buckles. "Those kids just couldn't resist trying to lick it off, and every winter someone's tongue would get stuck to

---

2 **sodbusters:** farmers who break sod
3 **Union Jacks:** flags of the United Kingdom, also flown in Canada to symbolize allegiance to the British crown

the cold metal. I'd run to the house and get Grandma to heat the kettle and then run back out and pour hot water on the metal to get them unstuck. They always left a little blood and skin behind."

sloughs
(slüz) places of deep mud

Upstairs in the loft, not much had changed. Grandpa used to put up mountains of fresh loose hay cut from **sloughs**. We put up our hay in bales now. We'd look up there anyway, stopping to listen to the low conversations of pigeons in the cupola.[4] "Do you think they're the grandchildren of the pigeons that were here when you lived here?" I asked him once.

He had nodded his head. "Oh, without a doubt." That made me feel good.

Grandpa always carried a pencil in his pocket, and whenever he was milking cows, fixing machinery or just resting up after a day of work, he'd stop, take out his pencil and write something on the wall of the barn. It was a habit he got into, and over the years the barn walls filled up with his little notes. On the wall in front of me, above the drill press, beside the holes drilled into the wooden post where the drill bits were kept, he had written another of his messages:

July 17, 1935
Hauling wheat. Grasshoppers bad!
92 in the shade.
Ted

Outside, a crow cawed. A car crunched up the lane. Then another. I heard them stop. I imagined dust hanging behind them like jet trails. A door creaked open—and slammed shut. Half-ton. Then quiet. Just the liquid song of a robin, a few lazy notes from a sun-warmed cricket, the dry whir of a grasshopper flying. Then people talking quietly. Words tumbling, muffled, like a distant stream. Someone laughed! *How can they laugh, for crying out loud? He's dead!* I couldn't go out there. I couldn't face those church-step smiles, the perfumed hugs, the awkward handshakes. I'd had enough of them already today.

A barn cat appeared like a ghost and rubbed against my leg. "Hi there, Bandit." He arched his back and purred loudly as I stroked his long grey fur. Mom used to cut my hair, always used to just chop it

---

4 **cupola:** a raised, often rounded structure on top of a roof with small windows and a pointed ceiling

Rick Book

off in a brush cut. Until one time when we were visiting Grandma and Grandpa in town and Dad said I needed a haircut. I had started to argue about it when Grandpa turned to Dad and said, "Let the boy grow his hair." No grown-up had ever stuck up for me before. From then on I kept my hair just the way I wanted.

When Grandma died I'd had the mumps and was sick in bed. So I'd never seen someone I knew dead before. Judy Davies, the town undertaker's daughter, had told me what her dad does to bodies. How he takes out their organs and sews up their chests. And then puts felt under their shirts so people can't feel the baseball stitches. There was no way I was going to touch Grandpa. Even though he had his arms folded over his chest and was holding his reading glasses in one hand.

They'd put makeup on him. You could see the smudges of powder around his hair. Reminded me of Aunt Gertie my parents used to have over at Christmas. Grandpa looked like an old doll sleeping in a box. It was scary to look at him. I wished he'd open his eyes and smile and say, "Hey there, sonny boy, how about a little walk?"

Grandpa and Grandma lived in town, but they loved the country. They always carried a wicker picnic basket and a red tartan blanket in their car. They'd pack a thermos of coffee and sandwiches and go on long Sunday drives, just looking at the crops. At harvest time Dad would be combining,[5] a cloud of dust on the horizon. I'd be in the truck, waiting for the **hopper** to fill up with wheat. And at lunch Grandpa and Grandma's car would appear. Mom would arrive, too, with my sisters and a car full of smells: a big Dutch oven with hot roast beef, with corn on the cob and new potatoes and fresh peas and carrots from the garden. Grandma would help spread the old quilts on the stubble beside the cars.

Grandpa and I'd wander out into the swath.[6] He'd bend over and grab some wheat, break off a few big heads and grind them between his palms. Then he'd hold them close to his mouth and blow the husks and chaff[7] away. He'd peer at the gold kernels in his deeply lined palm like the watch repairman at Eaton's, poke them

hopper
a funnel-shaped object used to hold grain

---

5 **combining:** using a combine, a machine that harvests wheat

6 **swath:** rows of cut grain left behind by the combine

7 **husks and chaff:** shells and seed coverings of the wheat left behind after the harvest

Saying Good-bye to the Tall Man

with his bony finger, check for color, see how fat or shriveled they were. "What do you think?" I knew it was a test.

"Number One," I'd say. And he'd smile, pop the wheat into his mouth and chew to see how hard and dry it was. I followed each step, threw the wheat into my mouth but didn't swallow. I kept chewing until it turned into gum, just like he'd showed me one time, until Dad came round with the combine and it was time to eat.

The meals were feasts. And while we ate, Grandpa and Grandma would hear all the news from my sisters and me. What we'd been doing, where we'd been fishing, whether we were looking forward to school. After pie and coffee, Dad would say good-bye and start up. Mom would clean up, then take my sisters off to a slough to look for frogs. Grandpa and Grandma would lie down in the shade beside the car tire, Grandma with her head on Grandpa's chest and they'd have a snooze. "Just forty winks," Grandpa would say.

More cars were coming up the lane. More people. More words. The ache in my gut wasn't going away. It just sat there like red coals. I still didn't want to go out there.

An old aluminum milk pail hung from an iron hook on a rafter. Cobwebs draped over the handle like lace, the bottom dented where a cow had stepped in it. Instantly I saw Grandpa with the pail tied to his belt, wading into a chokecherry patch in some coulee.[8] The trees were black with berries. The sun was hot. It was quiet, just the odd bee buzzing, the rustling of branches as we milked clumps of berries into the pail, the plip-plip-plip of berries hitting the bottom when the pail was empty; the quieter plopping sounds as it filled up. Sometimes we'd talk. Sometimes the conversation would slow to a trickle, just the odd word passed back and forth in a conspiracy, a comment, a laugh. Often there was just silence.

3-day blizzard
−35. Drifts over garage.
Jan 11/29
Ted

"Want some tea, Kat?" Grandpa'd stand over Grandma as she sat in her recliner. Her arthritis was bad and the chair had heating pads and a vibrator built right into it. Outside it was blizzarding again. I'd

---

8 **coulee:** a small, shallow stream

Rick Book

stayed in town after school for hockey practice, but now it was storming too hard to get home to the farm. Coming to Grandpa and Grandma's was always the reward you got for being stuck in town. Grandpa'd make potato pancakes with hash and canned peas and corn. I'd watch as he poured the tea in the kitchen. Dad and Mom used to laugh about it. He always held the pot so far from the teacup you never thought the tea would make it. But somehow it arced across the distance and into the cup before gravity knew what was up.

Sometimes an uncle or older cousin would be storm-stayed, too. I'd listen to their conversations—about politics, about the news. After everyone got all talked out, we'd sit in the living room and Grandpa would turn on the radio and Grandma would turn out the lights. The radio was brown wood with a cloth cover over the speaker and was set into an alcove by Grandpa's chair. In the dark the numbers on the dial glowed. I was drawn to that light like a moth, hungry for stories of the world beyond Saskatchewan. We listened to the CBC, to classical music, which was boring, to radio plays and, best of all, mysteries. I often woke up the next morning on the couch where I'd fallen asleep in my pajamas. Grandpa and Grandma would have put a comforter over me and given me a pillow with a picture of a wolf howling at the moon and the words *Waskesiu, Prince Albert National Park* on it.

I walked out of the shop, over to the old sleigh that was wedged into one of the stalls. It had been there as long as I could remember. I'd never seen it outside the barn. It was an enclosed horse-drawn sleigh. A big yellow plywood box on wood and steel runners. Inside there were two plate glass windows, and there were two round holes beneath it for the reins to the horses to pass through. Grandpa said they'd had a kerosene heater and buffalo robes and cowhides to keep them warm.

"We'd hook up old Queen and Bess and go across the fields to neighbors to play cards, have a big feed and maybe a singsong around the piano. Later the horses would follow their own tracks home again right to the barn. You could hear the harness bells jingling for a mile in the cold air. And the stars would be so bright and your Grandma would be singing—" Grandpa stopped and I wondered what he was thinking of, and if it was possible at his age to still be in love. And if he missed his old friends and neighbors who were now dying off.

In church today it felt like everyone was looking at me just waiting to see if I was going to cry. Dad didn't. None of my uncles did, but my aunts sure did. So did Mom especially. She loved Grandpa best of all, I think. We were always stopping in at their house, bringing baking, fresh-cooked meals that Grandpa could just freeze and then pop into the oven. Last time we were there, though, I noticed Grandpa had had an accident going to the bathroom and his pants were a mess, even his hands. Mom and Dad whispered about it in the car on the way home. We were all pretty sad. But old Grandpa, he still stood straight as an arrow, and he still loved to throw back his head and laugh. When he had his heart attack a few days ago, my uncles were there within minutes to take him to the hospital in Riverside. As they were carrying him out he looked up at George and said, "Well, I guess this is it." Grandpa knew he wasn't coming home again.

The cemetery is just outside of town past the **elevators**—a square acre of grass surrounded by tall poplars on the edge of a field

elevators
buildings for elevating, storing, and delivering grain

that had just been combined. Grandpa's grave was right next to Grandma's. The headstone on his side was empty. Gunnar, Sigurd, Rudy, Axle, Pat and Johnny were pallbearers, all farmers. Slowly they pulled the coffin out of the long black Cadillac that had come from Saskatoon. With big hands and weathered faces, these friends carried Grandpa to his grave. Axle stumbled and the coffin tilted. I wondered if Grandpa's body was rolling inside. I wondered if Grandpa was watching from somewhere. I wondered what he thought.

The men set the coffin down on two canvas straps stretched across the black hole. It was neat and tidy and awful. They were going to put Grandpa down there! In all that dirt. That's where he'd be until the coffin rotted and his bones turned to dust. My teeth were clenched like a vice. My tie was choking me. A puff of wind brought perfume and aftershave, stubble field, fresh-cut grass and dirt. Someone cleared their throat. Someone sobbed. The minister, a gray-haired Dutchman, was a friend of Grandpa's and Grandma's even though they didn't go to church. He stood in his long black robe by Grandpa's head, the elevators in the distance behind him, and he smiled. "This is a day to celebrate life," he said. "A man that loved and was loved by his family and his community." I bit down on my tongue. I stared hard at the orange lilies on top of the coffin.

There was a prayer and then the minister grabbed a handful of dirt and sprinkled it on Grandpa's coffin. And then he shook hands with Dad and Mom and my aunts and uncles. People started talking again quietly. Shaking hands. Hugs. Smiles. It was over. My sisters and I didn't know what to do, so we got into the back seat of our car and waited. Mom and Dad finally got in, looking gray and grim. As Dad started the car I turned and looked out the back window. Mr. Davies, the undertaker, bent over and released something holding the straps. Grandpa's casket started going down, smoothly, like a car on a hoist. In seconds he and the lilies were gone. A breeze sprang up as we drove out; poplar leaves clattered like applause—for Grandpa with his glasses in his hand, in his blue pinstripe suit, with formaldehyde in his veins.

Picnicked today in Beaton Coulee
2 inches of rain last night. Crops look good.
Ted & Kat June 30, 1947

Someone was at the door. It rolled open a bit. A footstep on the cement floor. "You in there?" It was Mom.

"Yeah, in here." I straightened and turned to face her. It was strange to see Mom in the barn, especially in her good church dress and with lipstick on.

"Hi," she said, scanning my face with radar eyes. "You okay?"

I shook my head. And then it happened. All the feelings that had been bottled inside me for the last week, the last three days, welled up like water in a cistern pump. A piston started moving inside my chest, heaving up and down, shaking my shoulders, building up pressure. I stood there, fists clenched at my side, and finally the tears came.

Mom put her arms around me. "I know," she whispered. "I..." She stopped, waited, tried to say something but couldn't. Her grip on me tightened. Her shoulders shook. We both stood there crying.

Finally Mom pulled back and looked at me, wiping her eyes. "You know he'll always be right here, don't you?"

Clang. A metallic ring came from outside. "They're playing horseshoes!"

"Yes. Don't you think Grandpa would like that?"

"Yeah, I guess so."

"Well, think you're ready to come out now and say hello?"

"Yeah." I wiped my face and sniffed. "I'll be there in a minute. I have something to do first."

"Okay." Mom moved to the door and stepped out into the light. She stopped and looked up. "Perfect day for a picnic. Bet you that's what they're doing right now." And then she was gone.

I stood there for a minute, then turned and walked back into the shop to the workbench and reached for a can on the shelf. There was the yellow stub of an old carpenter's pencil in it. I looked for a space on the wall.

Edward (Ted) Anderson buried today. Age 92.
All his friends and family here.
Sunny, 78 degrees.
Eric
September 19, 1965

✳ **THE POET'S PERSPECTIVE**

Because I could not stop for Death

Emily Dickinson

Because I could not stop for Death—
He kindly stopped for me—
The Carriage held but just Ourselves—
And **Immortality**.

We slowly drove—He knew no haste
And I had put away
My labor and my leisure too,
For His Civility—

We passed the School, where Children strove
At Recess—in the Ring—
We passed the Fields of Gazing Grain—
We passed the Setting Sun—

Or rather—He passed Us—
The Dews drew quivering and chill—
For only Gossamer, my Gown—
My Tippet—only Tulle[1]—

We paused before a House that seemed
A Swelling of the Ground—
The Roof was scarcely visible—
The Cornice[2]—in the Ground—

Since then—'tis Centuries—and yet
Feels shorter than the Day
I first surmised[3] the Horses' Heads
Were toward Eternity—

immortality
*unending existence;
being alive forever*

LITERARY LENS

*Why do you think Rick Book
uses a barn as the place
where Eric remembers his
grandfather and Dickinson
uses a carriage as the setting
for her poem?*

---

1 **My Tippet—only Tulle:** a shawl made of lightweight net cloth
2 **cornice:** a horizontal piece along the top of a wall, pillar, or building
3 **surmised:** guessed; inferred

RESPONDING TO UNIT TWO
Family Album

REFLECTING

1. There are many different kinds of families in this unit. Some include only one parent. Others include grandparents and brothers and sisters. Based on what you have read, what do you think makes a family?

2. Of all the families you read about in this unit, which would you most like to have as your next-door neighbor? Why?

3. Think about Ashleigh's predicament in "Ashes." What do you think she will do? What would you do in her place?

4. What does the minister mean when he says at Grandpa's funeral, "This is a day to celebrate life"?

ANALYZING

5. Each of the families featured in this unit has strengths and weaknesses. Develop a chart like the one below and list the strengths and weaknesses of each family.

Selection	Family Members	Strengths	Weaknesses
Looking for Work	*Gary* *Sister* *Brother* *Mother*	*Laughter* *Caring* *Support*	*No money* *Mom overworked* *Kids on their own a lot*
A Plate of Peas			
Ashes			
After the Divorce			
Atomic Blue Pieces			
The Night the Bear Ate Goombaw			
Saying Good-bye to the Tall Man			

6. What is the main idea, or major theme, of Gary Soto's autobiographical account, "Looking for Work"?

7. "The Night the Bear Ate Goombaw" might be called a "comedy of errors." Analyze the mix-ups in this story that help to make it amusing.

8. The mood of a piece of writing is the primary feeling it conveys. For example, "The Night the Bear Ate Goombaw" has a light-hearted mood. How would you describe the mood in the poem "Because I could not stop for Death"?

9. Active Reading What events in the story "A Plate of Peas" were you able to **predict** in your reading? How often do you estimate you used the Active Reading strategies of questioning and predicting in this unit?

DISCUSSING

Different people in a family often take on different roles. For example, one person might be seen as the most responsible, another might be considered the most lighthearted, and a third might be thought of as the most emotional. What roles do you fulfill in your family? What roles do you perform in your life as a student and as a friend?

WRITING

Tales of Great Aunt Jack Most families have stories that are passed from person to person and generation to generation. Interview family members about another family member's famous adventure or about a long-standing family tradition—or simply make one up! Use your interviews to develop an essay or a short story.

Look at Us Find photos of your family to create an album of your history. Assemble the photos in a book of your own making, starting with pictures of you and others when you were a baby and progressing to the present. At each stage, write a short account of your impressions, memories, thoughts, or feelings about the people in the photographs.

WORK IN PROGRESS

Roots As a class, work together to decide what a family tree showing extended family members or a friendship tree showing a circle of friends might look like. When you have gathered all your ideas, choose either the family tree or the friendship tree to work on individually. Try to include birth and death dates in the family tree and phone numbers or email addresses in the friendship tree.

Families of the World, Unite! Choose a country you have never been to and research the culture and traditions of families in the country. Answer questions such as "What do families do for recreation?" "What is the average family size?" "What chores are assigned to the children?" Think of questions you'd like answered; then research the subject and give a short presentation.

Friendly Photos

That made me smile. Dan could almost always make me feel better, which is good. Because I'm a little miserable most of the time.

from "A Robot Doesn't Have a Curve Ball"
by Ron Koertge

Active Reading Alert!

CLARIFYING

As you read the selections in this unit, be sure to clear up anything that may be at all confusing right away. If something isn't quite clear, go back and reread until you understand what you've read. Think about the main idea of the passage or paragraph you have just finished reading. Continually clarify what the author is telling you throughout your reading.

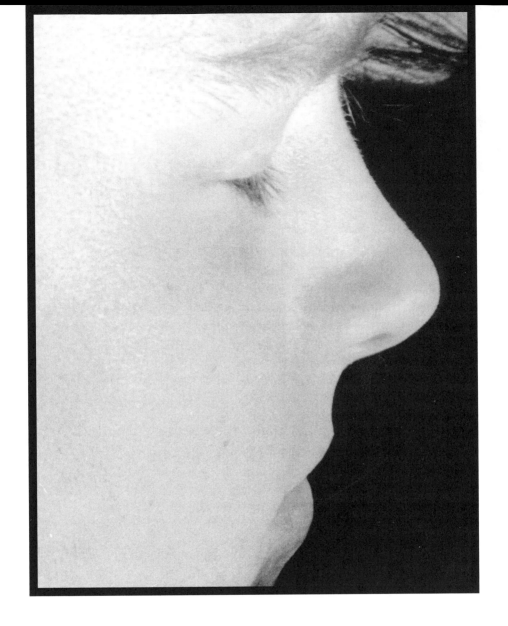

Kissing Tennessee

Kathi Appelt

*t*he answer wasn't clear at all to Peggy Lee Dixon, floating along the way she was, as if she were on a big, puffy cloud. But if a couple of birds flew by, one of them might look back over her shiny black wing and say, "Hey, did you see that girl over there? What's she doing up here in our sky?"

And the other one would say, "Leave her be, sister. That there is Peggy Lee Dixon, and all she's doin' is floatin'. No harm in floatin', is there?"

Then the first one would say, "But why's she floatin'?"

"'Cause Tennessee Jones finally passed the kiss test, that's why."

"The 'kiss test'! What in blue blazes is that?" By now the first bird would be gettin' agitated.

"Silly goose," bird number two would say. "That's when there's only one kiss in the whole movie, but that one kiss is worth the price of admission."

▪▪▪▪

LITERARY LENS

As you read the story and the accompanying poem, look for an image that is dominant in both.

It's not the first time he's kissed her.

No, the original kiss was in the first grade. There she was in her favorite pink Wrangler jeans and her new pink sweater that her grandmother had given her for Christmas, leaning up against the brick wall next to the door of the first-grade wing at Dogwood Elementary School, just standing there, pink, waiting for the bell to ring. Two or three other first graders were standing there with her, but not Tennessee.

He was out on the playground with a big group of other kids.

So there she was, leaning against the wall, when all of a sudden Tennessee shot from the playground crowd like a **meteor**, his blond hair blazing in the sun, his blue-jeans jacket streaming behind him. Faster than the speed of light, he blew by her, paused only long enough to kiss her right on the mouth, then zoomed back into orbit.

"Tennessee Jones!" Peggy Lee yelled. "I'm telling!" And she did, too.

That particular kiss earned Tennessee a trip to the office where Mr. Duncan, the principal, told him in no uncertain terms that kissing on school property was not allowed.

▪▪▪▪

meteor
a piece of matter that falls to earth from outer space with such speed that it glows

Tennessee. Now there's a name for you. His mama named him that on account of their last name being so regular. "With a plain vanilla name like Jones, you gotta have a first name that's special," she'd said. Tennessee, almost the exact same age as Peggy Lee and whose yard shares a fence with hers, who comes in and out of the Dixons' back door a million times a day. What a name.

Peggy Lee. She was named after an old singer her daddy thinks was the best thing this side of the Mississippi (and maybe the other side, too). Her daddy is just wild about this one song she sings. He knows all the words to it, and when Peggy Lee was really little, he used to pick her up in his arms, take her outside on the porch, and sing that song over and over, "Is That All There Is?"

Peggy Lee loved the song then, but now that she's thirteen, almost fourteen, it drives her crazy when her daddy starts singing it, because as soon as he does, it gets stuck in her head and she can't get it out. It just keeps playing over and over, like a scene from a movie sometimes does. And it's such a hard song to figure out. Is it happy? Is it sad? Happy? Sad? It seems all jumbled up.

■■■

The next time Tennessee kissed Peggy Lee, it was not on school property. It was at the Dogwood North Little League Park.

When they'd both been in the fourth grade, they'd played on the same baseball team, the Cardinals. The Cardinals made it all the way to the district playoffs. At the end of the championship game, they were behind by one run, 6–7, against the Lufkin Bearcats. It was the bottom of the ninth and the Cardinals were up to bat with two outs already. They had a runner on third base, and it was Peggy Lee's turn at bat.

None of the other boys on the team believed that she could hit against the Lufkin pitcher. But Tennessee yelled from the dugout, "Come on, Peggy Lee!"

That's one thing about Peggy Lee and Tennessee, they've always been there for each other. When Tennessee fell out of his tree house and broke his arm, Peggy Lee visited him at home every afternoon after school for the three whole days he was absent. She brought his homework to him and notes from the other kids, and told him all the jokes she could think up to make him feel better.

When Peggy Lee couldn't quite figure out how to do the multiplication tables, Tennessee showed her how to line up the numbers in columns and then look at them like pairs. He said it so that everything made perfect sense. Even today Peggy Lee knows her multiplication tables backward and forward because of that.

When Bodger, Tennessee's old dog, died one winter, Peggy Lee used her daddy's shovel to dig a hole in the backyard to bury him while Tennessee sat on the ground, cradling Bodger in his arms and crying. Then she sat next to Tennessee and cried and cried right along with him. And she never told anyone about Tennessee crying, either, not a single person.

So when it was Peggy Lee's turn to bat at the district playoffs, when everyone else thought they'd lose for sure because it was her, Peggy Lee, at bat, there was Tennessee yelling, "Come on, Peggy Lee! You can do it!"

And she did. When the pitcher threw the ball, she could see it heading straight for her swing, see it coming directly at the sweet spot on her bat, see it connect with the aluminum, leather against metal.

Pow! The ball went deep into left field, way behind the Bearcats' fielder, giving the runner on third base time to score—and Peggy Lee, too. Everyone on the bench poured out onto the field. They were all hugging and jumping and giving high fives. Cardinals everywhere.

And smack in the middle of all the commotion, Tennessee looked right at Peggy Lee and planted one right on her mouth. Then he just started jumping up and down with the rest of them, like it never happened.

Later, when they were eating their **complimentary** snow cones, Peggy Lee said, "Why'd you do that?"

complimentary
free; without charge

"Do what?" he asked, licking the red syrup that was running down the outside of his paper snowcone cup across the back of his hand.

"You know," she said, "kiss me like that."

He looked at her in total amazement. "Kiss you?" Then he leaned his head back and spit red ice straight up toward the stadium light. It glittered in the burning light.

But all of that was before tonight at the Stardust Dance.

Tennessee's daddy had dropped them off in front of the cafeteria right at eight o'clock, just as the band was beginning to play. When they'd walked in, the place was all sparkly. There was glitter everywhere, sprinkled on the table by the punch bowl and cookies, sprinkled on the floor, glued onto the decorations. It was even tucked into the napkins, so that when you picked one up, glitter floated through the air.

It was wonderful—the glitter, the music, all their friends dancing and talking. Pretty soon they were dancing, too. Peggy Lee with J.T. Sims and Tennessee with Tessie Adams. Peggy Lee didn't only dance with J.T., either. Nope. And Tennessee, he didn't only dance with Tessie. Peggy Lee saw him dancing with Julia Marsh and Patty Henderson, too.

The whole evening was filled with laughing and dancing and glitter. But especially dancing. And now it was almost over. Only a few dances left.

Peggy Lee was just getting ready to grab J.T.'s hand and pull him out onto the floor, when there was Tennessee, right in front of her, just like those times in first grade and at the Little League park. "Come on, Peggy Lee. This one's for me." And he wrapped his arms around her and pulled her close. All their lives they had been together, their houses backing up to each other. All their almost fourteen years they had been going in and out of each other's back doors without even knocking. Ever since they could remember, it had been Peggy Lee and Tennessee.

And in all that time, Peggy Lee didn't remember ever being so close to him as right then in the school cafeteria.

That's when she noticed how green his eyes were, and how tall he suddenly seemed to be, and how nice he smelled—like the spiced tea his mama made on cold afternoons when they came home from school to do their homework together. Like orange and cinnamon and cloves. Like that.

She closed her eyes and took a deep breath, and when she opened them, the whole room was filled with glitter. Glitter floating all around them. Right then the only place in the world she wanted to be was up close to Tennessee.

"I'm gonna get this right," he said. And as the band began to play the first chorus of an old Aerosmith song, he leaned down and kissed her. Just like that. Kissed her right on the mouth, right there in the Dogwood Junior High cafeteria that was all filled up with glitter.

Flash! She opened her eyes just in time to see Sky Williams take their picture.

And that's when the floating had started. The cafeteria floor just fell away beneath her feet. And even though Tennessee is holding her hand, she's still way up off the ground, like one of those helium balloons, floating up there with the clouds and the comets and the birds.

Later, when she gets back home, that song of her daddy's will keep on playing over and over in her head. "Is That All There Is?" Later she'll feel that way, happy and sad all jumbled up together.

But right now, her head on Tennessee's shoulder, the music swirling around them, one thing's for certain. That kiss? That single kiss? It was worth the price of admission.

 THE POET'S PERSPECTIVE

The Dream Keeper

Langston Hughes

Bring me all of your dreams,
You dreamers,
Bring me all of your
Heart melodies
That I may wrap them
In a blue cloud-cloth
Away from the too-rough fingers
Of the world.

LITERARY LENS

What image in "The Dream Keeper" is similar to the image in the opening passage in "Kissing Tennessee," in which birds watch Peggy Lee?

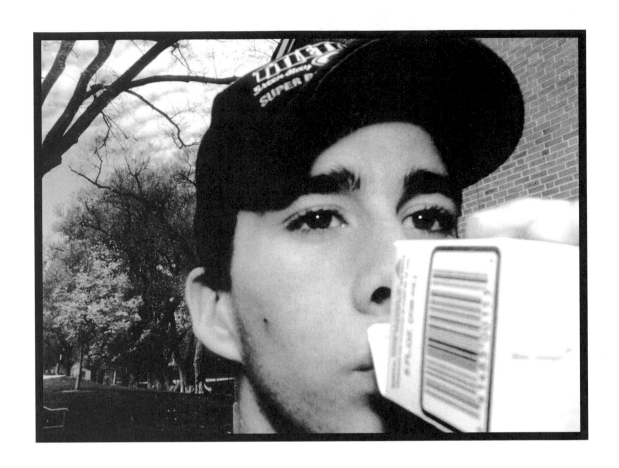

A Robot Doesn't Have a Curve Ball

Ron Koertge

I squatted behind the plate, pulled down my face mask, and got ready for the first pitch of the millennium.[1]

Sixty feet and six inches away, Dan blew on his fingers, then reached into his glove. He eyed me, shook off my first sign, nodded at the second.

"Take it easy," I yelled. "It's a long season."

His tight jaw didn't even twitch. He was practicing his game face. First time he'd had it on since summer league. He stretched and let it fly.

I had to reach. "What kind of slider was that? Try a curve this time."

"That was a curve." He rotated one arm, like a little kid playing windmill. "I'm stiff, man."

"I told you we should've played more catch." I faked a big overhand toss but didn't let go because it was great to feel the ball again, the code of the stitches in my hand. Great to feel my body move in ways it hadn't all winter.

Danny lobbed a few; then he turned on the heat. My left hand, buried in the mitt, started to sting a little.

I pressed on the air like catchers do, motioning for him to take it easy. I walked toward him maybe ten feet or so.

"You going to the dance?" I asked.

He was bringing up his knee, watching it descend. Working on his mechanics. "What dance?"

"The Spring Fling. Or at least that's what the banner across the front of the art building said."

"Oh, yeah." Dan frowned and stepped off the mound. "Are you going?"

"Everybody's going."

"So who'd you ask?"

"Nobody. How about you?"

"I asked Nobody, too. She said she was going with you."

That made me smile. Dan could almost always make me feel better, which is good. Because I'm a little miserable most of the time. Most kids are. Most *people* are. Especially since this is the year 2000 and nothing's changed. It's in all the papers and on TV; everybody thought it'd make such a difference, getting away from all those

LITERARY LENS

As you read the story, pay attention to the way Dan, Lee, and Walter talk to one another.

---

1 **millennium:** a period of one thousand years

nasty nineteen hundreds and into the terrific twos. And what really happened? Nada. Nothing. Zero. Zilch. Squat. Our folks go to work; we go to school.

At least we've got baseball.

He threw one sidearm, then flexed his wrist, checking for motion. I lobbed it back.

"We could go to the dance stag," I said.

"If we go together, we wouldn't be stag, would we?"

"We'd be two stags."

"Can stags do that, Lee?"

"If they don't rub each other's antlers."

"It's been a long winter, my friend. It's time you got out of the house."

My legs were starting to ache, so I stood up. "Let's say I ask somebody. My parents drive over to her house, I **trudge** up the walk and face her father; then my folks drop us off at the dance, pick us up again three hours later, and wait in the car while I walk her to the door. That sucks so intensely. In sixteen months I get my license. I'll start dancing then."

"Ethan asked Ann, and he said they're just going to meet there."

"Big Ann or Little Ann?"

"Big Ann. Why? Are you thinking about Little Ann?"

"No way. When you dance, her nose is like in your belly button."

"And that's a bad thing?" He stepped all the way off the mound. "So who?" he asked.

"Leslie."

"Yeah! Leslie is fresh!"

I covered my ears like he'd dropped a cherry bomb into the nearest trash can. "Do you think they heard you in Montana?"

"What's the problem? She likes you. Toby told me."

"Oh, great. Let's believe Toby, whose father said the world was going to end last year."

"Millennium fever. A lot of people had that."

"A lot of people didn't stop doing their homework like Toby."

"Speaking of homework," Dan interrupted, "don't look now; here comes Walter."

"In his blue Doc Martens."[2]

trudge
walk as though with great effort

---

2 **Doc Martens:** heavy shoes made by a European company of the same name

Ron Koertge

"They match his hair."

"It's kind of cool he did that," I said. "Most science geeks don't bother."

"Most science geeks don't play second base, either."

Walter found a fairly dry spot on the brown grass and stacked his textbooks like he was building a pyramid to Ra.[3] He watched Dan throw some smoke.[4]

"You guys are gonna go all the way to the majors together," he yelled. "You'll be the next great black-and-white battery."

"Dan is black?" I frowned and turned to my buddy. "You never told me you were black."

"Hey, you never asked."

"Very funny," said Walter taking a cling-wrapped sandwich out of his book bag.

We watched him eat. He took precise bites and chewed each one a long time. "Are you going to finish that in time for the dance?" I asked.

He took a swig of bottled water. "Dances are a waste of time."

"Which means," Dan said, "that he asked and got shot down."

"You don't get into Cal Tech going to dances, guys."

"That's where you're wrong, Walter," I said. "You have to rumba to get into Cal Tech. Everybody knows that."

"So who wouldn't go to the dance with you?" asked Dan. "Or is the list so long that we'll be late for dinner."

Walter tucked his long hair behind both ears, which seemed to have been created for exactly that. He lowered his head.

"It was so bad," he muttered. "I'm still, like, totally sick at my stomach. First of all, I had to wait about twenty years until she was alone."

Danny walked all the way to the baseline where Walter sat. He put a **consoling** hand on one thin shoulder. "You have to have that wolf mentality, buddy. Trail them until the weakest drops back; then you swoop down, cut her out of the herd, and ask her for a date."

"Actually, that's what I did. I followed them until Ann stopped to look in a store window."

consoling
offering comfort to an unhappy person

---

3 **pyramid to Ra:** the ancient Egyptians would build pyramids in honor of Ra, their sun god

4 **throw some smoke:** in this usage, throw a few pitches

"You asked Little Ann?"

"Who else, Lee? *I'm* little."

I looked at Walter. "You're little? You never told me you were little."

Dan scooted closer. "Just ignore him. I'm listening. You get her alone at the window, you ask her, and—?"

"Okay. So I do that. I get her alone. My heart's pounding, my palms are sweaty. I stutter. But I ask her." Walter dropped his head into both palms. "Oh, God."

"I take it she didn't say yes."

"She didn't say anything."

I nudged my mask higher on my forehead. "So what happened? She's not still standing there, is she?"

Walter sighed. "After about an hour, she yelled, 'Wait for me!' and ran up the block."

Dan rubbed a little dirt into the baseball. "In second grade when they ran away, it meant they liked you."

"But this is tenth grade," I told him, "and there's plenty of fish in the sea."

"Not short fish. And not as cute." Walter got to his feet. He clenched his fists. "This dating crap is so frustrating. Five years from now, ten tops, it'll be way better."

I cocked my head. "Why's that?"

"For one thing, absolutely everybody'll be online."

Dan shrugged. "So?"

"So we'll all be in the privacy of our own homes," Walter said. "Nobody'll be nervous."

I planted both feet and held out my arms like I was angling down the face of a wave. "You're not nervous when you surf the old net?"

Walter shook his head. "Nope. For one thing, I'm not short."

"Excuse me?"

"I mean nobody knows I'm short, so I don't think about it."

Dan leaned forward. "What do you say when somebody asks how tall you are?"

"They don't ask stuff like that."

"Pretty bogus chat room." Dan knocked some dirt out of his cleats.

"Well, okay. Sometimes. Like on weekends."

I nodded. "When the question of height often rears its ugly head."

"So," Dan asked, "what do you tell 'em on weekends, Walter?"

"The truth, okay? I tell 'em the truth. But it's, like, it doesn't matter so much because nobody can see me. In hyperspace, short is a **relative** term."

I told him that he was a braver man than I. "I'd lie about these zits."

"Well, pretty soon you won't be able to lie, cause you'll be sitting at your computer and there'll be, like, this red light that flashes if you do."

Dan scowled. "I don't even want to hear this, Walter."

"Well, it's coming. I saw a picture of it. You still use your mouse, okay? But there's this thing on it that's really a miniature polygraph."[5]

I held up my mitt like I was checking for rain, leaned forward, and let my mask tumble into it. "So it's Saturday night on Earth," I mused, "sometime in the future, and these super-unstressed people are sitting around with their fingers in these teensy-weensy lie detectors, and that's dating?"

"Right."

"But what do you do besides sit there?" asked Dan.

"Pretty much anything you do on a real date: watch the same movie, eat popcorn—"

"You're in different parts of the city eating popcorn?"

"But you can, like, hear the other person chew and stuff 'cause you're both wearing these like very high-tech, super-sensitive body suits," said Walter. "So you're virtually together."

"But not really," I said.

He held his thumb and forefinger a micromillimeter apart. "Very, very, very close."

I leaned toward him. "But not really."

"You can hardly tell the difference."

I leaned closer. "But there is a difference."

"Virtually none."

Dan pushed me out of the way. "Why don't people just listen to each other chew in a real movie?"

---

5 **polygraph:** a machine used to administer a lie-detector test

"'Cause virtual is better."

"Virtual kissing is better than real kissing? Are you nuts? Technology is never gonna be that good."

"Well, for sure it's safer: no mono, no bad breath . . ."

I took hold of his shirt and shook him a couple of times. "But, Walter, you hypertool, there's no breath at all!"

"Okay, forget kissing. Say Dan blows out a rotator cuff[6] Wednesday. Dr. Cyborg just makes him a new one, and he pitches again Thursday."

Dan frowned. "How'd I blow out a rotator cuff? I thought I was wearing my super-sensitive, high-tech body suit with one finger stuck in the lie detecting mouse."

"You'd find a way, ace. Or let's say you need some major organ; you just replace it. Everybody'll live forever."

"Sounds like long lines at the ATM," I said.

"Money will be in museums. Curiosity pieces. There'll just be debit chips. Everything'll be different."

"Well, not baseball. No way am I giving up baseball."

Walter shook his head. "You don't have to give it up, Dan. Just plug in a sports module."

"And then what? Have virtual Mom wash the virtual grass stains out of my virtual uniform? No way."

"Well, at least there won't be any more of that racial stuff."

"And why's that?"

Walter looked smug. "No races. No black people. Or yellow people or white people. We'll all be the same."

"Hey, I like being black."

"You can always jack into the black experience."

Dan looked suspicious. "I know I shouldn't ask this, but what color are we all going to be?"

"Beige."

Dan and I just about collapsed. We fell all over each other. A couple of kids walking home on the third base side stared at us, we were laughing so hard.

When I was pulled together again, I said, "My grandma told me that when she was our age, like back in the fifties, everybody was

---

6 **rotator cuff:** part of the shoulder that connects the muscles, tendons, and head of the humerus bone, the long bone of the upper arm

Ron Koertge

sure that by 2000 we'd all be wearing silver jumpsuits and zipping around in hovermobiles."

Dan tugged at his Cardinals cap. "And what'd we get instead? Extra wide, extra baggy jeans from the Gap and the new VW Beetle, which looks a whole lot like the old VW Beetle."

Walter leaned in. "But other stuff changed. Lee's grandma had never heard of computers, and now they're everywhere. And she couldn't have been friends with your grandma, Danny, because races were, like, almost totally separate back then."

Dan looked unimpressed. "Yeah, but we also got AIDS and a rain forest about as big as a patio." He tossed the ball into the air and caught it behind his back. "Man, remember midnight 1999? That was supposed to be such a big deal. And what really happened? A million people got drunk and puked, that's what happened."

"Not all at once," I pointed out. "They puked according to their time zones, moving from east to west."

"Whatever. So where were your robots with their mops and aspirins then?"

"They'll happen." Walter was decisive. "They're being built. And I sure wish I'd had one yesterday. I would've had it go meet Ann's robot, and I would've just stayed home and not got dumped on."

"Because you would've wisely programmed it to break it to you gently?" I asked.

"Anyway," Dan pointed out, "she didn't say no. She didn't say anything. What's your robot going to do with that?"

Walter acted patient. "You're thinking of replicants,[7] Lee. Robots just do whatever you tell them to."

"My grandma's really funny about robots," I said. "They *were* the year 2000 to her. She's totally steamed she hasn't got one. She was supposed to be able to sit around and these cute little aluminum guys would clean the toilet and vacuum and stuff. So now every time Granddad doesn't take out the garbage, she yells, "Where's the robot?"

"There'll probably be robot baseball," said Walter. "We'll watch it from the safety of our cocoons."

Only about three feet separated them, but Danny charged like he'd been brushed back hard. "There's not going to be any robot

---

7 **replicants:** sci-fi inventions; creatures that replicate the actions of their real-life counterparts

baseball! Robots don't have curve balls."

"Hey, you can build a robot that'd throw the wickedest—"

"No, no. Every curve is different." He appealed to me. "Right, Lee?"

I stepped up beside him. "Right."

"Guys, you program in the differences."

Dan shoved him. "Shut up, Walter!"

Walter shoved back. "Hey, I know what I know."

That's when I spotted the girls. "Break it up, you guys. There's Ann and Leslie."

"And," said Dan, "Heather Nyguen. Too bad she's going with Rasheed."

"They broke up," Walter informed us.

I asked where he got that scoop. "One of your chat rooms?"

"Toby told me."

"Man, Toby didn't used to know anything. Toby was totally out of it. How come all of a sudden Toby knows everything?"

Walter looked smug. "He's online, Lee. He's plugged in. So is Leslie, e-mail address and everything."

"Hey, if I want to talk to Leslie I'll call her on the phone. If I want to read on a screen, I'll go to a foreign film."

Then Dan leaned toward Walter. "You know, future boy, Little Ann is checking you out." He grabbed Walter's arm and hissed. "Don't look! Did you forget the rules, man? She looks at you, I see her doing it and tell you. Then you look at me; she sees that and knows that you know. If you want to look, look at Leslie, who should be looking at Lee."

"I just got an idea," said Walter.

"Put your hands around it and blow gently, or it'll go out."

"Let's all three of us go over there and talk to all three of them. If you guys asked Leslie and Heather to the dance, Ann'd probably say yes, too."

"Walter, buddy, I don't know. You've about got me convinced dating is a hassle. I might just stay home and download a few slow dances. How about you, Danny?"

"Sounds good. I could dance with myself, then—"

"They're leaving!" Walter sat up straight."

"No, it's okay." Dan pointed. "They just migrated a few yards."

"You know," I said, "I saw this show on the Animal Channel

where these little clusters of beasties do all this mysterioso **preening** and pawing the ground and—"

preening
making oneself sleek and smooth; primping

"Then," Dan said, "you and I have to butt heads, and the winner leads all three of those babes into a beautiful meadow with a brook."

"Either that or I've got brighter feathers and they choose me while you go up on Echo Mountain and cry."

Walter grabbed one of his books, opened it, and leaned into it **studiously**. "What are they doing now?" he hissed.

studiously
with purpose and intensity; as though studying

"They're wondering," Dan said, "if you're a real dork or a virtual dork."

Walter slammed the book shut. "God, I hate this. By 2050, we'll have these computer-generated ideal partners. Just type in what you want, and there she is."

"Is this like driving up to the clown," I asked, "and ordering two burgers and a malt?"

Walter wouldn't laugh. "You guys like baseball so much? Order a couple of girls who know every statistic since Abner Doubleday."

Dan put his mitt on his head like a hat. "Can you imagine how boring that would be?"

"Yeah, Walter. They'd know stuff, but it wouldn't mean anything to them."

"So?"

Dan retrieved his glove and pounded one fist into it. "Are you nuts, man? You seriously think it'd be fun to talk to some robo-babe who knew everything about a game she'd never played?"

I stepped between them. "Guys, while we debate the issue of virtual girls, some real ones are standing right over there wondering what's taking us so long."

Dan pointed Walter in the right direction. "C'mon, wirehead. We're going to stroll over there and ask them what's up. They're going to say they're on their way to Victoria's Secret and do we want to come along. Then we're going to say that we'll think about it."

Walter turned to me. "I'm serious, Lee."

"Okay. We're seriously going to go over there, say hi, and talk about how stupid school is."

Walter felt his stomach. "I'm so nervous. Who's gonna bring up the dance?"

"I'll take care of that," I said.

Walter brightened. "Maybe we should all ask at the same time?"

"What are we, the glee club?"

"You know," said Dan, "he's right for once. It doesn't have to be boy-girl, boy-girl, boy-girl. We can just go. All six of us. My grandma'll drive."

"Your grandma is so cool. Remember when she took us to get our ears pierced?"

"And Mom grounded *her* for a week?"

I nodded. "If I was going to order a grandma, I'd want one just like her. But I wouldn't know what to ask for, you know? She's, like, **unique**."

"Pretty soon," said Walter, "we can clone her. Then everybody'd have a cool grandma."

I glowered at him. "But she wouldn't be cool then, doofus. She's cool because there's just one of her."

Dan shoved him playfully. "Like there's just one of you, Walter. Which is one too many."

"Man, if I could, I'd just order a new everything." He looked down at his thin chest. "This skinny body is one major burden."

"You think Little Ann would like this brand-new, tall, totally buff Walter?"

"Are you kidding? Absolutely."

"You'd scare her, man. Ann's shy," I reminded him. "Everybody knows that. She likes you 'cause you're shy, too."

"If she likes me so much, why didn't she say anything when I asked her to the dance?" Walter groaned. "God, I hate this. Twenty years from now—"

I held up one hand, like a traffic cop. "Stop with the future, okay? The dance is Saturday."

Walter sagged. "I know, I know."

I got my friends on their feet. "C'mon."

"So we're not asking individuals, right? It's for sure let's-all-go-together?"

Dan nodded. "Trust the Animal Channel, Walter. Things'll naturally sort themselves out later on."

"Yeah," I said. "so just pretend you're grazing and nibble your way over there."

"I should have e-mailed her."

Dan shook his head. "Too late now."

We all took a deep breath and headed for Leslie, Ann, and Heather.

When we got there, when we were actually facing the three girls, Walter just froze. Even Dan lost his nerve and could only stare at Heather.

So it was up to me. I looked through my personal thesaurus for just the right thing to say, the perfect word that would break the ice and win their hearts, too.

"Hi," I said.

Leslie looked up, looked right at me, and smiled. "Hi."

"We were just thinking," I said, "about the dance. And we were wondering if you guys wanted to go, you know? With us. Danny's

grandma's got a van. She'd drive and phone all your folks if you want."

Heather nodded and Ann blushed.

Leslie smiled and said, "Great."

"All right! I'll call you," I said, "later."

"E-mail me," she replied, "lesliecool dot com."

Then they bolted.

Walter looked at me. "Is that it? They're gonna go?"

"Of course, they're gonna go," I said. "Let me tell you a story, okay? About a million years ago some nervous guys with clubs in one hand and wrist corsages in the other were going from cave to cave looking for dates for the rock concert, and I'm talking real rocks."

Dan grinned and held out his fist for me to tap.

"Well, we're part of that story, man. Some piece of DNA from back then is still tucked into us somewhere 'cause we're human, not some virtual hunk of virtual junk that just does what somebody tells it to."

"Whatever. I'm just glad it's over." Walter checked his watch. "I gotta go."

We watched him trudge off the field. Then Dan turned on his heel and trotted halfway to the mound. He stood there, rotating the ball in his palm. I stepped behind the plate.

All of a sudden, Danny **stalked** back to me. "There's not gonna be robot baseball, is there? 'Cause I'm not givin' this up." He pointed. "Most of the things I know I learned between here and home plate."

"Relax. There's two things that are never gonna change. There's always gonna be a spring dance, and guys are always gonna play ball."

"You're sure?"

"Absolutely."

"Even if there are robots, we'll come out anyway, okay?"

"We'll kick their aluminum butts."

"Good." He ground the rubber with his cleats. "That Walter, man. He gets on my nerves."

"Forget him. It's spring of the year 2000. You've got a great curve ball, a decent slider, and a baffling change. *And* a date for the dance." I squatted down. "So burn one in here. Show me what you've got."

LITERARY LENS

How would you characterize the friendship between Dan, Lee, and Walter?

Ron Koertge

Dawn

Tim Wynne-Jones

Barnsey met Dawn on the night bus to North Bay. His mother put him on at Ottawa, just after supper. His parents owned a store and the Christmas season was frantic, so for the third year in a row, Barnsey was going up to Grandma Barrymore's and his parents would follow Christmas day. He had cousins in North Bay,[1] so it was fine with Barnsey, as long as he didn't have to sit beside someone weird the whole way.

LITERARY LENS

Be aware of Dawn's impact on her young friend as you read this story.

"What if I have to sit beside someone weird the whole way?" he asked his mother in the bus terminal. She cast him a warning look. A let's-not-make-a-scene look. Barnsey figured she was in a hurry to get back to the store.

"You are thirteen, Matthew," she said. There was an edge in her voice that hadn't been there before. "Has anything bad happened to you yet?"

Barnsey was picking out a couple of magazines for the trip: *Guitar World* and *Sports Illustrated*. "I didn't say anything *bad* was going to happen. If anything *bad* happens, I make a racket and the bus driver deals with it. I know all that. I'm just talking about someone weird."

"For instance?" said his mother.

"Someone who smells. Someone really, really fat who spills over onto my seat. Someone who wants to talk about her liver operation."

His mother paid for the magazines and threw in a Kit Kat, too. Barnsey didn't remind her that she'd already bought him a Kit Kat, and let him buy a Coke, chips, and some gum. And this was apart from the healthy stuff she had already packed at home. She was usually pretty strict about junk food.

"I just asked," said Barnsey.

"Come on," said his mother, giving his shoulder a bit of a squeeze. "Or the only *weird* person you're going to be sitting beside is your mother on the way back to the store."

Barnsey didn't bother to ask if that was an option. His parents put a lot of stock in planning. They didn't put much stock in **spontaneity**.

"What if I end up in Thunder Bay by mistake?"

spontaneity
freedom; naturalness

---

1 **North Bay:** city in SE Ontario, Canada

Tim Wynne-Jones

His mother put her arm around him. He was almost as tall as she was now. "Matthew," she said in her let's-be-**rational** voice. "That would require quite a mistake on your part. But, if it were to happen, you have a good head on your shoulders *and* your own bank card."

His mother almost looked as if she was going to say something about how they had always encouraged him to be independent, but luckily she noticed it was boarding time.

They were at Bay 6, and his mother suddenly gave him a very uncharacteristic hug. A bear hug. They weren't a hugging kind of family. She looked him in the eyes.

"Matthew," she said. "It's not so long. Remember that."

"I know," said Barnsey. But he wasn't sure if his mother meant the trip or the time before he'd see her again. He couldn't tell.

They moved through the line toward the driver, who was taking tickets at the door of the bus.

"Don't do the thing with the money," Barnsey whispered to his mother.

"Why not?" she said. Barnsey didn't answer. "It's just good business. And besides, young man, I'll do what I please."

And she did. As Barnsey gave the driver his ticket, Barnsey's mother ripped a twenty-dollar bill in half **ceremoniously** in front of the driver's face. She gave half the bill to Barnsey, who shoved it quickly in his pocket.

"Here, my good man," said his mother to the bus driver in her store voice. "My son will give you the other half upon arrival in North Bay. Merry Christmas."

The driver thanked her. But he gave Barnsey a secret kind of cock-eyed look, as if to say, Does she pull this kind of stunt all the time?

Then Barnsey was on board the bus, and there was Dawn.

There was no other seat. His mother had once told him that if there weren't any seats left, the bus company would have to get a bus just for him. That was the way they did business. So Barnsey shuffled up and down the bus a couple of times even after he'd put his bag up top, looking—hoping—that someone would take the seat beside Dawn so he could triumphantly demand a bus of his own. But there were no other seats and no other passengers.

He suddenly wanted very much to go back out to his mother, even though she would say he was being irrational. But then when

rational
reasonable; sensible

ceremoniously
carefully; with precision

he caught a glimpse of her through the window, she looked almost as miserable as he felt. He remembered the bear hug with a shiver. It shook his resolve. Timidly he turned to Dawn.

"Is this seat taken?" he asked.

The girl took off her Walkman earphones and stared at the seat a bit, as if looking for someone. She took a long time.

"Doesn't look like it."

Barnsey sat down and made himself comfortable. He got out his own Walkman and arranged his tapes on his lap and thought about the order in which he was going to eat all the junk he had or whether he'd eat a bit of each thing—the chocolate bars, the chips, the Coke—in some kind of order so they all came out even. At home his mother had packed a loganberry soda and some trail mix. He'd keep those for last. Strictly emergency stuff.

Then the bus driver came on board and they were off.

"There's talk of big snow up the valley a way, so I'm gonna light a nice cozy fire," he said. People chuckled. There was already a cozy kind of nighttime we're-stuck-in-this-together mood on the bus. Nobody was drunk or too loud. And the girl beside Barnsey seemed to be completely engrossed in whatever was coming through her earphones.

It was only the way she looked that he had any problem with. The nine earrings, the nose rings, and the mohawk in particular— orange along the scalp and purple along the crest as if her skull was a planet and the sun was coming up on the horizon of her head. She was about twenty and dressed all in black, with clunky black Doc Martens. But as long as she was just going to listen to her music, then Barnsey would listen to his and everything would be fine.

And it was for the first hour or so. By then the bus had truly slipped into a comfortable humming silence. It was about nine, and some people were sleeping. Others were talking softly as if they didn't want to wake a baby in the next room. That's when the mix-up occurred.

There isn't much room in a bus seat. And there wasn't much room on Barnsey's lap. Somehow a couple of his tapes slid off him into the space between him and Dawn, the girl with the horizon on her head, though he didn't know her name yet. The weird thing was, the same thing had happened to her tapes. And the weirdest thing of all was that they both found out at just about the same time.

Tim Wynne-Jones

Barnsey shoved the new Xiphoid Process tape into his machine and punched it on. While he was waiting for the music to start, he dug the cassette out from his backpack and looked again at the hologram cover. The band was standing under lowering skies all around an eerie-looking gravestone. Then if you tipped the cover just right, the guys all seemed to pull back, and there was a hideous ghoul all covered with dirt and worms standing right in the middle of them where the grave marker had been. It was great.

Barnsey pulled a bag of chips from the backpack at his feet, squeezed it so that the pressure in the bag made it pop open, and crunched on a couple of chips as quietly as he could. He was busy enjoying the way the first sour cream and onion chip tastes, and it took him a minute to notice he wasn't hearing anything.

He turned the volume up a bit. Nothing. Then he realized there *was* something. A tinkling noise and a bit of whooshing noise, and a bit of what sounded like rain and some dripping and more tinkling.

Barnsey banged his Walkman. He thought the batteries were dying. Then Dawn changed tapes as well and suddenly yelled, as if she'd just touched a hot frying pan. Some people looked around angrily. The looks on their faces made Barnsey think they had just been waiting for a chance to glare at her. One lady glanced at him, too, in a pitying kind of way, as if to say, Poor young thing. Having to sit beside a banshee[2] like that.

Meanwhile, both of them opened up their Walkmans like Christmas presents. They held their tapes up to the little lights above them to check the titles.

"Rain Forest with Temple Bells?" Barnsey read out loud.

"Scream for Your Supper!" Dawn read out loud.

Barnsey apologized, nervously. Dawn just laughed. They made the switch, but before Barnsey could even say thank you, the girl suddenly took his tape back.

"Tell you what," she said. "You listen to that fer 'alf a mo, and I'll give this a try. 'Kay?"

She had a thick accent, British.

"Okay," said Barnsey, "but I think yours is broken or something."

---

2 **banshee:** a female spirit whose appearance foretells death. Here it means an undesirable person.

She took her tape back and tried it. She smiled, and her smile was good. It kind of stretched across her face and curled up at the ends.

"Naa," she said. "Ya just 'av ta listen, mate. Closely, like."

So Barnsey listened closely. He turned it up. There was a rain forest. There were ravens croaking and other birds twittering away. And there were bells. He thought someone was playing them, but after a while he realized that it was just the rain playing them, the wind. He kept waiting for the music to start. He didn't know what the music would be. Any moment a drum would kick in, he thought, then a synthesizer all warbly and a guitar keening high and distorted and a thumping bass and, last of all, a voice. Maybe singing about trees. About saving them.

But no drum kicked in. Maybe the tape *was* broken?

It took him a minute to realize Dawn was tapping him on the shoulder. She had his Xiphoid Process tape in her hand and a cranky look on her face.

"This is killer-diller," she said.

"You like X.P.?" he asked.

"It's **rubbish**."

Barnsey laughed. *Rubbish.* What a great word. He pulled out Rain Forest with Temple Bells.

"What ya think?" she asked.

"It's rubbish."

Then they both started to giggle. And now people stared at them as if they were in cahoots[3] and going to ruin the whole trip for everyone. Dawn hit him on the arm to shush him up.

He showed her the hologram cover of the X.P. tape.

"You think it's their mum?" she asked.

"Maybe," he said. He wished he could think of something to say. He just flipped the picture a few times. She leaned toward him. Her hand out.

"Dawn," she whispered.

It took him a minute to realize she was introducing herself. "Barnsey," he whispered back, as if it was a code. He shook her hand.

rubbish
British slang term for nonsense

---

3 **in cahoots:** planning with one another

He offered her some chips. She took the whole bag and made a big deal of holding it up to the light so she could read the ingredients. She shuddered.

"It's a bleedin' chemical plant in 'ere," she said.

"Rubbish," said Barnsey. Then he dug out the trail mix and they both settled down to listen to their own tapes. Barnsey turned X.P. down to 2 because there was no way Dawn would be able to hear her forest with Spice-box wailing on the guitar and Mickey Slick pounding on the drums. After a couple of cuts he switched it off altogether.

He found himself thinking of the time he had traveled with his father out to British Columbia, where he was from, to Denman Island. He remembered the forest there, like nothing he'd ever seen in southern Ontario. Vast and high. It had been a lovely summer day with the light sifting down through the trees. But, he thought, if it rained there, it would sound like Dawn's tape.

He didn't put a tape in his cassette. He left the earphones on and listened to the hum of the bus instead.

■■■■

"It's not so long."

It was the bus driver. Barnsey woke up with his mouth feeling like the inside of a bread box.

There was a stirring all around. People waking, stretching, chattering sleepily and my-my-ing as they looked out the windows. The bus was stopped.

"Will ya lookit that," said Dawn. Her nose was pressed up against the window. Outside was a nothingness of white.

They had pulled off the highway into a football field-sized parking lot. Another bus was parked up ahead. Through the swirling blizzard they could see lots of trucks and cars in the lot. It wasn't the stop Barnsey remembered from previous trips.

Barnsey could see the driver standing outside without his jacket, his shoulders hunched against the driving snow. He was talking to another bus driver, nodding his head a lot and stamping his feet to keep warm. Then he hopped back on the bus and closed the door behind him.

"Seems like we've got ourselves a little unscheduled stop," he said. "The road's bunged[4] up clear through to Mattawa."

Someone asked him a question. Somebody interrupted with another question. The driver did a lot of answering and nodding and shaking his head and reassuring. Barnsey just looked over Dawn's shoulder at the outside, shivering a bit from sleepiness and the sight of all that whirling snow. Dawn smelled nice. Not **exotic** like the perfume his mother wore, but kind of bracing and clean.

"This here place doesn't have a name," said the driver. People laughed. He was making it all sound like fun. "But the barn there with all the blinking lights is called the Cattle Yard, and the owner says yer'all welcome to come on down and warm yerself up a spell."

Passengers immediately started to get up and stretch and fish around for handbags and sweaters and things. There was an air of excitement on the bus. The Cattle Yard was a big roadhouse painted fire-engine red and lit up with spotlights. It was no ordinary way station.

Still sleepy, Barnsey made no effort to move as people started to file past him, pulling on their coats. Dawn still had her nose pressed up against the glass.

"D'ya know where I spent last Christmas?" she said. Barnsey thought for a moment, as if maybe she'd told him and he'd forgotten.

"In Bethlehem," she said.

"*The* Bethlehem?"

"That's right," she said. "In a bar."

Barnsey looked at Dawn. She was smiling but not like she was fooling. "There are bars in Bethlehem?"

She laughed. "Brilliant bars. Smashing litt'l town is Bethlehem."

Barnsey tried to imagine it.

Then the bus driver was beside him. "Here, you might need this," he said. And with a flick of his fingers he produced the half-a-twenty Barnsey's mother had given him. Barnsey was about to explain that it was meant to be a tip, but the driver waved his hand in protest. "Just don't get yourself all liquored up, son," he said, and then, laughing and clapping Barnsey on the back, he headed out of the bus.

"Wha's that then?" asked Dawn, looking at the half-a-twenty-

---

4 **bunged:** plugged

Tim Wynne-Jones

exotic
foreign; strange; unusual

dollar bill. Barnsey pulled the other half out of his pants pocket and held them side by side.

"Hungry?" he said.

■■■■

And she was hungry. He hadn't realized how skinny she was, but she stored away a grilled cheese sandwich in no time and two pieces of apple pie with ice cream. She ordered hot water and fished a tea bag from deep in her ratty black leather jacket.

"Ginseng, mate," she said. "Nothing illegal."

But Barnsey had only been noticing how stained the tea bag was and the little tab at the end of the string which had strange characters written on it.

It was all so strange. Strange for Barnsey to walk into a place with her, as if they were on a date—a thirteen-year-old and a twenty-year-old. He wondered if people thought she was his sister. He couldn't imagine his parents putting up with the way Dawn looked. She sure turned heads at the Cattle Yard. He wasn't sure if he minded or not. In his burgundy L. L. Bean coat, he didn't exactly look like he belonged in the place, either.

It was a huge smoke-filled bar with moose antlers on the knotty pine walls and two or three big TVs around the room tuned into the Nashville Network. There was a Leafs game on the TV over the bar. Just about everyone was wearing a trucker's hat, and nobody looked like they were leaving until maybe Christmas.

The bus passengers were herded down to one end where a section had been closed off but was now reopened. The bus drivers smoked and made phone calls and made jokes to their passengers about not getting on the wrong bus when they left and ending up in Timbuktu. Through the window and the blizzard of snow, Barnsey watched another bus roll in.

"I saw three ships cum sailin' in," sang Dawn. She was picking at Barnsey's leftover french fries—*chips*, she called them—trying to find ones that didn't have any burger juice on them. She was a vegetarian.

"Bloody heathen," she'd called him when he'd ordered a bacon burger with fries. He loved that.

"I've gotta go find the loo," she said.

"Bloody heathen," he said.

She flicked him on the nose with a chip as she clomped by in her Doc Martens. He wondered if it was possible to walk quietly in them.

"Rubbish," he said. He watched her walk through the bar toward the rest rooms. Somebody must have said something to her because she suddenly stopped and turned back to a table where five guys in trucking caps were sitting. They looked like all together they probably weighed a ton, but that didn't seem to bother Dawn. She leaned up close to one of them, her fists curled **menacingly**, and snarled something right at his face.

Barnsey watched in horror, imagining a scene from some movie where the whole place would erupt into a beer-slinging, window-smashing brawl. Instead, the guy whose face she was talking at suddenly roared with laughter and slapped the tabletop. The other four guys laughed, too. One of them ended up spitting half a mug of beer all over his friends. Then Dawn shook hands with her tormentors and **sauntered** off to the loo, as she called it.

Barnsey felt like he would burst with admiration. He picked up her teacup and smelled the ginseng. It smelled deadly. The writing on the little tab was Indian, he guessed. From India.

He looked around. On the big TV a country songstress with big country hair and dressed in a beautiful country-blue dress was draping silver tinsel on a Christmas tree while she sang about somebody being home for Christmas. Then the image would cut to that somebody in a half-ton truck fighting his way through a blizzard. Same boat we're in, thought Barnsey. Then the image would cut back to the Christmas tree and then to a flashback of the couple walking up a country road with a bouncy dog, having an argument in the rain and so on. Then back to the guy in the truck, the girl by the tree. It was a whole little minimovie.

Barnsey found himself trying to imagine X.P. dressing that same tinselly Christmas tree in that nice living room. But of course the guy in the truck trying to get home for Christmas would be the grim reaper or something, with worms crawling out of its eyes.

Then Dawn came back.

"What did you say to that guy?" Barnsey asked.

She smiled mysteriously. "I told 'im that if 'e'd said what 'e said to me in Afghanistan, 'e'd 'ave to marry me on the spot."

■■■■

menacingly
threateningly; showing intent to harm

sauntered
walked leisurely; strolled

It was around eleven before word came through that it was safe to leave. The drivers got everybody sorted out and back on board. Everyone at the Cattle Yard yelled Merry Christmas and held up their beer glasses in a toast. The guy who had been rude to Dawn stood and bowed as she passed by, and she curtsied. Then she made as if she was going to bite off his nose, which made his ton of friends roar again, their fat guts shaking with laughter.

By then Barnsey knew that Dawn had just got back from Nepal, where she'd been traveling with "'er mate" ever since she left Israel, where she'd been working on a kibbutz[5] after arriving there from Bloody Cairo, where she'd had all her kit[6] stolen. Before that she'd been in Ghana and before that art school. Barnsey didn't know what a kit was, or a kibbutz. He wasn't sure where Nepal was, either, or what or who 'er mate might be. But he didn't ask. She'd called him mate, too.

On the bus the excitement of the unscheduled stop soon died down. The roads were only passable so it was slow going. It was kind of nice that the three buses were traveling together. In a convoy, the driver had called it. It sounded reassuring. Soon people were falling asleep, snoring. But not Barnsey. He sat thinking. Trying to imagine working on a flower farm in Israel, the heat, the fragrance of it. Trying to imagine Bethlehem.

"Was it cold?"

"Freezin' at night," she said.

"See any stables?"

She laughed. "No, but I did see a good-sized shed behind a McDonald's."

Barnsey laughed. He tried to imagine the holy family pulling into Bethlehem today and huddling down in a shed out back of a McDonald's. Maybe Joseph would have a Big Mac. But Mary? Probably a vegetarian, he decided.

Quietness again.

"What kind of a store is it your people 'ave, master Barnsey?"

"A gift store," he said.

"Ah, well," said Dawn. "I can imagine a gift store would be busy at Christmas."

Finally, Barnsey dozed off. And the next thing he knew, the bus

---

5 **kibbutz:** a work commune
6 **kit:** traveling gear

was slowing down and driving through the deserted streets of North Bay. It was past 2:00 A.M.

"That'll be 'er," said Dawn as they pulled into the bus terminal. Somehow she had recognized his Grandma Barrymore in the little knot of worried folks waiting.

Barnsey just sat drowsily for a minute while people stirred around him. He felt like he weighed a ton.

"Get on with ya," said Dawn in a cheery voice. And she made a big joke of shoving him and roughhousing him out of his seat as if he was Dumbo the elephant. Then she gathered up all his wrappers and cans and threw them at him, saying, "'Ere—lookit this! Yer not leavin' this for me, I'ope." Barnsey found himself, weak with laughter, herded down the aisle. At the door he said good-bye and hoped that her trip to Vancouver would be nothing but rubbish the whole way. Grandma Barrymore was standing at the foot of the bus stairs. Much to her surprise, Dawn grabbed Barnsey by the head and scrubbed it hard with her knuckle.

"In Afghanistan, you'd have to marry me for that," said Barnsey.

"Toodle-oo, mate," said Dawn, blowing him a kiss. She blew one at Grandma Barrymore, too.

■■■

Dawn would arrive in Vancouver on Christmas Eve. Barnsey thought of her often over the next couple of days. He'd check his watch and imagine her arriving in Winnipeg, although all he knew of Winnipeg was the Blue Bombers football stadium which he'd seen on TV. And then Regina and Calgary. He imagined the three buses like wise men still traveling across the country in a convoy. But as much as Barnsey thought about Dawn, he gave up trying to talk to anyone about her. Grandma had seen her but only long enough to get the wrong impression. And when Barnsey tried to tell his cousins about her, it came out like a cartoon, with her wacky hair and her fat black boots. He couldn't get Dawn across to them—the *life* of her—only the image of her, so he stopped trying.

There was a lot to do, anyway. His cousins had arranged a skating party and Grandma wanted him to go shopping with her and help with some chores around the house. He enjoyed all the attention she showered on him. She spoiled him rotten just the way she'd spoiled his father rotten, she liked to say. But he'd never noticed it quite so much as this year. Anything he looked at, she asked him if he wanted it. It was spooky.

Then it was Christmas morning. It was a four-hour drive from Ottawa. His parents would arrive by 1:00 P.M. and that's when the celebration would start. When he saw his father's Mustang coming up the driveway at 10:30 A.M., Barnsey knew something was wrong.

He didn't go to the door. He watched from the window. They should have come in the big car. But there wasn't any they. Just his dad.

"Matthew, go help your dad with his parcels," said Grandma.

"No," said Barnsey. He was remembering the last time he had looked at his mother in the bus terminal, through the window. The look on her face. "It won't be so long," she had said.

It wasn't that his mother was sick or there was some problem at the store; they would have phoned. Barnsey's mind grew icy sharp. Everything was suddenly clear to him. He could see a trail of incidents leading to this if he thought about it. You just had to tilt life a bit, and there was a whole other picture.

His parents weren't very talkative. They didn't chatter; they didn't argue. And yet in the moments while his father unpacked the trunk of his salt-stained Mustang and made his way back and forth up the path Barnsey had shoveled so clean just the night before, Barnsey could hear in his head all the signs and hints stretching back through the months—how far, he wasn't sure. Right up to now, the past few days, with Grandma so attentive. Spoiling him rotten.

Then his father was in the living room, still in his coat, waiting for Barnsey to say something. His face didn't look good but to Barnsey he didn't look anywhere near bad enough, all things considered. Grandma Barrymore was standing behind him with her hand on her son's shoulder. She looked very sad. They waited. Barnsey looked out the window. Old-fashioned lace curtains hung across the living-room window. They were always there, even when the drapes were open. Barnsey stood between the lace and the cold glass. He turned and looked at his grandma through the veil of the curtain.

"I wish you'd told me," he said.

"She didn't know, Matthew," said his father. "Not for sure."

The ball was back in his court. That was the way his parents were with him. Lots of room. His father would not press him. He could wait forever and his father would never start saying stuff like "I'm sorry, honey," or "It's all for the better," or "Your mother still loves you, Matthew." Barnsey could wait forever and he wouldn't see his father cry. He would have done his crying already, if he had any crying to do. His parents didn't hold much with spontaneity.

He glanced at his father in his black coat and white silk scarf. He wanted him to do something.

Barnsey stared out the window.

"When did you get the ski rack," he said.

"When I needed something to carry skis."

There was a pair of skis on the top of the car. Rossignols.[7]

"They're yours," said his father. "I couldn't exactly wrap them."

Barnsey had been wanting downhill skis. And one of the large boxes piled in the hall was probably a good pair of ski boots. His parents would have read consumer reports about this. Even while they were breaking up.

"Your mother is hoping maybe you'll go on a skiing trip with her later in the holidays. Maybe Vermont."

"That would be nice," said Barnsey. Then he left the window and went to his room. His father didn't follow. It was his way of showing respect. He didn't say that; he didn't have to. He was there for him. He didn't say that, either, but it was something Barnsey had heard often. "We're here for you, chum."

Barnsey stayed in his room a long time, long enough to hear both sides of the new X.P. tape he hadn't had time to listen to on the bus. He flipped the cassette cover again and again. The ghoul glowed and vanished. Glowed and vanished.

Then his mother phoned. They had probably worked all this out, too.

"Must have been a terrible shock . . .

"Decided it was best this way . . .

"We couldn't dissolve the partnership in time for the shopping season . . .

"Couldn't see us play-acting our way through Christmas . . ."

Barnsey listened. Said the right things.

"Do you think we could head down to Mount Washington for a long weekend?" said his mother. "Give those new skis a workout?"

---

7 **Rossignols:** a high-quality brand of skis

Tim Wynne-Jones

"They aren't new," said Barnsey.

"They sure are," said his mother. "They're the best."

"There's a lot of snow between here and Ottawa," said Barnsey. It took his mother a minute to realize it was a joke. A lame kind of joke.

Then, with plans **tentatively** set and the call over and his mother's voice gone, Barnsey joined his father and his father's mother in the living room. They both gave him hugs.

"You okay?" his father asked.

"Yes."

"You want to talk now? Or later?"

"Later," he said.

"I think we all need a sherry,"[8] said Grandma. She poured Barnsey a glass. He liked the idea better than the sherry.

They ate lunch and then, since it was Christmas, they sat in the living room opening presents. Barnsey kept glancing at his father, expecting to see a little telltale tear or something. But all he ever glimpsed were the concerned looks his father was giving him.

He took his father's place as the hander-outer. When he came to his own present for his mother, he said, "Where should I put this?" His father piled the package on a chair in the hall.

Barnsey wasn't looking forward to Christmas dinner at his aunt's. His father had already taken that into consideration and would stay with him at Grandma's, if he liked. They'd make something special, just the two of them. But when he phoned to explain things, his sister wouldn't hear of them not coming, and his cousins got on the phone and begged Barnsey to come and try out their new computer game and in the end he went. Nobody talked about his mother not being there, at least not while Barnsey was around. Everyone was really considerate.

In bed he lay thinking about what kind of a place his mother would live in. She was the one leaving the relationship, so she was the one leaving the house. Barnsey wondered whether there would be a room for him or whether she'd just make up a couch when he came to visit. Then he wondered if his father would stay in Ottawa or move back to the west coast. He lay trying to think of as many things as could possibly go wrong so that he wouldn't be surprised by anything.

"I just wish someone had told me," he said.

tentatively
uncertainly; hesitantly

---

8 **sherry:** a type of wine

"We'll turn it around, Matthew," his father had said when he came to say good-night. "We'll make this into a beginning."

Was that from some kind of a book? How could he say that? Couldn't he tell the difference between a beginning and an ending?

There wasn't another man in his mother's life. His father hadn't found another woman.

"At least it isn't messy," his father said. He needn't have bothered. Nothing they ever did was messy.

In his sleep, Barnsey escaped. He found himself back on the bus.

"Rubbish," Dawn kept saying, and she pounded her fist into her palm every time she said it. Then the man in the seat ahead of them turned around, and it was the guy who had been in the country video heading home in his pickup through a blizzard to his tinsel-happy lady.

"Rubbish," he said. And then all of Xiphoid Process, who were *also* on the bus, turned around in their seats, pounding their fists and saying, "Rubbish. Rubbish. Rubbish." Soon the bus driver joined in and the whole bus sang a "Hallelujah Chorus" of "Rubbish, rubbish, rubbish."

Barnsey woke up, his head spinning. All he could think about was rubbish. He thought about the talk he had to have with his father that day. His father wouldn't insist, but he would be expecting it. He would say all the right things and, before Barnsey knew it, *he* would be saying all the right things, too. They'd talk it out. Get things out in the open. It would all make perfect sense.

Rubbish.

So he left.

He didn't pack a bag, only stuffed a couple of extra things in his backpack. He wasn't sure what a ticket to Vancouver cost, but it didn't matter. He had his bank card. He had no idea what he was going to do and he didn't care. He would not run away like his mother, carefully planning it all out first. How far did that get you?

And so, by nine o'clock on Boxing Day[9] morning, he was at the bus terminal, a ticket in his pocket, sitting, waiting. He had his Walkman with him and he rooted around in his backpack for a tape other than X.P. He didn't think he could take that right now.

He had five or six tapes in the bottom of his bag. He hadn't

---

9 **Boxing Day:** the day after Christmas, a Canadian and British holiday

Tim Wynne-Jones

emptied it since the trip. He pulled them out one by one: Alice in Chains, Guns 'n' Roses, Nirvana, Rain Forest with Temple Bells—

Rain Forest with Temple Bells?

Barnsey stared at the tape. He must have packed it up in the dark of the bus without noticing. Then he saw a piece of paper sticking out of the edge of the cassette. He opened the cassette and took out a folded-up note written in pencil.

dear barnsey this is for the meal and for the fun and for when the rubbish gets to be too much but you're snoring while i write this so maybe i'll shove the note in your gob!!! no i won't i'll hide it and it'll be your xmas present from dawn xox

Barnsey found himself shaking. He read the note again and again. He smelled it—trying to catch her scent—and held it and then folded it up carefully and put it back in the cassette. He took out the tape and put it on. He closed his eyes and let the rain on the bells and the ravens and the smaller birds and the ferns and the trees and the wind fill his ears.

How crazy it had been to wait for the music to start. You had to supply your own. Make it out of what was there. Because there was more than the rain forest. Beyond his earphones there were people talking, departure announcements, a man waxing the floor—they were all part of the music.

Then suddenly there was a voice much closer.

"Matthew," said the voice, and Matthew became part of the music. "Matthew." Barnsey opened his eyes and his father was sitting there beside him. He touched his son's knee so tentatively, it was as if he was afraid the boy might break, like some fragile ornament from the gift store. Barnsey wondered if he would break, but he wouldn't. He was going to Vancouver to find Dawn. He stared at his father, who could not know this.

His father was in his black coat and white scarf, but his hair was a complete mess. Barnsey had never seen his father out of the house unshaven and looking such a mess. His eyes were the worst mess of all.

"You look scared," said Barnsey. His father nodded. He didn't speak. He was waiting, giving Barnsey space. Then Barnsey looked closer into those wrecked eyes and suddenly it occurred to him that his father wasn't giving him space. He just didn't have any idea what to say or do. He was a million miles from the safe world of the gift store. He looked as if all his careful plans had fallen through.

Barnsey wanted to shake him, to knuckle his head, to throw stuff at him, laughing and shoving. To wake him up.

"Here," he said. He took off his earphones and put them on his father.

"What is it?" his father asked. "Is it broken?"

"No," said Barnsey. "Listen closely."

He watched his father listening. Barnsey listened, too. He didn't need the earphones to hear it.

LITERARY LENS

Use elements from the story to evaluate Dawn's influence on Barnsey.

Tim Wynne-Jones

Josh: The Smartest Dog in the World

Gary Paulsen

He sits now as I write this, watching me, waiting, his brown eyes soft but alert, full of love but without nonsense, his black-and-white coat shining in the New Mexico sun streaming through the window. He is old now—I think eighteen or twenty—and he is **staid** except when he feels like playing and he is full of a gentle honor that I will never come close to achieving.

Josh is the quintessential[1] Border collie. In many circles that would be all that needed to be said—he has all the traits of Border collies. He is loving, thoughtful, wonderfully intelligent—frighteningly so at times—and completely and totally devoted to the person he views as his master.

And yet . . .

Somehow, in some way he is different. Perhaps that is true of all Border collies, that they really *are* different, that they key in to the person they are with, and since all people are different all Border collies are different. I recently gave a Border collie pup to a friend who lives in a city—contrary to popular belief, they do not need to run all the time—and the dog (she named him Maddux after the incredible pitcher for the Braves) has keyed in to her life to the point where he *has* to help her carry her mail, *has* to help her open envelopes, *has* to have a coffee and bagel each morning with her, *has* to be with her wherever she is in the house, *has* to greet people at the door. He monitors all the street activity and reports anything he thinks is odd and protects her from the evil monster that lives in the vacuum cleaner—and he's only a pup.

But there is more with Josh.

He is . . . real. No, more than that, he is a person. I do not think in my heart that he is a dog. When I am riding with him in my truck and he sits next to me looking out the window I can speak to him, say, "Look at that nice lawn," or "They have a sale on fence at the lumberyard," and he will look and sometimes (I swear) turn back to me and nod.

Once while driving to get a submarine sandwich I took my baseball cap off at a stoplight and jokingly put it on Josh with the bill

---

1 **quintessential:** the most typical representation

backward and put a pair of sunglasses on him (I know—people shouldn't dress dogs but it was more a friend fooling around with a friend) and told him, "You look cool, man."

He looked at me and put his right front leg up on the ledge of the open window and kept the cap and glasses on (though he could have shaken them off easily) and really *did* look cool, caught in the moment, playacting with me, and when we pulled up to the drive-through window at the sub shop I said, "My friend and I would like a turkey sub." Josh looked over, through his shades, nodded and went back to looking out the window.

There are major stages that affect our lives. Enlisting in the army, marriage, success or failure at our careers—leaps forward or backward. Having Josh has had such an effect on me. He has, in wonderful ways, shaken my belief structures to the core and brought me to a level of understanding of other species that has been so profound it will last the rest of my life. Josh has changed me forever.

He came to me because he was a "naughty" dog. The woman who owned him had some pet ducks and Josh herded them—as Border collies are wont[2] to do—until he wore them out and one of them died. I had seen Josh earlier and thought he was a nice dog and jokingly said, "If you ever want to get rid of him let me know."

And so he arrived one day. He jumped out of the car, moved into the house and started—as near as I could figure it—to study me.

It was very **disconcerting** at first. I would catch him at odd times, at all times, watching me, watching every move, studying everything I did—or said.

disconcerting
upsetting; confusing

He once saw me hurry to a phone because I was expecting an important call and after that wherever he was when the phone rang he would run to it and wait until it was answered.

He saw me, just once, put on a Stetson,[3] go outside to saddle my mare and head out to ride fence. The next time I put the Stetson on he ran to the front door, slammed open the screen, loped to the corral, cut my mare away from the other horses and brought her to the gate, holding her there until I came to saddle her.

---

2 **wont:** inclined
3 **Stetson:** a type of broad-brimmed felt hat

communal
used by everyone;
shared

Once every nine days we get the flow of water in the **communal** irrigation ditch.[4] The process is rather involved. I must walk to the head of the ditch and open the valve, then move ahead of the water as it pours down the ditch and clean out brush and debris with a rake. When the water gets to the smaller ditches that run to the apple trees or the pecans, these side ditches must be fully cleared of leaves and grass before the water can run on to the next side ditch, and so on for seven side ditches.

Josh accompanied me the first time and watched what I did. Just once. The next time I went he actually tried to help open the valve with his teeth—cranking the steel-handled wheel—and when the water started he ran frantically ahead of it, scrabbling with his feet and claws to clean out the brush and junk. He went to each side ditch, one after the other, to clear it out carefully and make certain the water was running correctly, then on to the next ditch. I stood leaning on the rake, my mouth hanging open. Josh had actually figured it out quicker than I had the first time. And when the last ditch was running and too much water was coming—flooding out over the end—Josh studied the situation for a moment, then dug a cross ditch that made the water circle back into the ditch.

So many similar things happened that I thought maybe he was some kind of odd case—not normal even for a Border collie. When we had people to the house he would try to get them all in one room, gently pushing them into a group with his shoulder—it would take him thirty minutes to move a small child from one room to another—and I thought it might be some perversion[5] of the herding instinct. But it wasn't that so much as it was the fact that he simply wanted to see them all, watch over them. When somebody went to the kitchen or the bathroom he would accompany them if possible and watch over them until they came back, and then when it was time to leave he would escort each of them to their car, wait until they were gone and then escort the next one. He was, I believe now, merely being polite—trying to be a good host. Understand that I've had hundreds of dogs and loved them and, I hope, been loved by them, and I've been in God knows how many different kinds of situations with them, but I had never, ever seen anything like Josh. I

---

4 **irrigation ditch:** a ditch used to transport water to an area from a source
5 **perversion:** misuse

Gary Paulsen

half expected him to come out of the kitchen with a tray saying, "Canapés,[6] anyone?"

I thought I should learn if he really was unique and so one summer four years ago I went to the international Border collie field trials in Sheridan, Wyoming.

It was absolutely astonishing. Had I not seen it myself, had somebody written of it in a book, as I am trying to do now, I do not think I would have believed it.

A man would stand in one place and send a dog out half a mile to where some sheep stood, and following whistles, and sometimes gestures, the dog would bring the sheep back through gates, around in a circle by the man, then into a small holding pen—all without making a sound and without ever biting (called "gripping") or touching a sheep, using only eye contact and body language. That was incredible enough, but another thing was in some ways more incredible, and that was the behavior of the dogs themselves.

I have been to sled dog races where there were hundreds of dogs and if two or three of them got loose—which inevitably happened—there would be an uproar—barking and snarling and most often fights or attempted fights. The dogs had to be kept **tethered** and watched closely.

tethered
fastened; connected to something

All the collies were loose. There were hundreds of them, and I never saw a leash or a pen. Nor did I ever see a fight or even hear a bark. It was a hot summer day and a large stock tank had been brought in and filled with water. As each dog finished his work he (or she) would go to the tank, jump in, submerge until only eyes and nose showed, and stay that way for a few minutes, until he had cooled down. Then he would jump out and catch up with his master, who was by then a hundred yards off drinking lemonade and talking with other dog owners, and he would stop and sit by his owner's leg and look up and listen to the conversation.

And they do listen. All the time. To *all* talk. Josh has come to know dozens of individual words. To name just a few: *horse, mare, cow, truck, car, walk, run, bike, Dairy Queen* (also the initials *DQ*), *deer, cat, dog, sub sandwich, turkey sandwich, hamburger, pancake* (he *loves* blueberry pancakes), *gun* (he hates guns), *thunder* (the only thing I've ever seen truly terrify him—he comes to sit in my lap

---

6 **canapés:** bread or crackers topped with a spread, like cheese or caviar

when it thunders), *fence, elk, moose, bear, blabber* (a kind of candy I sometimes share with him), *telephone, bug* (he sometimes studies bugs as they crawl along the ground—never bothers them, just walks along studying them), *baby, snake* (he respects rattlers but doesn't fear them), *rabbit, flyswatter* (he leaves the room if you say the word—I don't know why), and several more Anglo-Saxon expressions he's heard me use when required, such as *Get the ------ horse off my ------ leg before I ------ bleed to ------ death!*

And he knows them out of context. I have often been having a conversation on the phone about, say, the weather, and inserted a word: "I think it's going to be cow a nice day," with no emphasis on the word at all. Wherever he is in the house he will rise, even if sleeping, and come in and look at me or wait by the door. More, he listens to everybody all the time. If several people are in a conversation and just one of them says a word—again, just in a normal tone—Josh will come in and look up and wait. It can be very disconcerting if you're having a conversation in which you might use one of the words a lot. I had a sick horse and called the vet and used the word *horse* several times in the conversation, and each time Josh went to the door and tried to get out, finally coming back to me and biting me on the leg to get my attention, gently at first and then harder when that didn't work and finally—he's learned this is particularly effective—grabbing my kneecap and exerting enough pressure to make me utter a profanity. Usually I react then and do what he wants.

He has wonderful limits. He will do anything I ask and many things I tell him to do, unless he thinks they are too stupid or repetitive or boring. He will retrieve, for instance, and do it with great élan,[7] leaping to fetch things thrown in water, over land, in brush, far away or near—but only five times. If you throw the ball the sixth time he will get it, look at you, then leave with the ball in his mouth and never bring it back. He hides it. If you want to play again the next day you must buy another ball. I was recently moving some old hay bales and when I lifted one that had been near the back corner of the storage area, I found eleven tennis balls and four Superballs and a professional retriever's canvas dummy bird. Josh had hidden them all when he thought the game had become too stupid.

---

7 **élan:** enthusiasm

158   Gary Paulsen

Josh is wonderfully **facile** and will humor me and learn dog tricks—up to a point. I taught him to sit up and hold a cookie on his nose until I commanded him to flip it in the air and catch it. He loves cookies and he learned the trick in less than ten minutes. And he did it five times. The sixth time, he looked at me over the cookie on his nose as if I was completely insane, then lowered his nose, let the cookie drop on the floor and walked away, and we don't do the cookie trick anymore. Not unless I want to sit up on *my* hind end and put the cookie on *my* nose and flip *my* head up and catch the cookie, we don't.

Living with Josh is a never-ending lesson in how we can never truly catch up with somebody who is smarter than we are. One day I was moving some sacks of feed and as I got down to the last sack I saw a rat run in back of it and hide. There was nowhere for it to go and Josh was there so I looked at him and grabbed the bag and told him, "Get ready—get ready now. There's something there. Are you ready? Ready?" until he was excited enough to jump out of his skin, and then I moved the sack and the rat made its break. Josh grabbed it without hesitation but didn't kill it. Holding it in his mouth, he looked up at me in total disgust as if to say, "You fool—I've got a *rat* in my mouth," then turned sideways and spit it out—he distinctly made the sound *ptui* as he did it—and then walked away from me.

It wasn't finished either. The next morning in my boot there was a dead gopher. It had been dead for some time and smelled as rotten as old, long-dead gophers dragged off the highway can smell, and I shook it out in the trash and thought, Fine, message received.

I discovered one day by accident that Josh is wonderfully, wildly ticklish on his ribs and sometimes when he seems to be getting too serious about things—say two or three dozen times a day—I will grab him and flip him on his back and tickle his ribs while he woof-laughs and wiggles and air-snaps his fangs, always just missing my hands and arms. It's a ritual we have both come to love and sometimes when he is feeling a bit glum he will come up to me and flop over and invite me to tickle him.

Life is not always up and once I had about a three-day run of luck that was all bad and I never smiled. Some complete jerk shot a new Border collie pup I had gotten for Josh to train. (The pup's name is Walt and he has more or less recovered but it was so stupid and ridiculously violent—the idiot just shot him to see if his damn gun worked—that it made me sick of the whole human race for a time.) I also had a friend die and couldn't get to his funeral in time . . . just misery. At the height of this I was sitting in an old easy chair with my legs stretched out thinking dark thoughts and Josh came up in front of me and sat, studying me for a full minute, his eyes clear and calm. Then he seemed to shrug, turned around so he had his back to me, straddled my boot, then backed up my leg until his teeth were even with my foot. I had never seen him do anything like it and thought he might be going crazy when suddenly he reached down, grabbed my boot and with a mighty lunge jerked me completely out of the chair on my butt and then jumped on me and pretended to be biting my ribs, back and forth, tickling me.

Enough of the blues, by God—it was time to laugh. And I did, rolling on the floor with him, and we tickled each other until we knocked over an end table and had to quit.

Then—his job completed; I was cheerful again—he was sober once more, sitting quietly, listening in case I said a word he needed to respond to, watching me, anticipating where I would go, what I would do, out ahead of me like an infantry point—no, like a spirit, like an extension of my mind.

If possible Josh is always with me. Sleeping, awake—I even took him on an author tour once—he is always, always there. When I ran sled dogs he tried to go, put himself in the team, and when I threw a harness on him he pulled wonderfully. But he was too ... too **refined** for that work. The sled dogs are wonderful but they are primitive, basic, grandly prehistoric and animal. It was like putting a neurosurgeon in the middle of a professional hockey team and expecting him to be able to function, so I took Josh out.

refined
above the ordinary; cultured

■■■■

A last picture of Josh:

I am riding a horse, leading a packhorse up into the Bighorn Mountains out of Story, Wyoming. All mountains are beautiful but there is something about the Bighorns that is particularly wonderful, and I have trained one horse to carry a pack so I can head up and spend some time alone wandering, looking.

Gary Paulsen

Well, not alone. The horses are there, of course, and they provide some company, and there is Josh.

When I left the sled dogs because of my heart and went to horses, Josh fit right in, as I should have known he would. At first he trailed along on rides—just at first; then he saw that most of the problems with horses come from the front: deer, snakes, moose, bear, mountain lions—anything that would scare the horses and make them shy and throw me (which happened several times). Then he moved of his own **volition** to the front.

Josh knew his job was to lead always, to handle problems, to run ahead, out there about forty to fifty yards, trotting up the trail leading bear off, turning moose and elk away, dodging around snakes; doing all this day in, day out, until the mare knew him, understood what he was doing and trusted him. I think in a way the mare came to love Josh, because she would sometimes come up to him when he wasn't looking and nuzzle the back of his head as if petting him.

But that one picture of him is always clear in my mind. Head and tail down slightly, body relaxed but still somehow tensed and ready. The Bighorn Mountains wild across the sky above us and Josh trotting up the trail ahead, looking back at me on the horse, to make sure I'm coming.

volition
act of making a choice; free will

LITERARY LENS

How do Gary Paulsen's descriptions of Josh support the title?

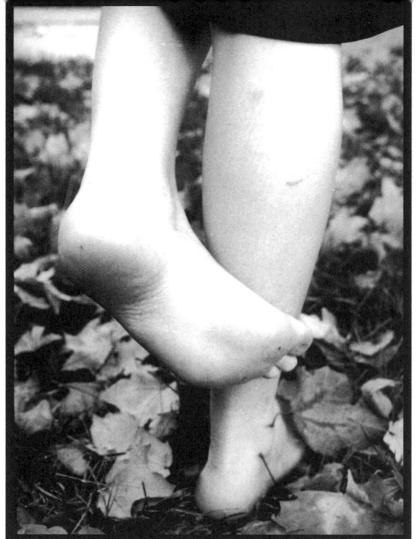

The
Fitting of the Slipper

William J. Brooke

"**P**lease," implored the Prince, stepping back in some distress, "this is not fitting."

"Not yet, but it will in a minute," she muttered between clenched teeth.

"No, I mean it is not right."

She looked at the slipper in confusion for a moment. Then she took it off her right foot and began jamming it onto her left. "You might have said something sooner," she grumbled. "Your Highness," she added, remembering that she hoped to marry the Prince and must not snap at him until after the wedding.

She wore the daintiest little socklets, creamy white lawns with tiny red flowers strewn across them. They would have been enchanting but for the red that blossomed between the flowers as she tried to put herself in the royal shoe by any means available.

"I thank you for trying," the Prince began to say as he gestured for his Lord Chamberlain to **retrieve** the slipper.

She swung her foot away from him on the pretense of getting a better angle of entry. "No trouble, no trouble, just I've been on my feet all day and they're a bit swollen." She shoved a finger behind her heel and tried to force her way in.

The Prince stared, **appalled**. "This cannot go on," he sighed to his Lord Chamberlain, who knelt at this woman's feet.

"It can! It can!" she said, redoubling her efforts as she saw her chances slipping away. "It's almost on now." Four toes had found a lodging place and she seemed perfectly determined to abandon the last to make its own way in the world.

"No! No!" He pushed forward and grabbed the slipper from her. A smear of red appeared on his snowy-white garments. "I am on a mission of romance. I am seeking love and finding naught but greed and grotesque self-mutilation."[1]

She pursed up her mouth like a prune and said, "Well, I never heard of shoe size being a sound basis for matrimony,[2] but if Your Highness chooses to place his future on that footing, I don't suppose he can blame anyone for trying to cut a few corners."

retrieve
to collect and bring back

appalled
shocked; horrified; dismayed

---

1 **grotesque self-mutilation:** unnatural, purposeful self-destruction
2 **matrimony:** marriage

"Silence, woman," the Lord Chamberlain snapped automatically, but he looked as if he probably agreed with her.

"You do not understand," the Prince sighed. He stood open-mouthed, as if looking for words, then shook his head. "You did not see her. You do not know the feeling of . . . Oh, what is the use?"

The Lord Chamberlain tried to take control. "If Your Highness will step outside, we have three more houses to visit in this street."

"No! No more! No more feet, no more blood, no more women who wish only to crush me beneath their heels! I cannot bear it!"

And with that he clutched the bloody slipper to his bosom and swept out the door.

Only it was the wrong door, and he found himself in a dark little hallway instead of on the street where the royal retinue[3] waited. The door behind him started to open again and he knew it would be the Lord Chamberlain.

"You are not to open that door on pain of . . ." The only punishment he could think of at the moment was decapitation,[4] and that seemed excessive. ". . . Of my severe displeasure," he finished, rather lamely. The door closed again and he was alone.

Before anything else could happen, he slipped down the hall and through another door. He was not sure where he was going or what he wanted, but he knew that he wanted to be away from what was behind him. He closed the door and dropped a bar into place. He listened for any movement, but there was none. He was alone.

For a moment the Prince was so thrilled to be by himself that he paid no attention to his surroundings. He took a deep breath and listened. There was nothing. No one asking, "Is Your Highness ready to meet with your ministers?" No one imploring, "If Your Highness would only listen to my suit . . ." No one hinting, "Would Your Highness care to dine now?" Strange that it always sounded as if he were being asked his pleasure when in fact he was being told to do this or that right away. For being a Highness and a Majesty, he was always being bossed around by someone or other. The only time he was left alone was when he went to the bathroom. And even then it wasn't long before there would be a **discreet** knock and "Does Your Majesty wish to review the troops now?" Sometimes he would imag-

discreet
showing good judgment in conduct

---

3 **retinue:** group of attendants
4 **decapitation:** beheading

William J. Brooke

ine himself replying, "Why, certainly, My Majesty always likes to review the troops with his pants around his ankles. It is a little hard to walk but it sets a good example for the recruits."[5] But he knew he would never say anything remotely like that. And whenever he got that sort of thought, he would blush and say to himself, "This is not fitting." Then he would hurry up and be more **obedient** than ever.

For he knew he should be grateful for his wealth and position and that he owed it all to the love and good will of his people, and it was his responsibility and blah blah blah. Sometimes he felt that a very wicked Prince lived inside him and would leap out and take over if he gave it the least chance. But he had never given it that chance. Until now.

For a while he just listened to the quiet. It was dark and shadowy with only a little fire at the far end of the room and he could not see very much. But he could hear lots of lovely silence, and when he put out his hand he could feel the rough wood of the door. It felt wonderful to him, all uneven and knotted and slivery, and it squirmed with lovely deep-red shadows in the flicker of the fire. He could feel the glass slipper in his other hand. *That* was what he was used to in his life, everything smooth and silky and featureless. He held it up and looked at its crystalline **transparency**, beautiful and perfect and boring. In sheer delight, he ran his hand across the rough landscape of the door.

And gave a howl as a big splinter slid into his palm.

He stuck the glass slipper under one arm and tried to ease the pain with his other hand. Then he froze and caught his breath again to listen.

Something had moved at the far end of the room. Near the fire, but in the shadows. In fact, one of the shadows itself.

He peered as hard as he could, but the harder he looked, the less he saw. When he moved his eyes, blue images of the fire danced in the dark. Even when he shut his eyes, the blue fire flitted about until he wasn't sure whether his eyes were open or closed.

He held his breath as tight as he could. But he noticed now that the breath he held was full of smells. They were kitchen smells, and to anyone who had grown up in a snug little cottage, they would have been comforting and comfortable smells. To someone like the

obedient
doing what you are told to do; willing to obey

transparency
ability to be seen through

---

5 **recruits:** soldiers in training

Prince, though, who had grown up perfumed and scented and protected, they smelled like a wild beast in its lair.

He found himself wishing he had at least one of his guards or even a fawning courtier[6] with him. Stories he had been told as a child came back to him, tales of witches and demons and unspeakable stews boiling on heathen hearths.

He had not thought of those stories in many years. They had been told him by an old peasant woman who had been his wet nurse[7] when he was tiny. The infant Prince cried whenever she left him, and the Royal Nurse could not abide a squawling child, even if it was a Princeling. So the old woman had been allowed to stay until the child was old enough to learn that neither listening to silly stories nor crying was part of his responsibilities toward his people. One day he noticed he had not seen the old woman for a while. Eventually he forgot to notice when he never saw her again. He had outgrown her stories and her warm, soft hugs and her wet kisses.

Now he wondered how he had forgotten her. Her memory made the room a lovely warm haven again. Even the smells seemed to belong to her, and they comforted him like the low murmur of music from a distant place.

Suddenly a bent and twisted shadow stepped in front of the fire. The Prince gasped and grabbed for the door and gave out another howl when the splinter slid in a little deeper. The shadow pushed something into the fire. There was a little burst of light as a twig caught and then the shadow turned and thrust it at him, bright-blazing and shadow-twisting.

The Prince fell back against the door in absolute terror. He could see nothing past the light but a filthy hand, a coarse sleeve, and the dark bent shape beyond.

They were frozen like that for a moment of silence. Then the shape gave a low sigh in a rough, woman's voice. "Aaow. You am come then. I can't believe you really come."

There was something familiar about the voice, and the Prince straightened up to try to see. The shape abruptly dropped to its knees and the light lowered. "Your 'Ighness! I'm forgettin' me place! 'Ere is me all dirty an' bent over with scrubbin' an' stickin' the fire right in yer face like I 'ad any right at all. Please say yer fergivin' of me!"

---

6 **fawning courtier:** a flattering attendant

7 **wet nurse:** a woman who breast-feeds children who are not her own

William J. Brooke

The Prince stared down over the flame, at the wild, tangled hair and dirt-laden face, as if searching a dark thicket for a wounded boar. But instead of a ravening beast, that face held eyes bright and darting as twin harts[8] startled by the hunt. He was still frightened but it was different now. And she sounded somehow familiar. . . .

The silence stretched out, with him looking thoughtfully down at her and her looking up at him with a question and a hope that belied dirt and rags. Then he blinked and pulled himself together.

"I believe that you have the most awful grammar that I have ever heard," he finally said.

She didn't reply but slowly lowered her eyes from his.

"I do not mean that as an insult. It is actually quite interesting to me. Everyone makes such a point of being precisely correct with me, it is rather refreshing to hear someone jabbering away." She stiffened at that. "Well, I do not really mean 'jabbering,' just…"

Her eyes, which had veiled themselves, suddenly widened with concern. "Yer 'urt! Why din't you tell me?" She was staring at the blood on his clothes.

"Oh, that is not my blood," he said. "That came from this." He held out the slipper. She looked hard at the glass shoe and then raised eyes filled with some terrible emotion.

He found it impossible to meet those pain-filled eyes, so he held out his hand. "I do have a slight injury, however—a splinter from your door."

She took his hand without a word and led him to the fire. She pulled a rough chair close to it and seated him, respectfully but firmly. Then she knelt before him, studying his hand in the firelight. She glanced up to see that he was ready, then seized the splinter and pulled it out.

It actually hurt rather a lot, but he was determined not to show it. "Thank you, my good woman." He wasn't sure if she was a woman or a girl. Even close to the fire, the layers of dirt and ragged clothes hid her almost completely.

He started to rise, but she took his hand again and examined it. "Not all out," she pronounced and hurried away to a dark corner where she sorted through the contents of a box with a great clanking of metal and wood.

---

8 **harts:** male deer

"Actually, it feels much better and perhaps I will wait for the Court Surgeon." But she was back then with a long, sharp darning needle, which caught the light like a dagger. She thrust its point into the fire and waited silently for it to heat up. The Prince felt distinctly ill at ease.

There was a faint scraping in the hall outside and a low tap on the door. The voice of the Lord Chamberlain sounded deliberately unconcerned, as though pretending that nothing was out of the ordinary. "Is Your Majesty ready to proceed to the next house?"

The Prince looked nervously at the needle, which was beginning to glow red at its tip, and at the girl whose shoulders tightened at the voice. He wondered what the Lord Chamberlain would think if he knew he was closeted with a strange serving girl who was about to apply a red-hot point to the royal person. The thought almost made him giggle.

"Perhaps Your Highness does not realize the lateness . . ."

"My Highness is perfectly capable of telling time. Even now I am looking at a clock above the mantel. I shall come out when I am ready."

"Very good, Your Majesty." After a moment, the steps scraped away down the hall again.

She looked at him warily. "We got no clock in 'ere."

He looked abashed. "I know. It was a lie."

"You lie a lot, then, do ya?"

"Never! I just . . . It wasn't me, it was . . ."

"Was what?"

Something made him blurt it out before he could think. "The Wicked Prince who lives inside me and tries to get out." He held his breath. He had never told anyone about the Wicked Prince.

She didn't laugh. "The Wicked Prince 'oo tries to get out. Well, I guess 'e succeeded this time, din't 'e? Don't seem to 'ave done much damage. Maybe you should let 'im out more often. Maybe 'e woun't be so wicked if 'e just got a breath o' fresh air every onc't in a while." She smiled. And her smile cut right through the dirt like a spray of clear, crisp spring water and made him smile back.

"Let's see if we can't cut 'im some air 'oles right now." She wiped the glowing needle on a rag and **brandished** it in the air with a piratical grin.

brandished
waved or shook in a frightening way

William J. Brooke

The Prince lost his smile. "Perhaps I should be going. There is a great deal of…"

She didn't answer, but knelt before him, grabbed his hand, and turned her back to him so that his arm was immobilized[9] under her own, pressed against her side. It took only a moment, she was so quick, and he was left with the curious feeling of being completely defenseless and completely protected at the same time. She plunged the needle in swiftly and deftly. He tried not to think of the pain, and after a moment he didn't. His face was very close to her shoulder and all along the inside of his arm he was touching her. He could feel roundness and softness beneath the coarse fabrics. He could smell her smell, which was the scent that rises from under the earth after rainfall. And in the play of the firelight on her cheek he felt he could see beneath the dirt to some kind of shining **essence** that . . .

"I said, 'All finished.'"

He realized it was not the first time she had spoken. Yet she had not moved from where he half leaned against her, just waited for his pleasure. He sat back, embarrassed, and she turned and seated herself on the floor beside her fire.

"Not too bad? Yer 'and," she added when he showed no sign of comprehension.

"Oh! Oh, that. Fine. No pain at all. I am sorry that I am a little dreamy, but I was thinking of my old Nurse Reba. You make me think of her."

"Well, I don't know if I want to remind you of any old nurse."

"Not that you are old. I mean, I do not know if you are old. I mean, what is your name?"

She smiled to show that there was no offense. "Ella, Yer 'Ighness."

"Ella," he repeated. "A good . . . plain name. Fitting for a . . ."

"A good plain girl?" She suggested.

"A good and faithful servant," he finished, trying to make it sound like a hearty compliment.

"Actually, I'm more in the line of poor relation than yer outright 'ouse'old servant."

"Ah, I see. A cousin of the house whose own family fell on hard times?"

essence
the pure, true nature of something

---

9 **immobilized:** unable to move

She looked sadly at the walls around her. "This 'ouse is the 'ouse of me father."

The Prince couldn't take it in. "Your father? You are the daughter of this house? But this is a substantial house, so why are you . . ." He gestured mutely at their surroundings.

"Me mother died when I was a tiny one. Me father married agin an' 'ad two more daughters an' no more 'appiness afore 'e went to join me mother. Since then, this room 'as been me 'ome."

The Prince didn't know what to say. He felt deeply ashamed that he had ever felt ill-treated in his royal position.

Ella felt his pity and hastened to add, "It 'asn't been as bad as 'ow it might seem. There's good in anything if you know where to look for it."

The Prince felt deeply uncomfortable. He decided it was time to return to his duties. He tried to find something cheerful to say. "I am quite sure you are right. And we thank you for your good service to your Prince. Now we must be going, for there is much of importance to be done."

He started for the door, but she was in front of him suddenly, eyes flashing. " 'Much of importance to be done.' More customers to try on, ya mean."

"What!" he exclaimed, drawing himself up into a state of outraged dignity. "How dare you judge your betters! You should remember your place!"

She fell instantly into a deep and clumsy curtsy. "Fergive me, Yer 'Ighness. I just want the best for you."

He was sorry for her, but determined to be dignified. "It is all right, my girl. It was really our fault for encouraging you in a way we should never have done. You have your Prince's gratitude and his kind thoughts."

She held her face in shadow and spoke low. "I just wanted you to know as 'ow I wasn't just what I seemed."

"Of course. Thank you and farewell." He strode to the door.

He was starting to lift the bar when he was stopped by a gentle rap at the door. He sighed resignedly and said, "Yes, my Lord Chamberlain?"

But it was the voice of the older woman who had greeted them at the door. "If Your Highness please, my other daughter is still waiting to try her fortune. Or if Your Highness wishes to stay by the fire awhile, I wonder if you might send Cinderella out so she can get to her chores."

The Prince looked at Ella. She had slunk back into the corner by the fire, merging into the shadows from which she had appeared. "Cinderella?" he called through the door. She raised her eyes to him then, but he could not read them in the dark.

"Yes," called back the woman. "Cinderella, our kitchen maid." She laughed. "Unless Your Highness was figuring to try the slipper on her as well."

The Prince hurled the bar into a corner and threw the door open. The woman fell into a deep curtsy at his wrathful expression. "Your Highness!" she gasped, not at all sure what she had done.

"Yes," he said after a moment. "You are quite right. Please rise." She did so, uncertainly. "It was my intention to try the fit of the slipper on all the ladies of respectable houses. So of course I shall try it on Ella. If there is time, I shall do the same for your other daughter."

The woman was speechless for a moment. "Ella! A lady?"

The Prince silenced her with a look. "She has treated us as a lady should treat her liege[10] and as others have not. Await us without." He closed the door on the woman's white, startled face.

The Prince was furious but also delighted. It was the sort of thing the Wicked Prince would have urged him to and yet it seemed entirely in keeping with royal behavior. He might find a way to reconcile himself[11] yet.

He turned to the shadow that was frozen by the fire. "All right, my girl, come over here and try this . . ." He stopped in surprise as she burst past him and tried to get out the door. He reached past her and slammed it.

"No, no!" she cried, fleeing into shadow. "Please, my Prince, don't make me do it!"

"Come, girl, do not be silly. Stop it! The sooner you do it, the sooner we are done. Come, that is a good girl."

She came to him slowly, unwillingly.

"If Yer 'Ighness insists . . ."

"I do. I command it."

---

10 **liege:** royal superior to whom allegiance is due
11 **reconcile himself:** in this case, bring his two sides to agreement

"Then I must tell Yer 'Ighness somethin' afore I try on that shoe."

"What is it, girl?"

"It's my shoe."

The Prince blinked. "What?"

"It's my shoe. It fell off o' me when I was runnin' . . ."

"What! Listen, girl, I am doing this out of the goodness of my heart, and you are wasting my time. Just put your foot . . ."

"'Me birthright for yer name,' " she said, and his breath caught in his throat. " 'If I stay another moment, I'll lose everything.'"

"How do you know that?" he gasped out. He grabbed her shoulders and shook her. "I have told no one except my father our last words to each other. How do you know them?"

She broke away from him and stood up proudly. "I know 'cause I was there!"

"But you . . . you . . . Look at you!"

She did not lower her eyes. "I clean up better than you'd expect."

"But you jabber away like a trained bird and dart about like a ferret! *She* spoke so precisely and moved with a stateliness that shamed the court!"

"You try 'avin' a conversation without usin' any 'H' words an' see 'ow precise you sound. An' if you want stateliness, just you 'op up onto a pair o' glass 'eels. Believe me, it's either stately or fall down in them things."

"Your gown! Your coach! Whence came they?"

"Well, whence they come was a friend o' mine. A person o' some power, I might add. An' don't ask to meet 'er, cause she operates on 'er own schedule and only shows up when I need 'er. An' she's the one as decides when that is, 'owever much me own opinion may disagree."

The Prince sat in the chair and began to rub his temples. "You do not understand what I am feeling. You cannot be the person. And yet you know things you could not know if you were not."

She stood behind him. "Why can't I be 'er?"

"You would not ask if you had seen her."

She began to rub his neck and shoulders. "Tell me about 'er."

He knew it was an unpardonable liberty, both her touch and her request, but the warmth and the shadowy darkness and the smells gave him a sense that ordinary rules had been **suspended**.

suspended
temporarily discontinued until further notice

William J. Brooke

And her closeness.

"She was beauty beyond beauty. She moved like a spirit slipping the bonds of earth. She was light in my eyes and light in my arms. Each moment with her was molten gold, slipping away all the faster the harder I clutched to hold it. And with the stroke of twelve, the dream was broken and I fell back to earth. I do not expect you to understand."

She massaged his neck in silence while they stared into the fire. Her hands were rough and firm and knowing. He felt unfathomably content.

"You was so tall an' so 'andsome," she said from the darkness at his back. "When we danced, you 'eld me like a big dog with a egg in 'is mouth, like if you chose you could of crushed me in a second. Which you couldn't of, you know." And she gave his neck a teasing little slap. "But it was good to be treated fragile, even if I wasn't. You was so strong an' gentle. The music was playin' just for us, an' there was colors everywhere but I couldn't see nothin' but you. It was the best night I'll ever 'ave."

Her hands were still upon his shoulders. They waited in silence. Finally he spoke into the fire.

"If you feel that way, try on the slipper."

She let her hands drop. "No. You'd 'ave to marry me, an' that ain't what you want."

He turned in the chair and took her hands. "If the slipper fits, I want you."

"No. You don't want the slipper to fit nobody."

"That is mad. Why do you think I am going through the whole kingdom on my knees to every woman who wants to try her foot at winning a prince?"

She smiled. "It's actually yer Lord Chamberlain 'oo is on 'is knees."

"Figuratively on my knees. Why am I doing it? Tell me."

She shrugged. "To prove that no one is fitting." He started to object, but she silenced him. "You don't know that, but it's true. If you found 'er, she might turn out to be real.

"You felt sorry for me, but I feel sorry for you. Our night was like a beautiful dream for me, too, but I can wake up an' get on with it. I've got me little kitchen an' me work and I can be 'appy. And if me stepmother someday needs to make a connection with a rich 'ouse, she'll clean me up an' marry me off to some stupid, ugly oaf of a merchant's son. And I'll be 'appy 'cause I'll keep me 'ouse tidy an' me kitchen cozy and afore I goes to sleep, I'll think a secret thought about me Prince. And I'll sleep smilin'.

"But I can see *you* in twenty year. You'll be King an' they'll 'ave married you off to someone or other 'oo you only see at dinnertime. An' you'll drink too much wine an' shed a tear for what might 'ave been. An' you could 'ave been a good King, but you won't be, 'cause you won't want to get down an' dirty yourself in what's real an' common. You'll just be thinkin' about yer dream Princess. It'll be sad but it'll be better than if you found 'er an' married 'er an' discovered that 'er breath smelt bad in the mornin' just like real people."

He had sat down again as she talked. "What's wrong with wanting to live a dream?" he mused into the fire.

"In a dream, you got to play by its rules, an' there's more nightmares than sweet dreams in my experience. In real life, you got a chance to make yer own rules, especially if yer a prince to start off with." She stroked his hair. "Forget yer dream Princess. Be the King you can be. Think kindly of me now an' then, but don't let me 'old ya back. There's a beauty in what's real, too."

He sat silent a moment. She gave him a little push to get him moving. He stood and slowly moved to the door.

"Don't forget this." She picked up the slipper, saw it was stained, and dipped it in a bucket of water and dried it on her skirts. "Good as new. Drink me a toast out of it now and agin. Onc't a year. No more."

He nodded, took it, and turned to the door. He put his hand on the latch, then leaned his head against the rough wood. "I have to know," he said.

She gave a sigh. "Are ya sure?"

"Yes. As sure as I am of anything." He turned and knelt to place the slipper before her.

She started to lift her foot, then set it down. "There's one thing you ought to know afore I try it on."

"And that is?"

She rolled her eyes up for a minute, then looked back to him. "It may not fit."

From his kneeling position, he slowly slumped down into a sprawl on the floor. He cradled his head in his hands. "What are you doing to me?"

"Just tryin' to be honest with ya."

"But you knew our last words. It *must* have been you."

"Everybody in the kingdom knows your last words."

"That's impossible! I told no one but my father. He would never have repeated it to anyone."

"Yer sure nobody could 'ave over'eard?"

"There was no one else there!"

She counted off on her fingers. "Nobody 'cept for six guards, three table servants, two butlers an' one old falconer 'oo pretended 'e needed the King's advice about where to tie the pigeons for the next 'unt just so's 'e coud 'ear the story for 'isself. Twelve people. Eleven versions of the story was all over the kingdom within twenty-four hours, an' the twelfth was a day late only 'cause one of the guards had laryngitis."[12]

The Prince knit his brow. "I never noticed them."

She nodded. "You wouldn't 'ave paid them much mind."

"And that is how you knew what I said."

"No, I knew 'cause I was there. I'm just sayin' you 'aven't been quite as secret as you thought."

"Then why will the slipper not fit you?"

"Might not fit," she corrected. "Because it was got by magic. See, the person I mentioned 'oo got me me gown and all was me fairy godmother. She did the coach out of a punkin an' the 'orses out o' mice an' so on. So I don't know if me foot really fit in that glass shoe or if that was more of 'er doin'."

He rose from the floor and stood before her, looking deep into her eyes. He spoke softly.

"That is the most ridiculous story I have ever heard."

She nodded. "I guess I'd 'ave to agree with ya. Bein' true is no excuse for bein' ridiculous."

He laughed. "But I do not care." He thought a moment. "I don't care. I have felt more in the last hour with you than I have felt in all the rest of my life. Except for one night. And I can live with that one night as a golden, receding memory if I know that I can have every

---

12 **laryngitis:** a sore throat that inhibits the vocal cords

day with you. I love you, Cinderella."

She was troubled even as she felt the stirring of hope. "I don't like that name."

"But it is part of your life and I must have it. I want to know all of you." He smiled with a **contentment** he had never known. "Marry me, Cinderella."

contentment
*feeling of extreme
happiness and
satisfaction*

She burst into tears then. "No, no! It can't be. Look at me! Listen to me!"

"That's all I want to do. That and hold you forever." He longed to touch her, but he waited.

She dried her tears on a sleeve and tried to laugh, but it was a desperate sort of attempt. "I'll say yes, 'cause there's no way I could say no." He stepped toward her. "But first—I'll try on the slipper."

He stepped away from her and his brow was furrowed. "You don't have to do that. I don't care."

"Not now, maybe. But in five years or ten years, you'd start regrettin' it. An' regret is the only thing that love can't cure. So gimme that slipper. What's the worst that could 'appen?"

Hollow-eyed, he looked at her. "It might fit," he whispered.

She started at that, but looked him straight in the face and said, "Give it to me."

He set the slipper in front of her, then straightened. She touched her hand to his face and knelt to the fitting.

They stood, then, face to face. And there was so much hope and joy and fear and pain that neither one could have said which of them was feeling what.

"Look," she said.

He tried not to, but he couldn't help it.

The slipper didn't fit.

It didn't near fit.

He raised his eyes to hers and saw the hope in them change to a terrible fear.

"It isn't fitting," he said. "It is not fitting." She cringed. The Wicked Prince was out for good.

"It isn't fitting that a Princess dance on her wedding night in shoes that do not fit her."

Her face was crumpling. He could do nothing but go on.

"I shall have to summon the royal glassblower."

William J. Brooke

Her eyes flashed the question at him.

"To make you shoes that fit. The shoe must fit the foot. It's madness to try to make the foot fit the shoe."

She kicked it off and stepped close, and they stood a moment, savoring together the bittersweet of the last instant of aloneness they would ever know.

Then he swept her up into his arms, so strong yet gentle, as if he feared to crush her, which he couldn't have.

And the first step of all the many they took together smashed the glass slipper past all fitting.

 THE POET'S PERSPECTIVE

Interview

Sara Henderson Hay

Yes, this is where she lived before she won
The title Miss Glass Slipper of the Year,
And went to the ball and married the king's son.
You're from the local press, and want to hear
About her early life? Young man, sit down.
These are my *own* two daughters; you'll not find
Nicer, more biddable girls in all the town,
And lucky, I tell them, not to be the kind

That Cinderella was, spreading those lies,
Telling those shameless tales about the way
We treated her. Oh, nobody denies
That she was pretty, if you like those curls.
But looks aren't everything, I always say.
Be sweet and natural, I tell my girls,
And Mr. Right will come along, some day.

LITERARY LENS

List all the ways the story and the poem differ from the Cinderella tale that you know, and determine the most striking difference.

RESPONDING TO UNIT THREE
Friendly Photos

REFLECTING

1. Ralph Waldo Emerson once said, "The only way to have a friend is to be one." Which character in this unit do you think best follows this rule? Why?

2. Do you think an animal such as Josh, the Border collie in Gary Paulsen's biography, can teach us anything about human interaction? Explain your answer.

3. Friends come in many different shapes, sizes, colors, and even species. What interesting aspect of friendship did you discover in the unit you have just read?

4. If you were going to create a friendly snapshot of someone, how would you go about doing it?

ANALYZING

5. Make a list of all the qualities you think a good friend should have. Then match the following characters to the qualities you have listed: Tennessee, Danny, Dawn, Josh, and Cinderella.

6. Write a short summary of the story "The Fitting of the Slipper."

7. Look at the chart below. On a separate piece of paper, create a similar chart. Write the name of the character from Unit Three who *might* have said each quote. Then add your own made-up quote and character name to the chart.

Quote	Character Name
"I'd like to go to the dance with Walter, but I just can't seem to talk to him."	
"The third time is definitely the charm! That last one had me floating on a cloud."	
"I'm smart, thoughtful, alert, and love to be tickled. And...I'd do anything for Gary."	
"If the shoe doesn't fit, don't bother with it!"	
Your Quote	**Character Name**

8. How does Dawn turn what appear to be her "tormentors" in "trucking caps" into friends?

9. **Active Reading** How did you go about **clarifying** any confusing passages while reading "The Fitting of the Slipper"? What other Active Reading strategies did you use while reading the selections in this unit?

DISCUSSING

You've probably seen the commercial on television advising, "Friends don't let friends drive drunk." What, in your opinion, do people your age try to stop friends from doing?

WRITING

Hello, Mate! Imagine that on her travels, Dawn meets up with Walter, the "science geek" in "A Robot Doesn't Have a Curve Ball." Write their conversation. Be sure to use a few direct quotations.

That's What I Like About You The subject of friendship has long inspired poets and songwriters. Write a poem or song about a friend of yours. Remember, it doesn't have to be "sappy," just honest and from the heart.

WORK IN PROGRESS

Friends Don't Let Friends _____? You've discussed in class the kinds of issues in which friends try to help friends avoid inappropriate choices. Now get together in groups of four and work up an ad campaign to help put your message across. Use as many advertising strategies as you can, including catchy phrases or slogans (written and recorded), striking visual images, testimonials, and so on.

Dos and Don'ts of Friendship As a class, discuss the things you think are important in a friend and things you feel a friend should never do. Then create a graphic organizer like the one below on the chalkboard to keep track of your ideas. When you have gathered all your ideas, write a *Statement of Friendship* and hang it on the wall as reminder. Read it aloud from time to time.

What a Friend Does	What a Friend Does Not Do

School Pictures

"I think you've always assumed that I want to be like you. But I want you to know something about kids like me. We don't want to."

from "A Letter from the Fringe"
by Joan Bauer

Active Reading Alert!

CONNECTING

As you read the selections in this unit, try to connect what you are reading to something in your own experience, or to something you have read or seen. Ask yourself, "What does this remind me of?" When you connect with the characters or situations as you read, your reading is livelier.

Pig Brains

Alden R. Carter

I was headed for the outside doors and the fall afternoon when a voice behind me boomed, "Hey, Shadis!"

I turned, smile fixed, resigned to taking the usual load of garbage from my favorite Neanderthal: the Doughnut. Now, Doughnut's a big guy, about six four and maybe 260, making him a foot taller and about 120 pounds fatter than I am. Fortunately, the brain that knocks around inside his massive skull is inversely proportional[1] to his overall size. Put another way, I'm twice as smart. Which is handy. "Hey, Doughnut," I said.

He flopped a python-thick arm around my shoulders. "When you coming out for football, Donny? I could use a blocking dummy." He guffawed. Nitwit.

"Maybe next year," I said, and changed the subject. "What are you bringing to O'Brien's class tomorrow?"

"Huh?" he said.

"Food, Doughnut. We're supposed to bring something that reflects our ethnic heritage." *Which in your case is probably raw mastodon,* I thought, but didn't say.

"Oh, yeah," he said. "I nearly forgot. My ma's going to make some doughnuts. We're German, and Germans eat a lot of doughnuts."

"Do they?" I said, to be polite.

"Yeah. At least my family does." He grabbed a fistful of his belly with typical lineman's[2] pride. "Doughnuts put lead in our pants so we can block better. Coach O'Brien loves how I block. And he loves my mom's doughnuts, too."

"Really?" I said.

"Yep. I brought six dozen to practice just last week. They were all gone in five minutes."

"Do tell?" I said.

"Yep. So, who else is bringing food tomorrow?"

"It's you, me, and Melinda Riolo this week."

"Melinda? Hey, you kinda liked her last year, didn't you?"

"She's okay," I said.

"I think she thinks you're a nerd." He laughed.

LITERARY LENS

As you read this story, think about the relationship between Shadis and the Doughnut.

---

1 **inversely proportional:** equally opposite in size; here, the bigger his head, the smaller his brain

2 **lineman:** the position in football that is responsible for defending or advancing on the line of scrimmage

Well, she thinks you're a baboon! So we're even, jerk. "Makes no difference to me," I said.

He grinned, knowing better. "Yeah, right. So, what are you bringing?"

"Brains," I said. "Lithuanians eat a lot of brains."

He stared at me. "You're kidding!"

"Nope. Calf brains, sheep brains, goat brains, all sorts of brains."

He let his arm drop from my shoulder. "That's gross."

"Not really. I like pig brains best. They've got kind of a nutty flavor."

Suddenly his hand was back on my shoulder, and it wasn't friendly. He turned me to face him, his eyes mean. "You're putting the Doughnut on, man. I don't like it when people do that. It's like they think I'm stupid or something."

But you are, Doughnut. You are. I just wish you weren't so big. "I'm not putting you on, Doughnut. I swear."

He stared at me for a long minute, his hand slowly kneading my shoulder. "If you're lying, you'd better tell me now. I might just hurt you a little bit."

I gave the Boy Scout sign. "I swear, Doughnut. I'm bringing Lithuanian fried brains."

He grunted, still looking suspicious, and let me go.

I made it to the street on wobbly knees and started the walk home past the grade school and down the hill into the Third Ward. What had I done? If I didn't show up tomorrow with Lithuanian fried brains, I'd better show up with a doggone good excuse. Or else Doughnut was going to hurt me a lot more than a little bit.

The only sane, logical thing to do was come up with a good excuse. But the more I thought about it, the more I really wanted to bring fried brains. I wanted to gross Doughnut out. I mean, the guy grossed me out just by being alive. Now it was my turn.

■■■

There really is a recipe for fried brains in the Lithuanian cookbook my mom has. She wrote away for it last spring so she could make a special dinner for my grandpa's eightieth birthday. I helped her pick out the menu: "Hey, Mom, here's one we could try. Lithuanian fried brains. Soak the brains overnight in a pan of water in the refrigerator, then—"

"Stop," she said. "I don't want to hear it."

"But, Mom! Maybe he had them growing up. Maybe he's been longing for some fried brains ever since he left Lithuania."

"Believe me, he hasn't. He's a finicky eater. It drove your grandma nuts."

"Aw, Mom—," I whined.

"No brains! Find something else."

■■■■

By the time I got home the sheer brilliance of my inspiration had produced some blind spots in my usually **acute** vision. Except for twenty or thirty sound, sane reasons, I couldn't see why I shouldn't bring fried brains. Oh, there were a few complications—like where to get the basic ingredient—but that was minor stuff. I could make this happen.

acute
sharp; precise

I called Lerner's Meat Market and asked if they had any brains. Mr. Lerner laughed. "No, I haven't seen brains on sale in thirty years. Nobody around here cooks brains. Maybe in Albania or someplace, but not central Wisconsin."

"Rats," I muttered.

"Nope, we don't have them, either. You might try Albertson's Supermarket, though. They might have rats."

"Ha, ha," I said. "Very funny."

"We try. What do you want the brains for?"

"A science project."

"Oh. Well, you might try the stockyards over in Stuart."

How was I supposed to get to Stuart without a car, a license, or a **gullible** parent? (My mom was decidedly ungullible, my dad permanently absent without leave.) "Do you suppose Albertson's might have some brains?" I asked.

gullible
easily tricked; believing

"You could ask, but I'd bet a thousand to one against."

"Thanks, Mr. Lerner."

"Sure enough. Good luck."

I slumped in the chair. No brains, no gross-out of the Doughnut. Rats and double rats. (Or words to that effect.) But the idea wouldn't let go, and I had my second inspiration of the day. Remember the Halloween game where squealing kids pass the pieces of Frankenstein's monster from hand to hand under a sheet: grapes for the eyes, a carrot for the nose, pepper slices for the ears, *spaghetti for the brains? Shadis*, I told myself, *you are brilliant*.

I pedaled my mountain bike down to Albertson's and inspected the pasta selections. I finally decided on fettuccine,[3] although I was briefly tempted by some green linguine.[4]

Mom was meeting a client for supper and my sister was studying at a friend's, so I had the kitchen to myself. Good thing, because making some passable brains out of fettuccine took quite a bit of experimentation. I finally managed what I thought was a pretty good facsimile[5] by cooking the noodles al dente,[6] rolling them in cornmeal, and frying them in some oil. I drained them on paper towels, stuffed them into a loaf pan, and stuck it in the refrigerator.

By then I was on a pretty good roll. *A dip*, I thought. *We need some brain dip.* I searched the refrigerator and found half a bottle of cocktail sauce. I poured it into a neutral container and wrote "Lithuanian Brain Dip" on a label. Nah, I could do better than that. I tore it off and wrote "Cozzackakus: Blood of the Cossacks."[7] Much better.

■■■

Digging in the refrigerator at breakfast the next morning, my sister yelped, "Oh, gross!"

Mom looked over Amy's shoulder. "What on earth?"

"Don't touch," I said. "Social studies project."

"What could this possibly have to do with social studies?" Mom asked.

"Really!" my sister said.

"I meant science," I said. "You don't want to know any more."

"You've got that right," Mom said. "Just get it out of my refrigerator."

By this time the dazzle of my idea had faded considerably and I was having some decidedly unpleasant second thoughts. Playing a joke on Doughnut was dangerous enough, but getting caught by Mr. O'Brien might be even worse. Mr. O'Brien doesn't fit the stereotype of a football coach. He doesn't have a big belly, he doesn't **glower** a lot, and he doesn't think football is the most important thing in the

glower
look unhappy; frown; scowl

---

3 **fettuccine:** a long, flat pasta noodle
4 **linguine:** a long, thin pasta noodle—in this case, made with spinach
5 **facsimile:** copy
6 **al dente:** Italian for "to the tooth," or pasta cooked just long enough to retain a firm texture
7 **Cossacks:** Russian warriors, known throughout history for their willingness to defend their country in battle

Alden R. Carter

world. He thinks social studies is. He expects a lot, even from Doughnut, who sits in the back of the class trying to look interested. (Doughnut thinks O'Brien is God. Or just about.)

Mr. O'Brien pegs the needle on his hyper meter at least four or five times a day. He crashes around the room, slapping his pointer on maps, globes, and time lines. He pounds his fist on his desk, climbs on his chair, playacts at being this or that historical figure, even beats his head against the wall if that's what it takes to make a point. In other words, he's a heck of a teacher. But he isn't someone to mess with, and I was beginning to wish I was bringing Lithuanian sponge cake or something. Maybe I'd tell everybody that I'd brought Lithuanian cornmeal-coated fried noodles. Big **delicacy**, if you're into that kind of thing. Then I'd lie like crazy to Doughnut and hope that he only broke a couple of my bones.

delicacy
food considered rare and delicious

■■■■

Melinda Riolo didn't bother to go to her desk but marched right to the front of the room with her casserole dish. She stood there, tapping her foot, while Mr. O'Brien finished the roll. He smiled at her. "All right, Miss Riolo, go ahead."

She uncovered the dish and tilted it for everybody to see. "I brought eggplant parmigiana, which I like because it doesn't have a lot of calories. Since I lost all that extra weight last year in junior high, I don't eat a lot of the fattening stuff Italians like. I mean all the cheese and stuff. But this is pretty good. Enjoy." She set down the dish and marched to her desk across the aisle from mine. My heart bumped a couple of times with longing.

Doughnut swaggered to the front. He opened a big plastic pail of greasy sugar doughnuts. "They're really good," he said. "My mom fries 'em in real lard."

Melinda muttered, "Oh, charming. Now they're an extra five hundred calories." She eyed me narrowly. "You're being quiet today. Did you forget to bring something?"

"No, I've got it right here in the bag."

"What is it?"

"Brains," I said.

"You're putting me on!"

I looked at her and couldn't lie. "Yeah, but don't tell anybody else. It could cost me about sixteen broken bones."

Doughnut finished telling how he could put away a dozen doughnuts straight from the boiling deep fryer. "Two dozen if they're small. They don't call me the Doughnut for nothing!" He grinned, using both hands to grab fistfuls of his belly. People laughed, and he swaggered back to his desk.

I took a deep breath, followed it with a short prayer, and stumbled confidently to the front of the class. I whipped the towel from the top of the loaf pan. "Ladies and gentlemen, boys and girls, these are Lithuanian fried brains. They're an old delicacy in traditional Lithuanian homes. When we're up at my grandpa's, we play a lot of pinochle.[8] And while we play, we usually have popcorn, chips, or fried brains."

I prodded at the greasy tangle with a finger. Jeez, it was obvious they were noodles. Even Doughnut must have guessed by now. "It's kind of hard to find brains to fry sometimes. Sheep and goat brains are supposed to be the best, but there just aren't many sheep and goats around here. Calf brains are easier to find and they're really good. But I like pig brains best and that's what I brought today."

Up to this point I'd been too nervous to look directly at my classmates. But now I chanced it and was greeted by a lot of open mouths, screwed-up noses, and generally horrified expressions. Doughnut was absolutely gray. Good Lord, they believed me! I took a breath and put the accelerator to the floor.[9] "Now, when we get the brains, we soak them overnight in a big pan in the refrigerator. It's kind of a good thing to remember they're in there. Otherwise, the next time you open the refrigerator, it's—*whoa*—Frankenstein's laboratory! But"—I shrugged—"you kind of get used to that sort of thing around my grandpa's house."

I dug into the tangle, separated a sticky wad of three or four noodles, and held it up. "The next morning we slice the brain and it falls apart into these sort of floppy, wormlike things." (There were some very satisfying groans. Doughnut had gone from gray to ashen.) "We roll them in cornmeal and fry them in oil. We drain them on some paper towels and then put them on the table in a big bowl. Brains are really best served hot, but they're still good cold. Like popcorn's good hot or cold."

---

8 **pinochle:** a card game
9 **put the accelerator to the floor:** a metaphor for "hurried"

Alden R. Carter

I headed the wad of noodles toward my mouth, then pulled it back at the last second. "Whoops, I almost forgot. There's also the dip my mom makes from an old recipe my grandma brought from the old country. It's called *Cozzackakus*, which means 'blood of the Cossacks.' I asked my grandpa about the name and he said it's because Lithuanians don't like Cossacks, who used to be these real tough bandit types who raided a lot. My grandpa says not even Cossacks like Cossacks that much, so—"

Mr. O'Brien interrupted. "This would be an example of an ethnic prejudice, class. As we discussed, many older people have them. Go ahead, Don. This is just great."

"Ah, thanks. Anyway, I'm not sure my grandpa ever actually knew any Cossacks, but that's how the sauce got its name. So here's how you eat pig brains." I dipped the noodles in the shrimp sauce, stuck them in my mouth, and chewed. They were terrible, but I grinned. "This is a really good batch. Pig brains are just so much better than calf or beef. Did I mention beef brains? The butchers stopped selling them because people started worrying about mad cow disease. But my grandpa says all Lithuanians are already pretty crazy, so they probably wouldn't get any worse if they caught it. So, anyway, who'd like to try some Lithuanian fried brains?"

Nobody moved for a long minute. Then Melinda stood and strode to the front of the class. She gave me a look that was at least half glare. "I bet these are fattening as all get-out."

"I don't know, Melinda. Maybe a little."

She plucked a few noodles from the pan, dipped them in the cocktail sauce, and popped them in her mouth. She chewed and then shrugged. "Not bad. Could use some salt, maybe."

Mr. O'Brien jumped up. "Okay, everybody line up. You know the rule: Everybody's got to try everything, unless you've got a genuine, doctor-certified food allergy." He rubbed his hands together. "This is great! Just great. This is what we want. Something unusual. Something really **authentic**. Come on, everybody. Line up. Paper plates and spoons are right here. Don and Melinda, go ahead. No standing on ceremony here."

When we were back at our desks, Melinda glared at the doughnut on her plate. "I'd rather have brains." She leaned over and started to whisper, "You were kid—"

authentic
real; genuine; exactly what is claimed

"Hold on, Doughnut!" Mr. O'Brien shouted. "You missed the brains. No cheating."

Doughnut grinned sheepishly and dug a few noodles from the pan.

"Don't forget the blood sauce, Doughnut," I called. "Makes them even better."

Leaning against his desk, Mr. O'Brien was digging into a big serving of brains. He smacked his lips. "You know, Don. If I didn't know better, I'd swear these were noodles."

I almost choked on a bite of eggplant but managed a weak smile. "Yeah, they're kind of similar, aren't they?"

"Sure are. What do you think, Doughnut?"

Doughnut was sitting at his desk, staring at his plate. He looked up pleadingly at Mr. O'Brien, who gave him a now-be-a-man stare. Doughnut sighed, picked up a shred of brains, and stuck it in his mouth. It was a moment of high drama, but I couldn't help glancing at Melinda to see if she was **savoring** it as much as I was. That's how I missed Doughnut's bolt for the bathroom. He only made it as far as the tall wastebasket beside the door. And when he let go, it was pretty awesome. The metal can **resonated** like a kettledrum, magnifying the heave into something truly stupendous—a barf worthy of the Doughnut in all his grossness. The sound and the smell set off a chain reaction that sent about a dozen girls and just as many guys out the door and down the hall to the rest rooms.

Mr. O'Brien stood at the front of the class, hands on hips, glaring at Doughnut's broad rear end as Doughnut heaved a couple more times. He shook his head. "Well, that's it for today, I guess." He waved a hand at the few of us who still sat frozen in our seats. "The rest of you can go. I've got to get Doughnut cleaned up. Don, Melinda, come get your dishes."

I picked up the half-empty loaf pan and followed Melinda out. At the door I paused. "I'm sorry, Mr. O'Brien."

He slapped me on the shoulder. "Not your fault we've got a bunch of sissies in this class. You did a great job. The most original ethnic dish we've ever had. An A+ all the way. Right, Doughnut?"

Doughnut leaned back on his heels, his face the color of dirty gym socks. "Right, Coach."

"As a matter of fact, we've got a big game Friday night," Mr. O'Brien went on. "Maybe I'll have Don bring a couple of pans of

savoring
*greatly enjoying;
relishing*

resonated
*sounded with a
repeating pattern*

Alden R. Carter

brains by the locker room. Some fried brains and some 'blood of the Cossacks' might be just the thing you boys need to fire up for a game against the conference champions. What do you think, Doughnut?"

Doughnut looked at Mr. O'Brien and then at me. *I am dead*, I thought. "Right, Coach. I'll do better. I promise. I'll be the first one to take some."

"Darn right you will. Now, are you man enough to take that wastebasket down to the custodian's room and wash it out?"

"Yes, sir."

We watched him trudge down the hall, head hanging. Mr. O'Brien slapped me on the shoulder a final time. "Good work, Shadis. See you tomorrow."

■■■■

A half block from the school, Melinda was sitting on one of the swings in the playground behind the grade school. "Okay," she said. "What were they really?"

"Fettuccine."

"Yeah, I thought so. Did O'Brien catch on?"

I shrugged. "Who knows? If he did, he decided to go along with the joke."

"You're lucky. You were way out on the edge. What did he say to you?"

"Not much. He said maybe he'd have me bring a couple of pans of brains to the locker room before Friday night's game."

She laughed. "Cool. I bet half those jocks would lose their lunch. Are you going to do it?"

"Are you kidding? I don't have that kind of death wish. I think pig brains may be real hard to find for the next few weeks."

"And sheep, goat, and calf brains?"

"Them, too," I said.

She laughed again. "I'm glad you did it. Took Doughnut down a notch." She grinned at me. "And put you up a couple, even if nobody knows what you really had in that pan but me."

I shrugged. "That's okay. I don't want to be a dead hero. . . . Hey, you walking my way?"

"Yeah, I could do that," she said. "Definitely."

LITERARY LENS

Why do you think Shadis wanted to take Doughnut "down a notch"?

The Metaphor

Budge Wilson

*M*iss Hancock was plump and unmarried and over-enthusiastic. She was fond of peasant blouses encrusted with embroidery, from which loose threads invariably dangled. Like a heavy bird, she fluttered and flitted from desk to desk, inspecting notebooks, making suggestions, dispensing eager praise. Miss Hancock was our teacher of literature and creative writing.

If one tired of scrutinizing Miss Hancock's clothes, which were nearly always as flamboyant as her nature, one could still contemplate her face with considerable satisfaction. It was clear that this was a face that had once been pretty, although cloakroom discussions of her age never resulted in any firm conclusions. In any case, by now it was too late for simple, unadorned prettiness. What time had taken away from her, Miss Hancock tried to replace by artificial means, and she applied her makeup with an excess of zeal and a minimum of control. Her face was truly amazing. She was fond of **luminous** frosted lipsticks—in hot pink, or something closer to purple or magenta. Her eyelashes curled up and out singly, like a row of tiny bent sticks. Surrounding her eyes, the modulations of colour, toners, shadows could keep a student interested for half an hour if he or she were bored with a grammar assignment. Her head was covered with a **profusion** of small busy curls, which were brightly, aggressively golden—"in bad taste," my mother said, "like the rest of her."

However, do not misunderstand me. We were fond of Miss Hancock. In fact, almost to a person, we loved her. Our class, like most groups that are together for long periods of time, had developed a definite personality. By some fluke of geography or biology or school administration, ours was a **cohesive** group composed of remarkably backward grade 7 pupils—backward in that we had not yet embraced sophistication, boredom, cruelty, drugs, alcohol, or sex. Those who did not fit into our mould were in the minority and made little mark upon us. We were free to respond positively to Miss Hancock's literary excesses without fear of the mockery of our peers, and with an open and uninhibited delight that is often hard to find in any classroom about the level of grade 5. So Miss Hancock was able to survive, even to flourish, in our unique, sheltered environment.

LITERARY LENS

Pay attention to the metaphors that describe the characters in this story and the poem that follows.

luminous
shiny; glowing

profusion
very many; an abundance

cohesive
working well together; united

modulated
sounding well pitched

Miss Hancock was equally at home in her two fields of creative writing and literature. It was the first time I had been excited, genuinely moved, by poems, plays, stories. She could analyze without destroying a piece of literature, and we argued about meanings and methods and creative intentions with passionate caring. She had a beautiful deeply **modulated** voice, and when she read poetry aloud, we sat bewitched, transformed. We could not have said which we loved best, Miss Hancock or her subject. They were all of a piece.

But it was in the area of composition, in her creative writing class, that Miss Hancock made the deepest mark upon me. She had that gift of making most of us want to write, to communicate, to make a blank sheet of paper into a beautiful or at least an interesting thing. We were as drugged by words as some children are by electronic games.

One October day, just after Thanksgiving,[1] Miss Hancock came into the classroom and faced us, eyes aglitter, hands clasped in front of her embroidered breasts.

"Today," she announced, clapping her dimpled hands together, her charm bracelets jingling, "we are going to do a lovely exercise. Such *fun!*" She lifted her astonishing eyes to the classroom ceiling. "A whole new world of composition is about to open for you in one glorious *whoosh*." She stood there, arms now raised, elbows bent, palms facing us, enjoying her dramatic pause. "After today," she announced in a loud confidential whisper, "you will have a brand-new weapon in your arsenal of writing skills. You will possess . . . (pause again) The Metaphor!" Her arms fell, and she clicked to the blackboard in her patent-leather pumps to start the lesson. Her dazzling curls shone in the afternoon sunlight and jiggled as she wrote. Then, with a board full of examples and suggestions, she began her impassioned discourse on The Metaphor. I listened, entranced. Miss Hancock may have been in poor taste, but at that time in my life she was my entry to something I did not yet fully understand but that I knew I wanted.

"And now," Miss Hancock announced, after the lucid and fervent[2] presentation of her subject, "The Metaphor is yours—to *use*, to *enjoy*,

---

1 **One . . . Thanksgiving:** in Canada, where this story takes place, Thanksgiving is celebrated on October 14.

2 **lucid and fervent:** clear and impassioned

Budge Wilson

to *relish*." She stood poised, savouring one of her breathless pauses. "I now want you to take out your notebooks," she continued, "and make a list. Write down the members of your family, your home, your pets, anything about which you feel *deeply*. Then," she went on, "I want you to describe everyone and everything on your list with a pungent and a telling metaphor." She gave a little clap. "Now *start*!" she cried. She sat down at her desk, clasping her hands together so tightly that the knuckles looked polished. Smiling tensely, frilled eyes shining, she waited.

All but the dullest of us were excited. This was an unfamiliar way of looking at things. Better still, it was a brand-new method of talking about them.

Miss Hancock interrupted us just one more time. "Write quickly," she urged from her glowing, expectant position at the desk. "Don't think too hard. Let your writing, your words, emerge from you like a mysterious and elegant blossom. Let it all *out*"—she closed her lacy eyes—"without restraint, without inhibition, with *verve*."

Well, we did. The results, when we read them out to her, were, as one might expect, **hackneyed**, undistinguished, ordinary. But we were delighted with ourselves. And she with us. She wrote our metaphors on the blackboard and expressed her pleasure with small, delighted gasping sounds.

"My dog is a clown in a spotted suit."

"My little brother George is a whirling top."

"The spruce tree was a tall lady in a stiff dress."

"My dad is a warm wood stove."

And so it went. Finally it was my turn. I offered metaphors for my father, my grandmother, my best friend, the waves at Peggy's Cove. Then I looked at the metaphor for my mother. I had not realized I had written so much.

"Miss Hancock," I hesitated, "the one for my mother is awfully long. You probably don't want to write all this stuff down."

"Oh, *heavens*, Charlotte," breathed Miss Hancock, "of *course* I want it! Read it all to us. Do, Charlotte. Oh, *do*!"

I began: "My mother is a flawless modern building, created of glass and the smoothest of pale concrete. Inside are business offices furnished with beige carpets and gleaming chromium.[3] In every

hackneyed
unoriginal; ordinary

---

3 **chromium:** a type of metal

room there are machines—telex machines, mimeograph machines, and sleek typewriters. They are buzzing and clicking away, absorbing and spitting out information with a speed and skill that is not normal. Downstairs, at ground level, people walk in and out, tracking mud and dirt over the steel-grey tiles, marring the cool perfection of the building. There are no comfortable chairs in the lobby."

I sat down, eyes on my desk. There was a pause so long that I finally felt forced to look up. Miss Hancock was standing there at the front of the room, chalk poised, perfectly still. Then she turned around quickly and wrote the whole metaphor **verbatim** (verbatim!) on the board. When she faced us again, she looked normal once more. Smiling brightly, she said, "Very, *very* good, class! I had planned to discuss with you what you all *meant* by your metaphors; I had hoped to probe their *significance*. But I have to leave early today because of a dental appointment." Then, with five vigorous sweeps of her blackboard eraser, the whole enticing parade of metaphors disappeared from the board, leaving us feeling vaguely deprived. It also left me feeling more than vaguely relieved. "Class dismissed!" said Miss Hancock cheerily, and then, "Charlotte. May I see you for a moment before you go."

When the others had gathered up their books and their leftover lunches, they disappeared into the corridor. I went up to the front of the room to Miss Hancock's desk. She was sitting there soberly, hands still, eyes quiet.

"Yes, Miss Hancock?" I inquired, mystified.

"Charlotte," she began, "your metaphors were unusually good, unusually interesting. For someone your age, you have quite a complex vocabulary, a truly promising way of expressing yourself."

Ah. So this was why she wanted to see me. But apparently it was not.

"I wonder," she continued slowly, carefully. "Do you have anything you would like to discuss about your mother's metaphor?"

I thought about that.

"No," I replied. "I don't think so. I don't really know what it means. It just sort of came out. I feel kind of funny about it."

"Lots of things just sort of come out when you're writing," said Miss Hancock quietly, oh so quietly, as though she were afraid something fragile might break if she spoke too quickly, too loudly. "And

verbatim
word for word; exactly as heard

there's no need to feel funny about it. I don't want to push you even a little bit, but are you really sure you don't want to discuss it?" I could tell that she was feeling concerned and kind, not nosy.

"Lookit," I said, using an expression that my mother particularly disliked, "that's really nice of you, but I can't think of anything at all to say. Besides, even though you say there's no need to feel funny, I really do feel sort of creepy about it. And I'm not all that crazy about the feeling." I paused, not sure of what else to say.

Miss Hancock was suddenly her old self again. "Well!" she said cheerfully, as she rose. "That's perfectly fine. I just wanted you to know that your writing was very **intriguing** today, and that it showed a certain maturity that surprised and delighted me." She gathered up her books, her purse, her pink angora cardigan,[4] and started off toward the corridor. At the door, she stopped and turned around, solemn and quiet once more. "Charlotte," she said, "if you ever need any help—with your writing, or, well, with any other kind of problem—just let me know." Then she turned abruptly and clicked off in the direction of the staff room waving her hand in a fluttery farewell. "My dental appointment," she called merrily.

intriguing
interesting; stimulating

I walked home slowly, hugging my books to my chest. The mid-October sun shone down upon the coloured leaves that littered the sidewalk, and I kicked and shuffled as I walked, enjoying the swish and scrunch, savouring the sad-sweet feeling of doom that October always gives me. I thought for a while about my metaphor—the one Miss Hancock had asked about—and then I decided to push it out of my head.

When I arrived home, I opened the door with my key, entered the front porch, took off my shoes, and read the note on the hall table. It was written in flawless script on a small piece of bond paper. It said: "At a Children's Aid board meeting. Home by 5. Please tidy your room."

The hall table was polished, antique, perfect. It contained one silver salver for messages and a small ebony lamp with a white shade. The floor of the entrance hall was tiled. The black and white tiles shone in the sunlight, unmarked by any sign of human contact. I walked over them carefully, slowly, having slipped and fallen once too often.

---

4 **angora cardigan:** a sweater made of a soft, fuzzy fabric

Hunger. I went into the kitchen and surveyed it thoughtfully. More black and white tiles dazzled the eye, and the cupboards and walls were a blinding spotless white. The counters shone, empty of jars, leftovers, canisters, appliances. The whole room looked as though it were waiting for the movers to arrive with the furniture and dishes. I made myself a peanut-butter sandwich, washed the knife and plate, and put everything away. Then I went upstairs to my room, walking up the grey stair carpet beside the off-white walls, glancing absently at the single lithograph[5] in its black frame. "My home," I said aloud, "is a box. It is cool and quiet and empty and uninteresting. Nobody lives in the box." Entering my room, I looked around. A few magazines were piled on the floor beside my bed. On my dresser, a T-shirt lay on top of my ivory brush and comb set. Two or three books were scattered over the top of my desk. I picked up the magazines, removed the T-shirt, and put the books back in the bookcase. There. Done.

Then I called Julia Parsons, who was my best friend, and went over to her house to talk about boys. When I returned at six o'clock, my mother, who had been home only one hour, had prepared a complicated three-course meal—expert, delicious, nutritious. "There's food in the box," I mused.

Since no one else had much to say at dinner, I talked about school. I told them about Miss Hancock's lesson on The Metaphor. I said what a marvellous teacher she was, how even the dumbest of us had learned to enjoy writing compositions, how she could make the poetry in our textbook so exciting to read and to hear.

My father listened attentively, enjoying my enthusiasm. He was not a lively or an original man, but he was an intelligent person who liked to watch eagerness in others. "You're very fortunate, Charlotte," he said, "to find a teacher who can wake you up and make you love literature."

"Is she that brassy Miss Hancock whom I met at the home and school meeting?" asked my mother.

"What do you mean, brassy?"

"Oh, you know. Overdone, too much enthusiasm. Flamboyant.[6] Orange hair. Is she the one?"

"Yes," I said.

---

5 **lithograph:** a print made by printing from a smooth stone or metal plate
6 **flamboyant:** behaving elaborately

"Oh," said my mother, without emphasis of any kind. "Her. Charlotte, would you please remove the dishes and bring in the dessert. Snow pudding. In the fridge, top left-hand side. Thank you."

That night I lay in the bath among the Estée Lauder bubbles (gift from my father on my last birthday) and created metaphors. I loved baths. The only thing nicer than one bath a day was two. Julia said that if I kept taking so many baths, my skin would get dry and crisp, and that I would be wrinkled before I was thirty. That was too far away to worry about. She also said that taking baths was disgusting and that showers were more hygienic. She pointed out that I was soaking in my own dirt, like bathers in the fetid Ganges. I thought this a bit excessive and said so. "For Pete's sake!" I exclaimed. "If I have two baths a day, I can't be sitting in very much dirt. Besides, it's *therapeutic.*"

"It's *what?*"

"Therapeutic. Water play. I read about it in *Reader's Digest* at the doctor's office. They let kids play with water when they're wild and upset. And now they're using warm baths to soothe the patients in mental hospitals."

"So?"

"So it could be useful if I happen to end up crazy," I laughed. I figured that would stop her. It did.

In the bath I always did a lot of things besides wash. I lifted up mounds of the tiny bubbles and held them against the fluorescent light over the sink. The patterns and shapes were delicate, like minute **filaments** of finest lace. I poked my toes through the bubbles and waved their hot pinkness to and fro among the static white waves. I hopefully examined my breasts for signs of sudden growth. If I lay down in the tub and brought the bubbles up over my body and squeezed my chest together by pressing my arms inward, I could convince myself that I was full-breasted and seductive. I did exercises to lengthen my hamstrings, in order to improve my splits for the gymnastics team. I thought about Charles Swinimer. I quoted poetry out loud with excessive feeling and dramatic emphasis, waving my soapy arms around and pressing my eloquent hand against my flat chest. And from now on, I also lay there and made up metaphors, most of them about my mother.

"My mother is a white picket fence—straight, level. The fence stands in a field of weeds. The field is bounded on all sides by thorny bushes and barbed wire."

filaments
long, hairlike strands

"My mother is a lofty mountain capped by virgin snow.[7] The air around the mountain is clear and clean and very cold." I turned on more hot water. "At the base of the mountain grow gnarled and crooked trees, surrounded by scrub brush and poison ivy."

Upon leaving the bath, I would feel no wiser. Then I would clean the tub very carefully indeed. It was necessary.

Not, mind you, that my mother ranted and raved about her cleanliness. Ranting and raving were not part of her style. "I know you will agree," she would say very oh ever so sweetly, implying in some **oblique** way that I certainly did not agree, "that it is an inconsiderate and really ugly thing to leave a dirty tub." Then she would lead me with a subtle soft-firm pressure into the bathroom so that we might inspect together a bathtub ringed with sludge, sprinkled with hair and dried suds. "Not," she would say quietly, "a very pretty sight."

And what, I would ask myself, is so terrible about that? Other mothers—I know; I had heard them—nagged, yelled, scolded, did terrible and noisy things. But what was it about my mother's methods that left me feeling so depraved, so unsalvageable?

But of course I was thirteen by now, and knew all about cleaning tubs and wiping off countertops and sweeping up the crumbs. A very small child must have been a terrible test to that cool and orderly spirit. I remember those days. A toy ceased to be a toy and began to be a mess the moment it left the toy cupboard. "I'm sure," she would say evenly, "that you don't want to have those blocks all over the carpet. Why not keep them all in one spot, over there behind Daddy's chair?" From time to time I attempted argument.

"But Mother, I'm making a garden."

"Then make a *little* garden. They're every bit as satisfying as huge, sprawling unmanageable farms."

And since no one who was a truly nice person would want a large, sprawling unmanageable farm, I would move my blocks behind the chair and make my small garden there. Outside, our backyard was composed of grass and flowers, plus one evergreen tree that dropped neither fuzzy buds in the spring nor ragged leaves in the fall. No swing set made brown spots on that perfect lawn, nor was there a sandbox. Cats were known to use sandboxes as community toilets. Or so my mother told me. I assume she used the term

7 **virgin snow:** snow that has just fallen and not yet been dirtied

oblique
indirect; offhand; subtle

toilet (a word not normally part of her vocabulary) instead of wash-room, lest there be any confusion as to her meaning.

But in grade 7, you no longer needed a sandbox. My friends marvelled when they came to visit, which was not often. How serene my mother seemed, how lovely to look at, with her dark-blond hair, her flawless figure, her smooth hands. She never acted frazzled or rushed or angry, and her forehead was unmarked by age or worry lines. Her hair always looked as though a hairdresser had arrived at six o'clock to ready her for the day. "Such a peaceful house," my friends would say, clearly impressed, "and no one arguing or fight-ing." Then they would leave and go somewhere else for their snacks, their music, their hanging around.

No indeed, I thought. No fights in this house. It would be like trying to down an angel with a BB gun—both sacrilegious and futile. My father, thin, and nervous, was careful about hanging up his clothes and keeping his sweaters in neat piles. He certainly did not fight with my mother. In fact, he said very little to her at all. He had probably learned early that to complain is weak, to rejoice is child-ish, to laugh is noisy. And moving around raises dust.

This civilized, this clean, this disciplined woman who was and is my mother, was also, if one were to believe her admirers, the mainstay of the community, the rock upon which the town was built. She chaired committees, ran bazaars, sat on boards. When I first heard about this, I thought it a very exciting thing that she sat on boards. If my mother, who sat so correctly on the needlepoint chair with her nylon knees pressed so firmly together, could actually sit on *boards*, there might be a rugged and reckless side to her that I had not yet met. The telephone rang constantly, and her softly con-trolled voice could be heard, hour after hour, arranging and steering and manipulating the affairs of the town.

Perhaps because she juggled her community jobs, her house-work, her cooking and her grooming with such quiet, calm effi-ciency, she felt scorn for those less able to cope. "Mrs. Langstreth says she's too *tired* to take on a table at the bazaar," she might say. It was not hard to imagine Mrs. Langstreth lounging on a sofa, probably in a turquoise chenille dressing gown, surrounded by full ashtrays and neglected children. Or my mother might comment quietly, but with unmistakable emphasis, "Gillian Munroe is having trouble with her children. And in my opinion, she has only herself to blame." The

implication seemed to be that if Gillian Munroe's children were left in my mother's care for a few weeks, she could make them all into a perfectly behaved family. Which was probably true.

Certainly in those days I was well behaved. I spoke quietly, never complained, ate whatever was put before me, and obeyed all rules without question or argument. I was probably not even very unhappy, though I enjoyed weekdays much more than weekends. Weekends did not yet include parties or boys. It is true that Julia and I spent a lot of our time together talking about boys. I also remember stationing myself on the fence of the vacant lot on Seymour Street at five o'clock, the hour when Charles Swinimer could be expected to return from high school. As he passed, I would be too absorbed in my own activity to look at him directly. I would be chipping the bark off the fence, or reading, or pulling petals from a daisy—he loves me, he loves me not. Out of the corner of my eye, I feasted upon his jaw line, his confident walk, his shoulders. On the rare days when he would toss me a careless "Hi" (crumbs to a pigeon), I would have to dig my nails into the wood to keep from falling off, from fainting dead away. But that was the extent of my thrills. No boys had yet materialized in the flesh to offer themselves to me. Whatever else they were looking for, it was not acne, brown stringy hair, or measurements of 32-32-32.

So weekdays were still best. Weekdays meant school and particularly English class, where Miss Hancock delivered up feasts of

succulent literature for our daily consumption. *Hamlet* was the thing that spring, the spring before we moved into junior high. So were a number of poems that left me weak and changed. And our composition class gathered force, filling us with a creative confidence that was heady stuff. We wrote short stories, played with similes, created poems that did and did not rhyme, felt we were capable of anything and everything; if Shakespeare, if Wordsworth, could do it, why couldn't we? Over it all, Miss Hancock presided, hands fluttering, voice atremble with a raw emotion.

But *Hamlet* dominated our literature classes from April to June. Like all serious students, we agonized and argued over its meaning, Hamlet's true intent, his sanity, his goal. Armed with rulers, we fought the final duel with its bloody sequence, and a four-foot Fortinbras stepped among the dead bodies between the desks to proclaim the ultimate significance of it all. At the end, Miss Hancock stood, hands clasped, knuckles white, tears standing in her eyes. And I cannot pretend that all of ours were dry.

At the close of the year, our class bought an enormous tasteless card of thanks and affixed it to a huge trophy. The trophy was composed of two brass-coloured Ionic pillars[8] that were topped by a near-naked athlete carrying a spiky wreath. On the plate below was inscribed: "For you and Hamlet with love. The grade 7 class. 1965."

When my mother saw it, she came close to losing her cool control.

"Who chose it?" she asked, tight-lipped.

"Horace Hannington," I answered. Oh, don't spoil it, don't spoil it.

"That explains it," she said, and mercifully that was all.

■■■■

Junior high school passed, and so did innocence and acne. Hair curled, makeup intact, I entered high school the year that Charles Swinimer left for university. But there would be other fish to fry. Outwardly blasé,[9] single-minded, and sixteen, I came into my first grade 10 class with a mixture of intense apprehension and a burning unequivocal belief that high school could and would deliver up to me all of life's most precious gifts—the admiration of my peers, local fame, boys, social triumphs. During August of that year, my family had moved to another school district. I entered high school with a clean state. It was terrifying to be so alone. I also knew that it was a rare and precious opportunity; I could approach life without being branded with my old failures, my old drawbacks. I was pretty; I had real curves; I was anonymous; I melted into the crowd. No one here would guess that I had once been such a skinny, pimply wretch.

Our first class was geography, and I knew enough of the material to be able to let my eyes and mind wander. Before the end of the period, I knew that the boy to pursue was Howard Oliver, that the most prominent and therefore the most potentially useful or dangerous girl was Gladys Simpson, that geography was uninteresting, that the teacher was strict. To this day I can smell the classroom during the first period—the dry and acrid smell of chalk, the cool, sweet

---

8 **Ionic pillars:** pillars typical in ancient Greek architecture
9 **blasé:** unconcerned

fragrance of the freshly waxed floors, the perspiration that traveled back to me from Joey Elliot's desk.

The next period was English. My new self-centered and self-conscious sophistication had not blunted my love of literature, my desire to write, to play with words, to express my discoveries and confusions. I awaited the arrival of the teacher with masked but real enthusiasm. I was not prepared for the entrance of Miss Hancock.

Miss Hancock's marked success with fifteen years of grade 7 students had finally transported her to high places. She entered the classroom, wings spread, ready to fly. She was used to success, and she was eager to sample the pleasure of a group of older and more perceptive minds. Clad in royal blue velour,[10] festooned with gold chains, hair glittering in the sun pouring in from the east window, fringed eyes darting, she faced the class, arms raised. She paused.

"Let us pray!" said a deep male voice from the back row. It was Howard Oliver. Laughter exploded in the room. Behind my Duo Tang folder, I snickered fiercely.

Miss Hancock's hands fluttered wildly. It was as though she were waving off an invasion of poisonous flies.

"Now, now, class!" she exclaimed with a mixture of tense jollity and clear panic. "We'll have none of *that*! Please turn to page seven in your textbook. I'll read the selection aloud to you first, and then we'll discuss it." She held the book high in the palm of one hand; the other was raised like an admonition,[11] an artistic beckoning.

The reading was from Tennyson's "Ulysses." I had never heard it before. As I listened to her beautiful voice, the old magic took hold, and no amount of peer pressure could keep me from thrilling to the first four lines she read:

> *"I am a part of all that I have met;*
> *Yet all experience is an arch wherethro'*
> *Gleams that untravell'd world, whose margin fades*
> *For ever and for ever when I move."*

But after that, it was difficult to hear her. Guffaws sprang up here and there throughout the room. Gladys Simpson whispered something behind her hand to the girl beside her and then broke into fits

---

10 **velour:** a velvetlike fabric
11 **admonition:** a gentle warning

of giggles. Paper airplanes flew. The wits of grade 10 offered comments: "Behold the Bard!"[12] "Bliss! Oh, poetic bliss!" "Hancock, Whocock, Hancock! Hurray!" "Don't faint, class! *Don't faint!*"

I was caught in a stranglehold somewhere between shocked embarrassment and a terrible desire for concealment. No other members of the class shared my knowledge of Miss Hancock or my misery. But I knew I could not hide behind that Duo Tang folder forever.

In was in fact ten days later when Miss Hancock recognized me. It could not have been easy to connect the eager skinny fan of grade 7 with the cool and careful person I had become. And she would not have expected to find a friend in that particular classroom. By then, stripped of fifteen years of overblown confidence, she offered her material shyly, hesitantly, certain of rejection, of humiliation. When our eyes met in class, she did not rush up to me to claim alliance or allegiance.[13] Her eyes merely held mine for a moment, slid off, and then periodically slid back. There was a desperate hope in them that I could hardly bear to witness. At the end of the period, I waited until everyone had gone before I walked toward her desk on the way to the corridor. Whatever was going to happen, I wanted to be sure that it would not be witnessed.

When I reached her, she was sitting quietly, hands folded on top of her lesson book. I was reminded of another day, another meeting. The details were blurred; but I knew I had seen this Miss Hancock before. She looked at me evenly and said quietly, simply, "Hello, Charlotte. How nice to see you."

I looked at her hands, the floor, the blackboard, anywhere but at those searching eyes. "Hello, Miss Hancock," I said.

"Still writing metaphors?" she asked with a tentative smile.

"Oh, I dunno," I replied. But I was. Nightly, in the bathtub. And I kept a notebook in which I wrote them all down.

"Your writing showed promise, Charlotte." Her eyes were quiet, pleading. "I hope you won't forget that."

Or anything else, I thought. Oh, Miss Hancock, let me go. Aloud I said, "French is next, and I'm late."

She looked directly into my eyes and held them for a moment. Then she spoke. "Go ahead, Charlotte. Don't let me keep you."

---

12 **the Bard:** William Shakespeare
13 **alliance or allegiance:** friendship or loyalty

She did not try to reach me again. She taught, or tried to teach her classes, as though I were not there. Week after week, she entered the room white with tension and left it defeated. I did not tell a living soul that I had seen her before.

One late afternoon in March of that year, Miss Hancock stepped off the curb in front of the school and was killed instantly by a school bus.

The next day, I was offered this piece of news with that mixture of horror and delight that so often attends the delivery of terrible tidings. When I heard it, I felt as though my chest and throat were constricted by bands of dry ice. During assembly, the principal came forward and delivered a short announcement of the tragedy, peppered with little complimentary phrases: ". . . a teacher of distinction . . ." ". . . a generous colleague . . ." ". . . a tragic end to a promising career . . ." Howard Oliver was sitting beside me; he had been showing me flattering attention of late. As we got up to disperse for classes, he said, "Poor old Whocock Hancock. Quoting poetry to the angels by now." He was no more surprised than I was when I slapped him full across his handsome face, before I ran down the aisle of the assembly room, up the long corridor of the first floor, down the steps, and out into the parking lot. Shaking with dry, unsatisfying sobs, I hurried home through the back streets of the town and let myself in by the back door.

"What on earth is wrong, Charlotte?" asked my mother when she saw my stricken look, my heaving shoulders. There was real concern in her face.

"Miss Hancock is dead," I whispered.

"Miss who? Charlotte, speak up please."

"Miss Hancock. She teaches—*taught*—us grade 10 English."

"You mean that same brassy creature from grade 7?"

I didn't answer. I was crying out loud, with the abandon of a preschooler or someone who is under the influence of drugs.

"Charlotte, do please blow your nose and try to get hold of yourself. I can't for the life of me see why you're so upset. You never even told us she was your teacher this year."

I was rocking back and forth on the kitchen chair, arms folded over my chest. My mother stood there erect, invulnerable.[14] It

---

14 **invulnerable:** not open to attack

crossed my mind that no grade 10 would throw paper airplanes in any group that *she* chose to teach.

"Well, then," she said, "why or how did she die?"

I heard myself shriek, "I killed her! I killed her!"

Halting, gasping, I told her all of it. I described her discipline problems, the cruelty of the students, my own blatant[15] betrayal.

"For goodness' sake, Charlotte," said my mother, quiet but clearly irritated, "don't lose perspective. She couldn't keep order, and she had only herself to blame." That phrase sounded familiar to me. "A woman like that can't survive for five minutes in the high schools of today. There was nothing you could have done."

I was silent. I could have *said something*. Like thank you for grade 7. Or yes, I still have fun with The Metaphor. Or once, just once this entire year, I could have *smiled* at her.

My mother was speaking again. "There's a great deal of ice. It would be very easy to slip under a school bus. And she didn't strike me as the sort of person who would exercise any kind of sensible caution."

"Oh, dear God," I was whispering, "I wish she hadn't chosen a *school bus.*"

I cried some more that day and excused myself from supper. I heard my father say, "I think I'll just go up and see if I can help." But my mother said, "Leave her alone, Arthur. She's sixteen years old. It's time she learned how to cope. She's acting like a hysterical child." My father did not appear. Betrayal, I thought, runs in the family.

The next day I stayed home from school. I kept having periods of uncontrollable weeping, and even my mother could not send me off in that condition. Once again I repeated to her, to my father, "I killed her. We all killed her. But especially me."

"Charlotte."

Oh, I knew that voice, that tone. So calm, so quiet, so able to silence me with one word. I stopped crying and curled up in a tight ball on the sofa.

"Charlotte. I know you will agree with what I'm going to say to you. There is no need to speak so extravagantly. A sure and perfect control is what separates the civilized from the uncivilized." She inspected her fingernails, pushing down the quick of her middle

---

15 **blatant:** obvious

finger with her thumb. "If you would examine this whole perfectly natural situation with a modicum[16] of rationality, you would see that she got exactly what she deserved."

I stared at her.

"Charlotte," she continued, "I'll have to ask you to stop this nonsense. You're disturbing the even tenor[17] of our home."

I said nothing. With a sure and perfect control, I uncoiled myself from my fetal position on the sofa. I stood up and left the living room.

Upstairs in my bedroom I sat down before my desk. I took my pen out of the drawer and opened my notebook. Extravagantly, without a modicum of rationality, I began to write.

"Miss Hancock was a birthday cake," I wrote. "This cake was frosted by someone unschooled in the art of cake decoration. It was adorned with a profusion of white roses and lime-green leaves, which drooped and dribbled at the edges where the pastry tube had slipped. The frosting was of an intense peppermint flavour, too sweet, too strong. Inside, the cake had two layers—chocolate and vanilla. The chocolate was rich and soft and very delicious. No one who stopped to taste it could have failed to enjoy it. The vanilla was subtle and delicate; only those thoroughly familiar with cakes, only those with great sensitivity of taste, could have perceived its true fine flavour. Because it was a birthday cake, it was filled with party favours. If you stayed long enough at the party, you could amass quite a large collection of these treasures. If you kept them for many years, they would amaze you by turning into pure gold. Most children would have been delighted by this cake. Most grown-ups would have thrown it away after one brief glance at the frosting.

"I wish that the party wasn't over."

---

16 **modicum:** a small amount
17 **tenor:** character

Budge Wilson

Mrs. Goldwasser

Ron Wallace

Shimmered like butterscotch; the sun
had nothing on her. She bangled
when she walked. No one
did not love her. She shone,
she glowed, she lit up any room,
her every gesture jewelry.
And O, when she called us all by name
how we all performed!

Her string of little beads,
her pearls, her rough-cut
gemstones, diamonds, we hung
about her neck. And when
the future pressed her flat,
the world unclasped, and tarnished.

LITERARY LENS

What metaphor would you invent to describe the narrator in "The Metaphor" and the speaker in "Mrs. Goldwasser"?

This Is a Test

Stephen Gregg

A classroom

Characters
ALAN   LOIS
MOTHER   TEACHER
EVAN   CHRIS   PAT
THE CHORUS   OTHER STUDENTS
THE VOICE

Time
The present

LITERARY LENS

As you read both the play and the poem, think about the relationship between reality and dreams.

There is a high-pitched whine of the type that comes on the television during the emergency broadcast system tests.

VOICE. This is a test. For the next sixty minutes, this classroom will conduct a test of your emergency information retrieval system. This is only a test.

Lights come up on five desks and, behind them, a large blackboard. Two of the desks are occupied by LOIS *and* ALAN. LOIS *is neatly groomed.* ALAN *is a mess. His shirt is buttoned incorrectly, his socks do not match, and his hair sticks out at odd angles. His expression is both dazed and frantic.*

ALAN. I shouldn't have done this.
LOIS. It's going to be worth it.
ALAN. This was not a good idea.
LOIS. You know the stuff, right?
ALAN. I don't feel good.
LOIS. You're going to get an A and you're going to thank me.
ALAN. No. I should have slept.
LOIS. I told you, a little sleep is worse than no sleep.
ALAN. For you maybe. You do this all the time. I'm not used to this. I shouldn't have done it. I should have taken my phone off the hook.
LOIS. You did the right thing.
ALAN. It didn't work! I don't know anything.
LOIS. Yes, you do.

ALAN. I don't. (*He reaches under his desk, gets his books, and frantically thumbs through them.*) I have to study some more.

LOIS. Relax!

ALAN (*stopping at a random place and seeing the word "Saladin"*). "Saladin. A Moslem sultan of Egypt in the twelfth century. (*He pauses.*) His name means 'keeper of the faith.' (*He pauses.*) He grew up in Lower Mesopotamia."

LOIS (*reaching over and shutting ALAN's book*). Stop it. It's too late to study now. You either know it or you don't. The best thing you can do now is just relax.

ALAN. I can't! I don't know anything! Nothing stuck with me. You know what I learned last night? I learned that the Battle of Hastings was in ten-sixty-six and I learned that Thomas Edison's middle name was Alva. That's it. That's all I know. If we're asked when the Battle of Hastings was, I can say, "The Battle of Hastings was in ten-sixty-six." If he asks, "What was Thomas Edison's middle name?" I can say, "Alva." Other than that, I'm completely sunk.

LOIS. No, you're not.

ALAN. Evan wouldn't have done this.

LOIS. What does Evan have to do with this?

ALAN. He has the best grades in the class and he didn't stay up all last night.

LOIS. Who cares?

ALAN. He's going to get a better grade than I am and he didn't have you calling him every half hour to say, "Are you still awake?" (*He snarls.*) Yes, Lois, I am still awake. I am still awake, Lois. I am still awake!

LOIS. Calm down!

ALAN (*after a pause, much calmer*). I'm sorry. (*He pauses.*) It's all that caffeine. It makes me nervous.

LOIS. I know.

ALAN. I lose my concentration.

LOIS. Me too.

ALAN. I lose my concentration.

LOIS. Don't worry.

ALAN. I have to study some more. (*He goes for his books. LOIS stops him.*)

LOIS. No! Trust me. Just close your eyes . . . (ALAN *closes his eyes. After a pause.*) . . . and relax. Think about something else.

(THE CHORUS, ONE, TWO, *and* THREE, *walks onstage.*)

LOIS. Are you thinking about something else?

ONE (*after a pause, holding a pen*). This is a pen.

ALAN. Yes.

TWO (*after a pause of about two beats*). A what?

ONE (*after the same length pause*). A pen.

TWO (*after a pause of about two beats*). A what?

ONE (*after the same length pause*). A pen.

TWO (*after a shorter pause, taking the pen from* ONE). Oh, a pen.
(TWO *turns and addresses* THREE.) This is a pen.

THREE. A what?

TWO. A pen.

THREE. A what?

TWO. A pen.

THREE. Oh, a pen.

ONE (to TWO, *holding a shoe*). This is a shoe. (ONE *and* TWO *go through the same dialogue:* "A what?" "A shoe." "A what?" "A shoe." "Oh, a shoe." When TWO *takes the shoe, he or she immediately turns to* THREE *and says,* "This is a shoe." Simultaneously, ONE—*holding a spoon—says,* "This is a spoon" *to* TWO. THREE *responds,* "A what?" *to* TWO *at the same time that* TWO *turns and responds,* "A what?" *to* ONE. ONE *and* TWO, *who turns back to* THREE, *say,* "A spoon" *and* "A shoe." TWO *and* THREE *respond,* "Oh, a spoon" *and* "Oh, a shoe" *and take the respective objects.* TWO *immediately says,* "This is a spoon" *to* THREE *while* ONE *says,* "This is a match" *to* TWO *and the process repeats with* ONE *presenting objects,* THREE *receiving them, and* TWO *both presenting to* THREE *and receiving from* ONE. *After the match, they pass these objects through the chain: a coin, a cup, a watch, a key, a shirt, a sock, a glass, a book, a bell, the time, a test. Soon after* THE CHORUS *begins to go through this routine,* ALAN *opens his eyes, squints, and shakes his head from side to side. When* ONE *says,* "This is a shirt," LOIS *notices* ALAN *shaking his head back and forth and the following dialogue—all the way down to* ALAN's *line,* "Fine!" *overlaps* THE CHORUS.)

LOIS. What's the matter?

ALAN. It's that drama exercise we did yesterday.

LOIS. What about it?

(*With no interruption in the dialogue,* PAT *and* CHRIS, *both students, enter and sit in the empty chairs. They notice* ALAN **contorting** *his face and banging his head.*)

contorting
*twisting or bending
out of shape*

ALAN. That's what I'm thinking about.

LOIS. So?

ALAN. It's stuck.

LOIS. What do you mean "it's stuck"?

ALAN. It's stuck in my head.

LOIS. Think about something else.

ALAN. I can't! (*A loud bell rings, signaling the beginning of class.*)

(*The* TEACHER *enters, carrying tests.*)

TEACHER. Good morning. (*The* STUDENTS *acknowledge him. He watches* ALAN *for a moment.*) I hope we're all rested and ready to go. I know I am. There are a couple of things I'd like for you to keep in mind while you take this test. First, you really shouldn't think of this as a test. It is a test, of course, but it's also quite a bit more. (*He has been watching* ALAN *who has been shaking back and forth and hitting the side of his head.*) Alan, are you all right?

ALAN (*a little wildly*). Fine! (THE CHORUS *stops, even if it isn't finished with the list of objects.*)

TEACHER. Good. As I was saying, keep in mind that this isn't only a test. This is your mid-term. How you do today, this morning, will determine to a large extent how you do for the rest of this course. And, of course, how you do in this class has a large impact on your overall grade point which is a major factor in determining what, if any, colleges you might be accepted into. It might help if you didn't think of this as a test so much as you think of it as your future. Your future in . . . (*He looks at his watch.*) fifty-eight minutes. Any last minute questions? (CHRIS *raises a hand.*) Chris?

CHRIS. Uh, what was Thomas Edison's middle name?

TEACHER. Alva. But don't worry. That's not on the test. Anything else? (*A pause*) All right then. Let's get going. (*He hands out the tests, face down.*) Think carefully about each question and be sure not to leave anything blank. Most of the questions come right off the review sheets, so if you studied them you'll be fine.

ALAN (*panicked*). Review sheets?

TEACHER. Yes. These. (*He holds up a stack of at least ten sheets of paper, stapled together.*) I handed them out last week. Didn't you get them?

ALAN. No.

TEACHER. Well, I don't know how that could have happened. Were you here last Monday?

ALAN. Of course.

TEACHER. I don't understand. Everyone who *did* get the review sheets, raise your hands. (*The* OTHER STUDENTS *raise their hands. The* TEACHER *stares at* ALAN *and shakes his head.*) That's a shame. They might have helped you. (*Pause*) But do your best, Alan. I'm sure you'll do fine. Is everyone ready? You have . . . (*He checks his watch.*) fifty-seven minutes to take this test. Begin. (*The students look at their papers.* PAT *immediately begins to write. A clock starts to tick loudly. It ticks through the entire play.* ALAN *reads his test.*)

VOICE. Section One. Multiple choice. Question One. In what year was the Battle of Hastings? (*Pause*) A: ten-sixty-two.

ALAN. No.

VOICE. B: ten-sixty-three.

ALAN. Nope.

VOICE. C: ten-sixty-four.

ALAN. No.

VOICE. D: ten-sixty-five.

ALAN. No.

VOICE. E: ten-sixty-seven.

ALAN. What? What happened to ten-sixty-six?

PAT (*raising a hand*). May I have another bluebook,[1] please?

TEACHER. Of course. (*He gives a bluebook to* PAT.)

ALAN (*frantically*). What happened to ten-sixty-six? (CHRIS *raises a hand.*)

TEACHER. Chris?

---

1 **bluebook**: a small booklet with lined paper and a blue cover, used for taking exams in college and some high schools

CHRIS. How much time to do we have left?

TEACHER. Fifty-six minutes.

ALAN. Where is ten-sixty-six?

TEACHER. Something the matter, Alan?

ALAN. No. It's just . . . (*He stares at the* TEACHER *for a moment.*) I can't answer the first question.

TEACHER. Well, that shouldn't be a problem. It's not worth too much, is it? (ALAN *looks at the test.*)

VOICE. Five points.

ALAN. No.

TEACHER. Then just go on to something you do know.

ALAN. But that was all I knew!

TEACHER. Really? Did you study?

ALAN. Yes, I did. I studied all night.

efficiently
without wasting time

TEACHER. Did you study **efficiently**?

ALAN. Well . . . yes, I did. I even made a list of all the things I needed to study. (*He stares straight ahead, daydreaming.* PAT *taps a pencil four times to the beat of* "This is a test." *Pause.* CHRIS *taps* "A what?" *Pause.* PAT *taps* "A test." *Pause.* CHRIS *taps* "Oh, a test," *then:*)

ONE. This is a desk. (*And so on while* ALAN *says:*)

ALAN. This desk is a mess. I can't work in a mess like this. I'll just clean everything up and then I'll be able to work.

ONE. This is a phone. (*And so on while* ALAN, *miming the phone, says:*)

ALAN. Oh, hi, Lois. Of course I'm still awake. No, I haven't quite started yet. I had to clean my room.

ONE. This is a book. (*And so on while* ALAN *picks up a book and pretends to read.*)

ALAN. *Flowers of Northern Michigan.* Wow, this is really interesting. I'll get to work in just a minute.

ONE. This is a phone. (*And so on while* ALAN, *miming the phone, says:*)

ALAN. Hi, Lois. No, I haven't done . . . a whole lot.

ONE. This is a Will.

TWO and THREE (*sincerely puzzled*). A what?

ONE. A Will.

ALAN (*staring at an imaginary television*). And Grace! My favorite show.

Stephen Gregg

TWO and THREE. A what?

ALAN. What's it doing on at two in the morning?

ONE. A Will.

ALAN. I'll just watch it for a quick study break.

TWO and THREE (*sarcastically*). Oh, a Will.

ONE. This is a phone. (*And so on while* ALAN, *miming the phone, says*:)

ALAN. Hi, Lois. 'Course I'm still awake. How's my studying going?

ONE. This is a lie.

ALAN. Great.

TWO and THREE. A what?

ALAN. It's going just great.

ONE. A lie.

TWO and THREE. A what?

ALAN. Study, study, study.

ONE. A lie.

ALAN. I'll see you in a few hours.

TWO and THREE. Oh, a lie.

ALAN. It's five in the morning.

ONE. This is the pits. (*And so on while* ALAN *stares blankly.*)

TEACHER (*after "oh, the pits," putting a hand on* ALAN's *shoulder and shaking him gently*). Alan? (*Pause*) Alan. (ALAN *looks up.*) This is a test.

ONE, TWO and THREE (*softly*). A what?

TEACHER. You seem to be daydreaming. Don't you think you should be writing something?

ALAN. Yes, of course. That first question threw me a bit is all. (*He smiles weakly.*)

TEACHER. Glad to hear it.

ALAN (*to himself*). Now concentrate. (CHRIS *raises a hand.*)

TEACHER. Chris? (ALAN *looks a bit annoyed.*)

CHRIS. How much time do we have left?

TEACHER. Fifty-three minutes.

ALAN (*to himself*). Concentrate. And remember, it could be worse. Sometimes caffeine doesn't just confuse me. Sometimes it actually makes me . . . paranoid.

(*As* ALAN *tries to concentrate,* PAT *slowly leans over and looks at* LOIS's *test.* LOIS *seems to be aware of this, but doesn't stop it.* ALAN *glances over to see* PAT *doing this and* PAT *immediately stops.* ALAN *looks horrified, but continues to try to concentrate. As he works,* CHRIS *slowly takes off his/her watch and begins to read something off the back of it. Again,* ALAN *catches him/her in the act and* CHRIS *quickly puts the watch back on. One by one, each of the students, except* ALAN, *develops a mannerism which is probably, though not initially certainly, a signal to at least one of the others.* LOIS *might, for example, begin to thumb her nose. After noticing this,* PAT *might develop a significant sounding cough.* CHRIS *might tap a pencil on the desk in ways that seem less and less random. And so on.*

In addition to developing an idiosyncrasy,[2] each student should occasionally notice what another student is doing and subtly acknowledge it or write down some information—all except ALAN *who is becoming more and more* **agitated** *by what's going on around him. He looks at the* OTHER STUDENTS *and then up at the* TEACHER *who always seems to be looking in the wrong place—glancing over someone's shoulder, perhaps, or just not paying attention. Finally, when he's certain that he's caught one of his classmates signaling to another,* ALAN *raises his hand to attract the* TEACHER's *attention.)*

> **agitated**
> *upset; disturbed*

    TEACHER (*pleasantly*). Alan?
    ALAN. I was just curious about something . . . that I forgot to ask.
       (*He hesitates.*)
    TEACHER. Yes?
    ALAN. Is this test going to be graded on a curve?
    TEACHER (*cheerfully, matter-of-factly*). Yes, of course. The better everyone else does, the worse you'll do.
    ALAN. Thank you. (*The* TEACHER *nods and then turns away. As* ALAN *starts to work,* PAT *takes out semaphore flags[3] and begins to calmly, with almost mechanical movements, send signals to the* OTHER STUDENTS. ALAN *notices and watches, horrified, as the* OTHER STUDENTS *watch and take down answers. The* TEACHER *doesn't notice. After this has gone on for a while,* CHRIS *pulls out a flashlight from his vest, points it at the* OTHER STUDENTS, *and begins to click it on and off, sending Morse code messages which everyone but* ALAN *dutifully copies down. Finally,* LOIS *removes a*

---

2 **idiosyncrasy**: a strange or unusual way of behaving
3 **semaphore flags**: flags used for sending signals. Each position of the flags has its own meaning.

    Stephen Gregg

large sign from underneath her desk or, better yet, she removes the entire top of the desk, on the bottom of which is a sign that says, "The answer to six is 'The Gaza Strip.'" LOIS waves the sign once to everyone. All, except ALAN, see it and copy it down. ALAN has seen what's happened and is horrified but he doesn't notice until it's too late to get the answer. He is panicked.) It's what? The answer to number six is what?

TEACHER (*suspiciously*). Question, Alan?

ALAN. No!

TEACHER. There's nothing you want to ask me or . . . (*With much meaning*) anyone else?

ALAN. No.

TEACHER. I'm sure I don't have to remind anyone here that we're all on our honor. (*Pause*) Not that it makes any sense to cheat anyway because when you think about it, when you really think about it, who is it that you're really hurting when you cheat?

CHRIS (*raising a hand, with much sincerity*). You're really only hurting yourself, sir.

TEACHER. That's right, Chris. You're really only hurting yourself. I'm glad you feel that way. (*He turns his back on* CHRIS.) All right, let's get back to work. (CHRIS *holds up a sign that says,* "Hurt me" *to* PAT. PAT *holds up a sign that says* "2D is False." CHRIS *holds up a sign that says* "Hurt me more." PAT *holds up a sign that says* "7 is Truman." ALAN *has been staring back and forth in open-mouthed astonishment. Suddenly, the* TEACHER *spins around.* CHRIS *and* PAT *both still have their signs up.*)

TEACHER. Well! I see we can't all keep our eyes on our own papers, can we . . . Mr. Lefenfeld?

ALAN. What?

TEACHER. Eyes on your own paper, Alan. I don't want to have to speak to you again.

ALAN. No, sir. (*To himself*) Don't pay any attention to them. Concentrate. Concentrate and ignore them. Go on to the next section.

VOICE. Section Two. True or false.

ALAN (*to himself*). Yes, much better. This is more my speed.

VOICE. Number One. Explain the nature of the universe.

ALAN. What? Wait a minute. That's not true or false. (*He frantically looks around, then looks down at his paper and mouths the words as the* VOICE *says:*)

VOICE. Explain the nature of the universe.

ALAN (*having no idea what to do*). I . . . I don't know. (*Pause*) Next question.

VOICE. Athens.

ALAN. What?

VOICE. Athens.

ALAN. Athens? (*Pause*) Athens. (*Pause*) False. Athens is false.

VOICE. Renaissance.

ALAN (*after a pause*). True.

VOICE. Geometry.

ALAN. True.

VOICE. Thomas Edison.

ALAN. False.

VOICE. One hundred and twelve.

ALAN (*growing more and more frenzied*). True.

VOICE. Athletic ability.

ALAN. False.

VOICE. Biceps.

ALAN. False.

VOICE. Facial hair.

ALAN. False!

VOICE. Social life.

ALAN. False! (*Pause. Calmer, but panting a bit.*) This isn't so hard. (*Pause*) Wait a minute! I have a social life. I've had dates. (*Pause*) I've had a date. (*Pause*)

ONE. This is a date (*and so on*). This is a girl (*and so on*). (*The girl may be represented by a Barbie doll, a mannequin, or a real girl.*) This is a zit (*and so on, while* ALAN, *grabbing a spot on his face, says:*)

ALAN. Why? Why always before a date?

ONE. This is a dance (*and so on, while* ALAN *says:*)

ALAN. I hate dancing. I'm a terrible dancer.

ONE. This is a hand (*and so on, while* ALAN *says:*)

ALAN (*pretending to hold a hand*). Does her hand always sweat this much?

ONE. This is a kiss (*and so on, while* ALAN *says:*)

ALAN. Stop it. This is so embarrassing.

ONE. This is a kiss (*and so on, while* ALAN *says:*)

ALAN. Still. Still the same kiss?

ONE. This is a kiss (*and so on. The* TEACHER *and the* OTHER STU-
DENTS *notice that* ALAN *is talking to himself.*)

ALAN. Still going? Listen, I think I'm in a little over my head here.

ONE. This is a breast (*and so on, while* ALAN *says:*)

ALAN. Put that away! I don't know what to do with it!

ONE. This is a faint (*and so on, while* ALAN *says:*)

ALAN (**defensively**). I did not faint. I just passed out momentarily!

ONE. This is his heart (*and so on. The response here is* "His what?"
ONE *holds, then slowly rips in half a large paper valentine heart,
while* ALAN *says:*)

ALAN (*desperately, almost angrily*). Go ahead. Break my heart! It's
only flesh!

TEACHER. Alan?

ALAN (*a little wildly*). What?

TEACHER. Are you all right?

ALAN. I'm fine! (*To himself.*) Now concentrate. Think hard.
(CHRIS *raises a hand.*)

TEACHER. Chris.

CHRIS. How much time do we have left?

ALAN (*to* CHRIS, *yelling*). Would you stop that! Why don't you get
a watch? Some of us are trying to concentrate here and it's
almost impossible with you asking the time every five minutes!

TEACHER. Alan, what is the matter with you?

ALAN (*suddenly meek*). I'm sorry. That's not really like me, is it?

TEACHER. Not at all.

ALAN (*addressing everyone*). I'm really sorry. I don't know what
came over me. I'm calm now. (*To* CHRIS) What was it you
wanted to know?

CHRIS. How much time do we have left?

TEACHER. Nine minutes.

ALAN. What? What happened to the last forty-five minutes?

TEACHER. They passed.

ALAN. Already?

TEACHER. Yes.

ALAN. Are you sure?

defensively
*trying to protect
oneself*

TEACHER. Lois, how much time do we have left?

LOIS (*looking at her watch*). Eight minutes.

TEACHER. Is everyone almost finished? (*all but ALAN ad lib[4] "just about," etc.*) How much more do you have to do, Alan?

ALAN (*flipping through at least six pages that he hasn't gotten to, lying*). A little bit.

(EVAN *walks in with a football sticking out of his backpack.*)

TEACHER. Hello, Evan.

EVEN. Hi, Teach. Sorry I'm late. I was at practice.

TEACHER. No problem. (*He hands a test to EVAN.*) Here's the test. I'll tell you what. You don't really have time to take it. Why don't you just look it over and see how you would have done.

EVAN (*looking at the test, nodding his head occasionally*). Mmm-hmm. Yeah. Yup. (*Pause*) I think I know all but the second to the last one.

TEACHER. Which one? Oh, that's a hard one. Here, let me show you. (*He takes EVAN's paper and begins to write on it. ALAN looks on, disgusted.*)

EVAN. Uh-huh. Yeah. Okay. That's pretty much what I would have put.

TEACHER. Is it?

EVAN. Yup.

TEACHER (*skeptically*). Is it really?

EVAN. Uh-huh.

TEACHER (*convinced*). All right, then. Nicely done. (*He writes on EVAN's test with red ink.*) One hundred percent. Congratulations. See you in class tomorrow. (*EVAN starts to leave.*)

ALAN. Wait a minute!

TEACHER. Alan?

ALAN. That's not fair!

TEACHER. I beg your pardon?

ALAN. He didn't answer the questions.

TEACHER. But he knew the answers.

ALAN. That's what he told you!

TEACHER. Alan, are you doubting the word of one of your classmates?

---

4 **ad lib**: improvise; say spontaneously

ALAN. Well . . . no.

TEACHER. Evan always gets hundreds. You know that.

ALAN. I know, but . . .

TEACHER. Besides . . . it really doesn't matter what Evan gets on his tests anymore.

ALAN. Why not?

TEACHER. Because he was recently admitted to the college of his choice.

ALAN (*to* EVAN). You were?

EVAN. Yeah. Early decision.

ALAN. To where?

TEACHER. Majestica University. I believe that's the school you were going to apply to, wasn't it, Alan?

ALAN. What? How? How could they let him in already?

TEACHER. Alan, do I detect within you the . . . green and withering voice of envy?

ALAN. No. Well, yes, of course. (*To* EVAN) I mean, I'm happy for you, but . . . It just seems so early.

TEACHER. I don't want to hear a word about it. Evan has worked hard and this is his reward.

ALAN. But it's only October.

TEACHER. Not another word.

ALAN (***despondently***). But we're only sophomores.

TEACHER. I don't want to hear it. Back to work.

despondently
in a hopeless, unhappy manner

ALAN (*to himself*). He's only a sophomore and he's already into Majestica. I'll never get in there. I'm not a good student. (*Pause*) Or a good athlete. And I'm funny looking.

ONE. This is his face (*and so on, while* THREE *draws the outline of a face on the chalkboard. The responses in this section are* "His what?").

ONE. This is his nose (*and so on, while* THREE *draws an exaggeration of* ALAN's *nose*).

ONE. These are his ears (*and so on, while* THREE *draws an enormous set of ears*).

ONE. This is his mouth (*and so on, while* THREE *draws a mouth, perhaps with large buck teeth*).

ONE. This is his hair (*and so on, while* THREE *draws wild hair*).

ONE. This is his skin (*and so on, while* TWO *and* THREE *draw spots all over the face and* ONE *labels the picture* "Alan").

TEACHER (*overlapping* "This is his skin"). And remember, how you do today can affect your whole future.

ALAN. My future?

ONE. This is your life (*and so on, holding and then passing a sign that says* "dull" *in large block letters, while* ALAN *says:*)

ALAN (*despondently*). My future.

ONE. This is your job (*and so on, passing a sign that says* "duller").

ONE. This is your town (*and so on, passing a sign that says* "dullsville").

ONE. This is your wife (*and so on, passing a sign that says* "dullard").

PAT. May I have two more bluebooks, please?

ALAN (*slowly, with building sadness*). It's true. My future is **bleak**. I'm a terrible student and everybody knows it. (*Pause*) I'm not an athlete. I don't debate. Or play chess. I'm funny looking. All my library books are overdue. I don't have any friends. I'm an orphan. (*Pause*) Well, I have parents but they probably don't like me very much. I wouldn't either. (*Pause*) Wait a minute. Snap out of it. Quit feeling sorry for yourself. You have plenty of fine qualities. (*A long pause*) What about my singing? Just last week Mrs. Mandell said that my voice had great potential. "With a little training," she said, "you could have been a very fine tenor." Those were her exact words. "A very fine tenor." And that's something that makes me different. It's just one example of the many fine qualities that make me unique. I can always remember that no matter what happens, I have my music to make me just a little bit special.

PAT (*to the tune of Hallelujah*). Mr. Williams!

TEACHER. Yes, Pat?

PAT, CHRIS and LOIS (*strongly, in unison, to the tune of Hallelujah*). Mr. Williams!

TEACHER. Class?

PAT, CHRIS and LOIS (*to the tune of the line* "And heav'n and nature sing" *from* Joy to the World). May we have another blue . . . May we have another blue . . . May we ha-a-a-ave another bluebook, please? (ALAN *puts his head down on his desk.*)

TEACHER. Well, of course you may. That was lovely. Thank you

bleak
hopeless

very much. And I'll tell you what. Just for that, everyone who sang is going to get ten points extra credit. (*He makes a mark on* PAT's, CHRIS's, *and* LOIS's *papers while handing them the bluebooks.*)

ALAN (*to himself*). Don't pay any attention to them. They are not your concern. Concentrate. What's the next question?

VOICE. Question Four. Essay question. Thirty points.

ALAN. Uh-oh.

VOICE. Opinion essay.

ALAN. Opinion essay! This is a breeze.

ONE. This is a breeze. (ALAN *shakes his head. The chorus members shake their heads.*)

TWO. This is a sneeze.

THREE. This is a cheese.

ONE. This is Louise.

TWO. This is Chinese.

ALAN. Stop it! (*He reads the test, looks puzzled, then panicked.*) Oh, no. (*He reads again.*) Oh, no. (*He calls over the* TEACHER.) Mr. Williams!

TEACHER. Yes?

ALAN. This essay question.

TEACHER. What about it?

ALAN. It's in Chinese.

TEACHER. Yes?

ALAN. I don't speak Chinese.

TEACHER. And why is that?

ALAN. I speak . . . English.

TEACHER. And why don't you speak Chinese?

ALAN. I've never learned it.

TEACHER. Never?

ALAN. No.

TEACHER. This may be something to take up with the Attendance Committee.

ALAN. Attendance! I'm never absent. You know that.

TEACHER (*opening the attendance book*). Oh? What about last Tuesday?

ALAN. Tuesday . . . Oh, that's right. I missed this period. I had a dental appointment.

TEACHER. I thought so. (*Pause*) We learned Chinese on Tuesday.

ALAN. The only day I ever missed.

TEACHER. I am sorry. But you know the policy on making up work. (*He recites.*) "All students are responsible for all classwork missed for any reason including medical emergencies, family vacations and dental appointments." I'm very sorry about that, Alan. Or should I say, "Ning chok no quo, Alan."

PAT. Ni how fan shen kik? (*May I have another bluebook, please?*)

TEACHER (*handing a bluebook to* PAT). Tau.

CHRIS. Da lee hen wah? (*How much time is left?*)

TEACHER (*looking at his watch and holding up five fingers*). Nye ma.

ALAN. Wait! This can't be happening! This is a nightmare. (*He puts his head on his desk. The lights dim, except for a spot on* ALAN. *All, except* ALAN, *wobble back and forth, then crumple forward, motionless.*) This is a nightmare.

(MOTHER *enters from offstage as the ticking stops. She taps* ALAN *gently on the shoulder.*)

MOTHER. Alan?

ALAN. Mom?

MOTHER. You were dreaming.

ALAN. Was I?

MOTHER. You fell asleep at your desk.

ALAN (*still groggy*). I guess you're right.

MOTHER. What were you dreaming about?

ALAN. It's dumb. I was taking a test. I didn't know any of the answers.

MOTHER. Son, you worry too much.

ALAN. I know.

MOTHER. Are you still studying for that test tomorrow?

ALAN. Uh-huh.

MOTHER. I can't believe how hard you've been working.

ALAN. It's a huge test. I don't know the stuff at all.

MOTHER. You always say that and you always do fine.

ALAN (*sarcastically*). Yeah.

MOTHER. Don't you have the best grades in the class?

ALAN (*shrugging it off*). I don't know.

MOTHER (*prodding*). Alan?

ALAN. I guess. But Evan's pretty close.

MOTHER. Don't worry about it. Just do your best. That's all we ask. (*She smiles.*) Besides . . .

ALAN. What?

MOTHER. I have a surprise for you downstairs.

ALAN (*sniffing*). Cookies.

MOTHER. And something else.

ALAN. What?

MOTHER. It's downstairs.

ALAN. What is it?

MOTHER. An envelope.

ALAN. From who?

MOTHER. Majestica University.

ALAN. Yeah?

MOTHER. It's an awfully thick envelope.

ALAN (*excitedly*). Really?

MOTHER (*kissing ALAN on the forehead*). Congratulations. You got in, and we're very proud of you.

ALAN (*dazed*). Thanks.

MOTHER (*walking to the side of the stage*). How about those cookies? (*The lights snap back up. MOTHER jumps offstage. All are instantly as they were before. The ticking resumes, even faster than it was before.*)

TEACHER. How about some answers, Alan?

ALAN. What?

TEACHER. You'd better stop daydreaming if you want to have a chance of passing this. (*The sound of a heartbeat comes up as ALAN begins to breathe hard.*)

ALAN. Oh, no!

TEACHER. What's the matter?

ALAN. I'm almost done and I haven't answered anything!

TEACHER. Have you tried all the questions?

ALAN. No. I skipped some of them.

TEACHER. Why don't you go back and look at the ones you skipped.

ALAN (*dejectedly*). All right.

VOICE. Section one. Multiple choice. Question Two. Which of the following students . . .

ALAN. Students?

VOICE. . . . is most likely to be accepted to Majestica University? A: Lois Flan. B: Elizabeth Zimmerman. C: Carlos O'Neill. D: Anthony Montagu. E: Alan Lefenfeld.

ALAN. I don't know. (*Pause*) Elizabeth is pretty smart, but her grades aren't as good as Carlos's. I think they're a little better than mine . . .

VOICE. Hint. It's not Alan Lefenfeld.

ALAN (*despondently*). Next question.

VOICE. Question Three. Which of Alan Lefenfeld's shortcomings do you find most annoying? (*Pause*) A: The way he shuffles when he walks. B: His poor posture. C: His bad breath. (ALAN *slaps his hand over his mouth.*) D: His irritating laugh. E: His sloppy **attire**. (*After a long pause,* ALAN *looks at the test, then turns to the next page.*) F: His whiny little voice. G: His bizarre sense of humor. H: His **dismal** standardized test scores. I: . . . (*Pause*) . . . The extremely embarrassing personal problem which Alan confided to the school counselor, Mrs. Fennelmeyer. (*Slight pause while* ALAN *looks up and then back down.*) Parentheses. Who is, by the way, a bit of a gossip but a wonderful cook.

ALAN. I hate this. I hate this test!

TEACHER. What's the matter now, Alan?

ALAN. I object to the third multiple choice question!

LOIS. Me, too.

CHRIS. I do, too.

ALAN. It's biased and it's mean.

LOIS. And it's too hard. (*To* CHRIS) I can't pick just one of these.

ALAN (*rattled*). And furthermore, It's subjective[5] . . .

PAT. And incomplete.

CHRIS. This must just be a partial list. (LOIS, PAT *and* CHRIS *ad lib agreement, along with suggestions for other possible answers.*)

TEACHER. All right, calm down. I'll tell you what. Let's strike the question and, to keep the number of points the same, why don't we say that Question . . . (*He looks through the test.*) . . . Nineteen is worth twice as much now. Okay?

ALAN (*thumbing through the pages*). Question Nineteen.

VOICE. Question Nineteen. Ten poi . . . (*The* VOICE *makes a*

---

5 **subjective**: influenced by personal feelings; not objective

Stephen Gregg

squawking sound as ALAN *scratches out the words "Ten Points" and writes "Twenty Points." Pause.*) Who was Saladin?

ALAN. Finally!

VOICE. What did his name mean?

ALAN. I know this!

VOICE. Where was he born?

ALAN (*throwing up his arms in joy*). Thank you! (*A bell rings and keeps ringing. The* TEACHER, *who was near* ALAN's *desk, snatches the test from his desk.*)

TEACHER. Kai foo len hee!

ALAN (*while the* TEACHER *grabs the other tests*). Wait!

TEACHER. Kai foo len hee which . . . (*He looks at* ALAN.) translated means what, Lois?

LOIS. Time's up. Kai foo len hee. (*The others begin to converse in Chinese as they gather up their books.*)

TEACHER (*He overlaps the students and no matter where he is in the speech, he should stop talking when* ALAN *shouts, "This is the end."*) Now I didn't want to tell you this earlier because I didn't want to make you nervous. I've decided it's too much work for me to make up these tests all the time so, instead of counting this as a mid-term, I'm going to let it serve as your final. How you did on this test will determine your grade for this semester and, probably, for the entire year. It's just too much work for me to have to sit down and write out all these tests and then grade them and then hand them back so we'll just say that whatever grade you got here is the grade you get for the course.

VOICE (*This overlaps with the Chinese conversation and the* TEACHER *and should begin when the* TEACHER *says, "I've decided."*) This concludes our test of your emergency information retrieval system. The teachers in your area, in voluntary cooperation with parents, the School Board, and local authorities, have combined to bring you this test. We now resume our regularly scheduled life.

ALAN (*He overlaps with everything else and should overlap with the very end of the* VOICE's *lines, shouting over the noise*). This is the end!

INSTANT BLACKOUT

Pass/Fail

Linda Pastan

Examination dreams are reported to persist even into old age . . .
—Time *magazine*

You will never graduate
from this dream
of blue books.
No matter how
you succeed awake,
asleep there is a test
waiting to be failed.
The dream beckons
with two dull pencils,
but you haven't even
taken the course;
when you reach for a book—
it closes its door
in your face; when
you **conjugate** a verb—
it is in the wrong
language.
Now the pillow becomes
a blank page. Turn it
to the cool side;
you will still smother
in all of the feathers
that have to be learned
by heart.

conjugate
give the forms of

LITERARY LENS

Why do you think the dreams in both the play and the poem are so convincing to the dreamers?

What Is and Ain't Grammatical

Dave Barry

I cannot overemphasize the importance of good grammar. What a crock.[1] I could easily overemphasize the importance of good grammar. For example, I could say: "Bad grammar is the leading cause of slow, painful death in North America," or "Without good grammar, the United States would have lost World War II."

The truth is that grammar is not the most important thing in the world. The Super Bowl is the most important thing in the world. But grammar is still important. For example, suppose you are being interviewed for a job as an airplane pilot, and your **prospective** employer asks you if you have any experience, and you answer: "Well, I ain't never actually flied no actual airplanes or nothing, but I got several pilot-style hats and several friends who I like to talk about airplanes with."

If you answer this way, the prospective employers will immediately realize that you have ended your sentence with a preposition. (What you should have said, of course, is "several friends with who I like to talk about airplanes.") So you will not get the job, because airplane pilots have to use good grammar when they get on the intercom and explain to the passengers that, because of high winds, the plane is going to take off several hours late and land in Pierre, South Dakota, instead of Los Angeles.

We did not always have grammar. In medieval England, people said whatever they wanted, without regard to rules, and as a result they sounded like morons. Take the poet Geoffrey Chaucer, who couldn't even spell his first name right. He wrote a large poem called *Canterbury Tales*, in which people from various professions—knight, monk, miller, reever, riveter, eeler, diver, stevedore, spinnaker, etc.—drone on and on like this:

In a somer sesun whon softe was the sunne
I kylled a younge birde ande I ate it on a bunne.

When Chaucer's poem was published, everybody read it and said: "My God, we need some grammar around here." So they formed a Grammar Commission, which developed the parts of

prospective
likely to be or become

LITERARY LENS
Sometimes humor is the best vehicle for making a point. Look for Dave Barry's message in this essay.

---

1 **crock:** slang for "lie"

Dave Barry

speech, the main ones being nouns, verbs, predicants, conjectures, particles, proverbs, adjoiners, coordinates, and rebuttals. Then the commission made up hundreds and hundreds of grammar rules, all of which were strictly enforced.

When the colonists came to America, they rebelled against British grammar. They openly used words like "ain't" and "finalize," and when they wrote the Declaration of Independence they deliberately misspelled many words. Thanks to their courage, today we Americans have only two rules of grammar:

Rule 1: The word "me" is always incorrect.

Most of us learn this rule as children, from our mothers. We say things like: "Mom, can Bobby and me roll the camping trailer over Mrs. Johnson's cat?" And our mothers say: "Remember your grammar, dear. You mean: 'Can Bobby and I roll the camping trailer over Mrs. Johnson's cat?' Of course you can, but be home by dinnertime."

The only exception to this rule is in formal business writing, where instead of "I" you must use "the undersigned." For example, this business letter is incorrect:

"Dear Hunky-Dory Canned Fruit Company: A couple days ago my wife bought a can of your cling peaches and served them to my mother who has a weak heart and she damn near died when she bit into a live grub. If I ever find out where you live, I am gonna whomp you on the head with a ax handle."

This should be corrected as follows:

". . . If the undersigned ever finds out where you live, the undersigned is gonna whomp you on the head with a ax handle."

Rule 2: You're not allowed to split infinitives.

An infinitive is the word "to" and whatever comes right behind it, such as "to a tee," "to the best of my ability," "tomato," etc. Splitting an infinitive is putting something between the "to" and the other words. For example, this is incorrect:

"Hey man, you got any, you know, spare change you could give to, like, me?"

The correct version is:

". . . spare change you could, like, give to me?"

■■■■

The advantage of American English is that, because there are so few rules, practically anybody can learn to speak it in just a few minutes. The disadvantage is that Americans generally sound like jerks, whereas the British sound really smart, especially to Americans. That's why Americans are so fond of those British dramas they're always showing on public television, the ones introduced by Alistair Cooke.[2] Americans *love* people who talk like Alistair Cooke. He could introduce old episodes of "Hawaii Five-O" and Americans would think they were extremely enlightening.

So the trick is to use American grammar, which is simple, but talk with a British accent, which is impressive. This technique is taught at all your really snotty private schools, where the kids learn to sound like Elliot Richardson.[3] Remember Elliot? He sounded extremely British, and as a result he got to be Attorney General, Secretary of State, Chief Justice of the Supreme Court and Vice President *at the same time.*

You can do it, too. Practice in your home, then approach someone on the street and say: "Tally-ho, old chap. I would consider it a great honour if you could favour me with some spare change." You're bound to get quick results.

LITERARY LENS

What point do you think Dave Barry is trying to make in this essay?

---

2 **Alistair Cooke:** (1908–) famous British-born broadcaster, known for his *Letter from America* radio program and 22-year tenure as host of PBS's *Masterpiece Theatre*

3 **Elliot Richardson:** (1920–1999) American government official who held many positions in Massachusetts and in President Nixon's cabinet

A Letter from the Fringe

Joan Bauer

*T*oday they got Sally.

She wasn't doing anything. Just eating a cookie that her aunt had made for her. It was a serious cookie too. She'd given me one. It was still in my mouth with the white chocolate and pecans and caramel all swirling together.

I saw Doug Booker before she did.

Saw his eyes get that hard glint[1] they always get right before he says something mean. Watched him walk toward us squeezing his hands into fists, getting psyched for the match. He's a champion varsity wrestler known for overwhelming his opponents in the first round. He was joined by Charlie Bass, brute ice hockey goalie, who was smirking and laughing and looking at Sally like the mere sight of her hurt his eyes.

Get the Geeks is a popular bonding ritual among the jock flock at Bronley High.

I swallowed my cookie. Felt my stomach tense. It was too late to grab Sally and walk off.

"Fun company at four o'clock," I warned her.

Sally looked up to smirks. Her face went pale.

Booker did that **vibrato** thing with his voice that he thinks is so funny. "So *Sals*, maybe you should be cutting back on those calories, huh?"

Charlie was laughing away.

"What have you got, Sals, about thirty pounds to lose? More?" He did a *tsk, tsk.* Looked her up and down with premium disgust.

All she could do was look down.

I stood up. "Get lost, Booker."

Sneer. Snort. "Now, how can I get lost in school?"

"Booker, I think you have the innate ability to get lost just about anywhere."

"Why don't you and your fat friend just get out of my face because the two of you are so butt ugly you're making me sick and I don't know if I can hold the puke in!"

He and Charlie strolled off.

There's no response to that kind of hate.

I looked at Sally, who was gripping her cookie bag.

---

1 **glint:** bright flash

I tried fighting through words like my mom and dad had taught me. Taking each one apart like I'm diffusing a bomb.

Was Sally fat?

I sucked in my stomach. She needed to lose some weight, but who doesn't?

Were she and I so disgusting we could make someone sick?

We're not Hollywood starlets, if that's his measuring stick.

If Booker said we were serial killers, we could have shrugged it off. But gifted bullies use partial truths. Doug knew how to march into personal territory.

I didn't know what to say. I blustered out, "They're total creeps, Sally."

No response.

"I mean, you've got a right to eat a cookie without getting hassled. You know those guys love hurting people. They think they've got some **inalienable** privilege—"

inalienable
not to be taken away

A tear rolled down her cheek. "I do have to lose weight, Dana."

"They don't have the right to say it! There are all kinds of sizes in this world that are perfectly fine!"

She sat there broken, holding the cookie bag that I just noticed had pictures of balloons on it.

"It's my birthday," she said quietly.

"Oh, Sally, I didn't know that."

■ ■ ■ ■

Sally and I were at the fringe table in the back of the lunchroom. It was as far away from the in-crowd table as you could get and still be in the cafeteria. The best thing about the fringe table is that everyone who sits at it is bonded together by the strands of social victimization.[2] We all just deal with it differently.

Present were:

Cedric Melville, arch techno whiz, hugely tall with wild-man hair and a beak nose. He has an unusual habit of standing on one leg like a flamingo. Booker calls him "Maggot."

Jewel Lardner, zany artist with pink-striped hair who has spent years studying the systems of the ICIs. ICIs are In-Crowd Individuals. She'd long ago stopped caring about being in, out, or in between.

---

2 **social victimization:** phrase meaning that society has cheated them

Gil Mishkin, whose car got covered with shaving cream last week in the parking lot. Gil doesn't have much hair because of a skin condition. His head has round, hairless patches and most of his eyebrows are gone. He can't shave and is embarrassed about it. Booker calls him "Bald Boy."

"Now, with big, popular Doug," Cedric said, "you can't give him much room to move, which is what you did. When you shot right back at him, he came back harder. He always does that."

"He'll do something else, though," said Gil. "Remember what happened to my car." His hand went self-consciously over his half-bald head.

"Look," said Jewel, "you're talking defensive moves here. You've got to think **offensively** so the ICIs leave you alone. First off, you guys need cell phones. That way, if any of us sees big trouble coming, we can warn the others. If a jock on the prowl comes close to me, I whip out my phone and start shouting into it, 'Are you kidding me? He's got *what* kind of disease? Is it catching?' People don't come near you when you're talking disease."

"But most important," said Ed Looper, plunking his lunch tray down, "is you can't seem like a victim."

"I don't seem like a victim!" Sally insisted.

She did, though.

Bad posture.

Flitting eye contact.

Mumbles a lot.

I used to be that way during freshman and sophomore years. I'd just dread having to go out in the hall to change classes. I felt like at any moment I could be **bludgeoned** for my sins of being too smart, not wearing expensive designer clothes, and hanging out with uncool people. I'd run in and out of the bathroom fast when the popular girls were in there.

Cedric used to skip school after getting hassled. Last year he decided he'd give it back in unusual ways. Now he'll walk up to a popular group, breathe like a degenerate,[3] and hiss, "I'm a *bibliophile*." A bibliophile is a person who loves books, but not many people know that. He'll approach a group of cheerleaders and announce, "You know, girls, I'm *bipedal* . . ." That means he has two

---

3 **degenerate:** someone who has degraded from the normal standard

Joan Bauer

feet, but those cheerleaders scatter like squirrels. "I'm a *thespian*," he'll say lustfully. This means he's an actor, but you know how it is with some words. If they sound bad, people don't always wait around for the vocab lesson.

Jewel also has her own unique defense mechanism. When a carload of ICIs once drove alongside her car blaring loud music, she cranked up her tape of Gregorian chants[4] to a deafening roar. Jewel said it put a new perspective on spirituality.

People were throwing jock-avoidance suggestions at Sally, but the advice wasn't sticking.

"I just want to ignore those people," she said sadly to the group.

"Can you do it, though?" I asked her.

She shrugged, mumbled, looked down.

See, for me, ignoring comes with its own set of problems. There are some people—Ed Looper is one of them—who can ignore the ICIs because he walks around in a cloud all day. If you want to get Looper's attention, it's best to trip him.

But *me*—sure, I can pretend I'm ignoring something or someone mean, but it doesn't help if deep down I'm steamed, and as I shove it farther and farther into the bottomless pit, the steam gets hotter.

So the biggest thing that's helped me cope is that I've stopped hoping that the mean in-crowders get punished for their cruelty. I think in some ways they have their punishments already. As my mom says, meanness never just goes out of a person—it goes back to them as well.

I look at the in-crowd table that's filling up. The beautiful Parker Cravens, Brent Fabrelli, the usual suspects. Doug Booker and Charlie Bass sit down too.

So what's inside you, Doug, that makes you so mean? If I were to put your heart under a microscope, what would I see?

Once Parker Cravens and I had to be lab partners. This was close to the worst news she'd gotten all year. She glared at me like I was a dead frog she had to dissect. Parker is stricken with *affluenza*, a condition that afflicts certain segments of the **excruciatingly** rich. She doesn't know or care how the other half lives; she thinks anyone who isn't wealthy is **subterranean**. At first I was ripped that she dis-

excruciatingly
very painfully

subterranean
one who lives underground

---

4 **Gregorian chants:** songs without rhythm, originally part of the liturgy of the Roman Catholic church in the mid-18th century

counted me; then I started looking at her under the emotional microscope. I have X-ray vision from years of being ignored.

"Parker, do you like this class?" I asked.

She glanced at my nondesigner sports watch that I'd gotten for two bucks at a yard sale and shuddered. "My dad's making me take it. He's a doctor and he said I've got to know this dense stuff."

"What class would you rather be taking?"

She flicked a speck off her cashmere[5] sweater and looked at me as if my question was totally **insipid**.

"No, really, Parker. Which one?"

"Art history," she said.

"Why don't you take it?"

Quiet voice. "My dad won't let me."

"Why not?"

"He wants me to be a doctor."

Parker would last two nanoseconds in med school.

"That's got to be hard," I offered.

"Like granite, Dana."

It's funny. No matter how mean she gets—and Parker can get mean—every time I see her now, I don't just think that she's the prettiest girl in school or the richest or the most popular; I think a little about how her father doesn't have a clue as to what she wants to be, and how much that must hurt.

■■■

My bedroom doesn't look like I feel. It's yellow and sunny. It's got posters of Albert Einstein and Eleanor Roosevelt and their best quotes.

Al's: *If at first the idea is not absurd, then there is no hope for it.*

Eleanor's: *No one can make you feel inferior without your consent.*

I flop on the bed wondering how come cruelty seems so easy for some people.

Wondering who decided how the boundary lines get drawn. You can never be too athletic, too popular, too gorgeous, or too rich, but you can be too smart and too nerdy.

My mom tells me that sometimes people try to control others when too many things are out of control in their own lives.

insipid
dull; flat; stupid

---

5 **cashmere:** soft fabric made from goat wool

I walk to my closet and pull down the Ziploc bag in which I keep my old stuffed koala bear, Qantas. He can't handle life on the bed like my other animals—he's close to falling apart. Think Velveteen Rabbit. He was a big part of my childhood. I got him when I was four and kids started giving me a hard time in nursery school because I used words that were too big for them to understand. I've talked to him ever since.

I take Qantas out of the bag, look into his scratched plastic eyes. This bear will not die.

I lost him at Disney World and found him. Lost him at the zoo and he turned up near the lion's cage. I always take him out when I've got a sticky problem. Maybe I'm remembering the power of childhood—the part that thinks a stuffed bear really holds the secret to life.

And it's funny. As I hold him now, all kinds of things seem possible.

Like the Letter. I've been tossing the idea around all year: how I could write a letter to the ICIs, explain what life is like from my end of the lunchroom, and maybe things would get better at my school.

At first I thought it would be easy to write. It isn't. This is as far as I've gotten:

To my classmates at the other end of the lunchroom:
   This is a difficult letter to write, but one that needs to be written.

Wrong, all wrong.

And there's the whole matter of how the letter will get distributed if I ever write it.

I could send it to the school paper.

Tack it to the front door with nails.[6]

Print it up on T-shirts.

I think about the mangy comments that have been hurled at me this month.

Were you born or were you hatched?

Do you have to be my lab partner?

Do you have to have your locker next to mine?

I hug my bear. Some people go on-line with their problems. I go marsupial.[7]

---

6 **Tack it . . . nails:** refers to the method Martin Luther used to announce his grievances with the Roman Catholic church in 1517

7 **marsupial:** refers to female mammals that carry their young in a protective pouch

"Qantas, if I had the guts to write a letter to the in crowd at my school, this is what I'd like to say:

"This letter could be from the nerd with the thick glasses in computer lab. It could be from the 'zit girl' who won't look people in the eye because she's embarrassed about her skin. It could be from the guy with the nose ring who you call queer, or any of the kids whose sizes don't balance with your ideal.

"You know, I've got things inside me—dreams and nightmares, plans and mess-ups. In that regard, we have things in common. But we never seem to connect through those common experiences because I'm so different from you.

"My being different doesn't mean that you're better than me. I think you've always assumed that I want to be like you. But I want you to know something about kids like me. We don't want to. We just want the freedom to walk down the hall without seeing your smirks, your contempt, and your looks of disgust.

"Sometimes I stand far away from you in the hall and watch what you do to other people. I wonder why you've chosen to make the world a worse place.

"I wonder, too, what really drives the whole thing. Is it hate? Is it power? Are you afraid if you get too close to me and my friends that some of our uncoolness might rub off on you? I think what could really happen is that tolerance could make us happier, freer people.

"What's it going to be like when we all get older? Will we be more tolerant, or less because we haven't practiced it much? I think of the butterflies in the science museum. There are hundreds of them in cases. Hundreds of different kinds. If they were all the same, it would be so boring. You can't look at the blue ones or the striped ones and say they shouldn't have been born. It seems like nature is trying to tell us something. Some trees are tall, some are short. Some places have mountains, others have deserts. Some cities are always warm, some have different seasons. Flowers are different. Animals. Why do human beings think they have the right to pick who's best— who's acceptable and who's not?

"I used to give you the control over my emotions. I figured that if you said I was gross and weird, it must be true. How you choose to respond to people is up to you, but I won't let you be my judge and jury. I'm going to remind you every chance I get that I have as much right to be on this earth as you."

I look at Qantas, remember bringing him to a teddy bear birthday party and being told he wasn't a real bear. I laugh about it now. He and I have never been mainstream.

I turn on my computer and begin to put it all down finally. The words just pour out, but I know the letter isn't for the ICIs and full-scale distribution.

It's for me.

And one other person.

I open my desk drawer where I keep my stash of emergency birthday cards. I pick one that reads: *It's your birthday. If you'd reminded me sooner, this card wouldn't be late.*

I sign the card; print the letter out, fold it in fourths so it will fit inside, and write Sally's name on the envelope.

LITERARY LENS

Compare how people in your school define themselves and others to how the narrator defines herself and others in her letter.

RESPONDING TO UNIT FOUR
School Pictures

REFLECTING

1. Which character in this unit do you think best reflects your school experiences so far? Why?

2. Don in "Pig Brains" and the kids in "A Letter from the Fringe" all come up with different ways to deal with bullying. Which coping strategy do you think is the best? Why?

3. Dave Barry makes his living as a writer, yet he makes fun of grammar. What subject or subjects do you think are overrated? Explain.

4. As a tribute to Miss Hancock, who encouraged her writing, Charlotte wrote a glowing metaphor about her teacher. Who in your life has been the most supportive of your growth as a student or simply as an individual?

ANALYZING

5. Each selection in this unit reveals a challenge with which many junior high students wrestle. Make a chart listing each selection and the problem the characters confront. Also identify the way in which the problem is confronted.

Selection	Challenge faced	Action taken
Pig Brains	*bullying*	*tricked the bully*
The Metaphor		
This Is a Test		
What Is and Ain't Grammatical		
A Letter from the Fringe		

6. Some of the characters featured in this unit are more successful than others in their quest to find their place in the school setting. Identify two characters you think succeed, and then compare their strategies.

7. "Pass/Fail" and "Mrs. Goldwasser" both recount school experiences using strong, almost authoritative voices. What gives each poem its authority?

8. If you were to direct the play "This Is a Test," how would you want the Voice to sound? Why?

9. Active Reading List three ways you went about **connecting** to Alan's situation in "This Is a Test." How often do you think you used this and other Active Reading strategies while reading the selections in this unit?

DISCUSSING

Imagine that you did a friend or teacher a disservice, such as Charlotte did Miss Hancock, or some students did to their classmates on "the fringe." What would you do to make things right?

WRITING

A Modest Proposal Dave Barry makes his point by satirizing the importance people give to grammar. In doing so, he places himself within a long tradition of satirists who make fun of something in the extreme. Satirize a rule or custom you think is unfair by advocating an extreme version of it.

Journal Journey Dana makes her point by writing a heartfelt letter about her circumstances in "A Letter from the Fringe." She addresses the letter to those who torment her and her friends, but she shares it only with her closest friend. Write a letter to someone about an issue of importance to you. Then keep it for your own reference or share it with someone.

WORK IN PROGRESS

You Are Here Develop a chart, diagram, or three-dimensional model showing your place in your family, your neighborhood, your school, or a club or team to which you belong. Be sure to use labels, captions, keys, and legends to explain your visuals.

The One Most Likely To . . . Appreciation of yourself and others can help combat bullying and peer pressure. To practice appreciation, use copies of your school pictures to create a miniature yearbook feature. As part of the feature, celebrate the talents of your classmates by identifying the strengths of each classmate and imagining successful careers they might develop as a result of those strengths. Identify each classmate as the person most likely to have a specific job. Be sure to indicate positive, productive futures.

Sing Along Songs are among the most inclusive ways to build community. Write the lyrics, tune, or both for a song that brings people together. If you like, you can teach the song to several or all of your classmates and then perform it.

Neighborhood Panorama

*But the garden's greatest benefit, I feel,
was not relief to the eyes, but to make the
eyes see our neighbors.*

from *"Amir"*
by Paul Fleischman

Active Reading Alert!

SUMMARIZING

Every now and again as you read each selection
in Unit Five, stop to review what you think has
happened so far. Determine what you know,
what you think you know, and what has changed
about what you thought you knew.

The Pill Factory

Anne Mazer

took the freight elevator to the seventh floor of the pill factory. Even though it wasn't yet 8:00 A.M., it was hot and the air smelled stale, with a faint **medicinal** overlay. One or two people drifted like bits of dust through the huge warehouse.

medicinal
smelling of medicine

I found the lunchroom where workers met before the start of the day, sat down at a scratched Formica table, and looked around. There was a coffee pot on a shelf, a small refrigerator, and some jackets on hooks. A battered romance novel lay face-down on the table. The single greasy window looked out on other brick warehouses painted with the faded names of long-gone companies.

"Well, well, our summer worker." A massive woman in denim overalls and a black T-shirt came into the room, carrying an open box of danishes, frosted doughnuts, and crullers[1] in one hand, and an umbrella in the other.

"Hello," I said.

LITERARY LENS

Notice how the narrator describes the things she sees as you read "The Pill Factory."

The woman plopped down on a chair, dropped the umbrella on the floor, grabbed a doughnut, and devoured half of it in one bite. Shiny red jelly oozed over the side of the doughnut and dripped onto the table.

"Want one?" Her stiff, oily hair was combed straight back. She shoved the pastry box in my direction.

"Oh, no, thanks."

"Go on, take one. You need the energy around here." Her eyes narrowed as she looked at me.

I pulled out a cruller. It was my first day. I didn't want to make a bad impression.

"You look twelve." A fine spray of doughnut crumbs flew out of her mouth as she spoke.

"I'm sixteen."

"No, you're not." She poured herself a cup of black coffee and dumped six packages of sugar into it. "Tastes like mud," she grunted. She leaned toward me, breathing heavily. "What's your name?"

"Meredith." I wanted to know her name, too, but was too shy to ask.

"Meredith, have you ever worked before?"

Did baby-sitting qualify? Did mowing the lawn or raking leaves? I was trying to think of an answer that would sound adult and

---

1 **crullers:** long, twisted doughnuts

respectable, when suddenly she looked up. "You're late again, Polly."

"No, I'm not, Barbara." Polly grinned crookedly. Her two front teeth were missing, and she had a black eye. I tried not to stare. "Are you the summer girl?" she asked.

I nodded.

Polly yanked a stained apron down from a wall hook, then fastened it around her dumplinglike body. Her hair was thin and brown, teased into a feathery pouf. "What did you come to this place for?"

"Money," I said, then blushed at my answer.

"That's the only reason to be here." Polly winked at me out of her good eye.

"Leave her alone," Barbara said. "Don't get her started with your bad attitude. And I told you. You're supposed to get here early."

"Oh, sure." Polly slid into the chair next to me and gave me a friendly poke in the ribs. "I love to work."

I had two older brothers in college; I had to work. There weren't a lot of jobs around for kids my age with no experience, and this one paid more than most. I was lucky to get it.

Barbara studied me. "We'll put her on the glue machine, don't you think?"

ominous
threatening; hinting of evil

It had an **ominous** sound. I imagined something sticky, vile, poisonous. Myself stuck to a machine, unable to escape.

"Sure, sure," Polly said, winking again. "It won't be too hard for her."

"Blaaatttt!" A bell rang insistently.

With the back of her fist, Barbara wiped the crumbs from her face. Her lips compressed into a thin line. "Punch-in time, girls!" she ordered. "Punch in!"

furtive
secretive; sly

Next to me, Polly's hand snaked toward the pastry box, disappeared inside, and snatched a danish. With a quick, **furtive** motion, she shoved it into her apron pocket and rushed out the door.

Barbara pushed me after her. Right outside the lunchroom was a time clock. She pulled a yellow card from a gray metal slot. "Write your name," she ordered. "Then punch in like this."

"Blaatt!" As I slid the card into place, the machine beeped angrily.

Anne Mazer

"Cooome on!" Barbara bellowed, balling her fists on her massive hips. "Time to work!"

Suddenly Polly dashed back into the lunch room.

Barbara breathed loudly through her mouth. Her face was red from chin to forehead. Hidden in the large, slablike cheeks were two gleaming, **shrewd** eyes. "Po-ol-*ly!*"

shrewd
calculating; intelligent

Polly darted back like a mouse flushed out of a hole. As she passed me, she pinched my arm and cackled. "Got the last drop of coffee," she whispered. "She couldn't stop me."

■■■■

I had never been in a factory before. I expected hundreds of workers siting at small tables and an unearthly din of machines, but there were only a few scattered in the vast space of the warehouse. Eleven people, Barbara told me when I asked her how many worked here.

She hurried me toward a rickety wooden table in the middle of the floor. A short distance away were rows and rows of high metal shelves stacked with boxes. Across from them, a stooped man stood at a narrow table and wound strips of sticky packing tape around a box. A single bare bulb burned above his head. In another corner of the warehouse were three machines with huge plastic funnels. A woman wearing green clothes and a mask over her nose like a hospital nurse turned the crank on one of them and pills clattered into an amber-colored bottle placed directly below the mouth of the funnel.

"Here," Barbara grunted. She indicated an old wooden chair in front of the rickety table, and lowered herself into the chair opposite. She pointed a huge red finger like a sausage at me. "I'm only going to say things once. This is the glue machine."

It was a small, unprepossessing[2] thing, barely a foot long and only eight or ten inches wide, with a couple of rollers on each end and a wide belt that reminded me of flypaper stretched between them. Barbara flicked on the switch, and the belt began to turn with a slow **monotonous** hum.

monotonous
repetitious; boring

"Now it's on. You got that?"

I nodded.

"Now. See this? A vitamin bottle. Understand?"

---

2 **unprepossessing:** creating an unfavorable impression

"Of course," I said, a bit impatiently. Maybe I had never had a job before, but I could recognize a vitamin bottle when I saw one.

She laid it in front of her and took a label from a stack at the side of the table.

"A label. For the bottle. Watch carefully." Her enormous fingers were surprisingly nimble as she fed the label face-up through the rollers, then snatched it by the edges as it came out the other end.

She held it up. With a **deft** motion, she centered the label, pressed it down on the bottle, and smoothed the edges. "See that?"

"Sure."

"Nothing crooked, nothing sloppy. And no air bubbles! You got it?"

"Uh-huh."

Standing up, Barbara kicked her chair back and slapped a label in front of me. "Then do it."

I picked up the label, inserted it between the rollers, watched the belt coat it with sticky glue, and grabbed it as it came out on the other end. Then I carefully stretched it over the glass bottle and smoothed it out from the middle toward the edges.

"There," I said, pleased I had done so well the first time.

Barbara frowned. "See that air bubble there? You'll have to do better than that."

I grabbed another label and put it through the machine. It tore as I pressed it over the bottle.

Silently Barbara handed me another label.

This time, the label slipped as I pressed it down. It ended up slanted on the bottle.

"If you can't do any better than that, don't bother coming back tomorrow."

I gritted my teeth and began again. The factory paid twice as much as baby-sitting, and I was sick of having milk spat in my face, of playing endless games of cards, of washing dishes and folding and ironing other people's laundry. And besides, I wanted to be out in the world, to prove that I was as smart and capable as the rest of my family, that I wasn't the baby anymore.

It wouldn't be easy to find another job either; I had put in thirty applications before I got offered this one.

I slid the label into the machine, retrieved it, and stretched it

deft
skillful; quick and easy

252   Anne Mazer

tight over the bottle. It didn't wrinkle, slide, or tear. "Yes!" I said triumphantly, holding up the neatly labeled bottle.

"Okay, you did one," Barbara grunted. She nodded in an almost friendly way. "Now do a thousand more."

■■■■

At first, I worked slowly: ten labels in three minutes. Then I picked up speed: fifteen labels in four minutes, then twenty in three. Every now and then I glanced at the large industrial clock mounted on the wall opposite. After two hours, I had several boxes of neatly stacked and labeled vitamin bottles.

"*Blaaattt!*" The bell rang again, bone-shattering and fierce. In spite of myself, I leaped from my chair. Then I forced myself back and picked up another label.

"What are you doing?" It was Polly, her hands and face covered with fine yellow dust. "It's break time!"

"Barbara told me to finish these."

"Are you crazy?" Polly reached over and switched off the machine. "You have to stop now."

"But…"

She gripped my arm with clawlike fingers and yanked me to my feet with surprising strength.

"It's okay," I explained. "I don't mind. I'm not tired."

Polly clucked in dismay. "Bad idea. You got to take your break." She pointed to the lunchroom. "Tomorrow you'll be running there."

I shook my head no.

Polly grinned, showing the gap in her teeth. "You'll see."

In the lunchroom, Barbara sat at the table, her massive legs splayed in front of her. She was breathing heavily through her mouth. The box of pastries was almost empty. "You're late," she said to me.

"I was finishing my work."

She snorted in contempt. "You only get fifteen minutes, by law, and if you miss it, it's your tough luck."

Next to me Polly cackled and pinched me hard, as if to say I told you so.

"Did you bring something to eat on break?" she asked. "No? I'll share mine with you." She reached into her apron pocket and pulled out the danish that I had seen her grab earlier. Only now, like her hands and face, it was coated with yellow dust.

"Here." She thrust half of it into my hand.

I looked down at it.

"Go on," Polly urged me. "I don't need it. You can have it."

"I'm not really hungry."

Barbara snorted again. "That's vitamin dust, girl. It won't hurt you; it'll make you healthy."

I nibbled at the edges of it.

"Isn't it good?" Polly said.

"Mmm." It was good. I took a larger bite, then went over to my backpack and pulled out a book. The two women stared at me.

"Oh, a smart girl." Barbara ran her fingers through her stiff, oily hair. "One of those."

"I knew she was," Polly said. "I knew it the minute I saw her."

I tried to concentrate on the words on the page, but they jumped around like insects. I could feel Barbara and Polly's gaze on me. I turned the pages and pretended to read while the large black and white clock above us ticked steadily; I imagined that its sound rose above the clattering din of the factory and overwhelmed it.

■■■

By the time the lunch bell rang two hours later, I had filled a dozen more boxes with labeled vitamin bottles: Best Rite, Serv You, American Vites, Health Kaps. They were cheap, inexpensively made vitamins, intended for local drugstore and supermarket generic brands, and their labels had bars of red, white, and blue on them, implying that it was not only healthy but patriotic to take your vitamins. I imagined vitamins making their way into my body, leaving **indelible** streams of color, then washing into my brain.

indelible
permanent;
not erasable

I was a gluer; I worked the glue machine. Those were the words that kept going through my head as I labeled vitamin C, multi-vitamins, and B complex. I had a good-paying job for the summer, and I was determined to succeed. My family would be proud of me. I was a baby no more.

A man came and hauled the labeled bottles over to Polly and another woman, who were filling them. Then they were capped, sealed, and taken away.

Just before the bell rang, Barbara came over to check on my progress. She was accompanied by a man I hadn't seen before. He was dressed up more than the other workers, in slacks, a white shirt, and a tie.

"This is the summer girl," Barbara's eyes narrowed as she looked down at me. "You can see her work."

"Not bad," the man said in a soft, nervous voice. He was tall and graying and blinked rapidly as he looked at me and my work.

"The manager, Mr. Kredler," Barbara announced.

"Nice to meet you," I said.

Barbara scowled at me. "She's one of those smart girls. How long do you think she'll last?"

I held my breath. Would I get thrown out before the day was even done? I needed the money. Money meant college. College meant I could choose what I wanted to be: lawyer, scientist, or teacher. But first I had to make it through this summer.

"Oh, she'll do," Mr. Kredler said mildly. He nodded at me as he turned away. "She'll do nicely."

■■■■

We had half an hour for lunch. It was hot in the lunchroom. I rolled up my sleeves and ate a peanut butter and jelly sandwich and an apple and drank a carton of juice. Barbara didn't show up, and Polly ate a meat stew. Another woman came in silently, took a brown paper bag off a shelf, and left. I opened my book and read a few pages. Next to me, Polly rolled up her sleeves and pulled out a nail file from her purse. Then she dug out a mirror and a comb and teased up her hair. When the bell rang, she gave me another friendly dig in the ribs. "Don't work too hard, kid, huh?"

"Okay," I agreed.

She winked at me out of her good eye.

■■■■

Break time again. It was two hours and many, many labels later. It was almost unbearably hot now. I drank three cups of water in the lunchroom, washed my hands and face, and wished I hadn't worn corduroy pants to work. Barbara sat at the table, drinking can after can of soda. Her eyes were thin, glittering slits between heat-swollen lids. Sweat dripped down her reddened face. Polly stripped off a long-sleeved shirt. She was wearing a light T-shirt underneath, one that revealed a tattoo of a rose on her plump, pale arm.

Blaaaattt! Before I could read even two pages, the bell rang again. I closed my book and stumbled to my chair.

Mechanically, I thrust label after label through the glue machine. My stiffened fingers worked in an automatic rhythm. I had a numbing feeling of unreality, as if I would never leave this factory, would never stop the endless round of bottles and labels.

At 4:45 P.M. I stood up and wiped my forehead with the bottom of my shirt. How was I going to get through the next fifteen minutes, much less the next ten weeks?

That evening, I wheeled my bicycle down the ramp. My hands were raw, my shoulders ached, my head was spinning. My fingertips crackled with glue. I stumbled out into the world, taking deep breaths of the hot, smoggy air.

■■■■

The next morning I was up early. My parents and older brothers had already left for work; the house was cool and silent. I took my bagel onto the patio and sat looking down at the garden, at the long sparkling trail of grass, and the roses bordering its edges. At 7:30 A.M. I wheeled my bike out of the garage and rode past the neat, orderly houses, down to the boulevard. Already there was a lot of traffic on the street.

I pedaled past gracious old houses with wide lawns, then past rapidly deteriorating neighborhoods and shabby storefronts, and into the decaying heart of downtown. At 7:55 I was riding up in the freight elevator with my bike. The doors opened. There were the shelves of jars waiting to be filled, and vats of pills that perfumed the air with their sharp, medicinal smell. I wheeled my bike onto the factory floor and left it standing in an empty corner.

The bell rang. "Punch in, smart girl!" Barbara hollered.

Another day in the pill factory.

■■■■

And another and another. The hum of the glue machine spoke to me. It said, "I have a job, I have a job." Or did the job have me? I wasn't sure any more. I lived by the bell. It was mounted near a greasy window, a huge bell, the size of a gong, and ushered us from one world to the next. Its furious bleat penetrated to the dustiest, most distant corner of the factory. The sound **reverberated** through my bones, muscles, and blood, drove all thoughts out of my mind, and let me know that I was part of a machine, that I was only as good as the labels I pasted. When I heard it, I jumped up like an automaton[3] and rushed to my station or abandoned it.

"I can't stand it!" I said to my parents after the second week. I pushed my hair away from my face with a sweaty hand. Tears came into my eyes.

"It's only for the summer," my father said. "Don't quit; it's not good for your self-respect. Finish what you start."

Then he reminded me that my grandmother had gone to work in a factory at age six; my grandfather had worked every day of his life driving a truck, flipping burgers at a hot grill, or doing manual labor; and both my parents had earned every cent of their college education. My brothers worked part-time during the year and all summer long. "Work or die" was the family motto.

My mother shot a reproachful look at my father. "If it's too hard for her, she can quit."

Did she think I couldn't handle it? Did she think I was too young, too immature, too weak? Too much of a baby? I sat up straighter and brushed away the tears. "I guess I can give it another try."

■■■■

In the factory, the sunlight beat through the dirt-smeared windows, and the temperature kept rising through the long afternoons. There was no air-conditioning. The air was gritty, almost a **palpable** force in the room, pressing against me. Rivers of sweat ran down my face and back. I sipped at glasses of water and tried to position myself in front of the floor fan, which sent a timid, ineffectual[4] breeze down the center of my table. My shoulders ached, my fingers were stiff, my mind was dazed by the clattering of the machines, the whirring of the fans, the ticking of the clocks that were everywhere. I worked in a big box that trapped hot air inside it, a noisy box with splintered wooden floors and large windows that didn't open. It was stifling, suffocating, maddening.

reverberated
echoed; resounded

palpable
able to be touched or felt

---

3 **automaton:** a self-operating machine; robot
4 **ineffectual:** without effect

But I could do it. At least for now. I could push myself a little farther every day.

After the first day, I had lost my name. "Summer girl," Mr. Kredler called me, during his rare appearances on the floor.

"Smart girl!" Barbara saluted me, her small eyes glittering as she inspected the boxes of labeled bottles.

"Hey, kid," Polly whispered, passing me half of a pastry and a dig in the ribs or a pinch on the arm to go along with it.

I answered to all of them and didn't mind that they seemed to have forgotten my name. After all, didn't Mr. Kredler often have a smile and a compliment for my work? Didn't Barbara sometimes offer a begrudging word of praise? Didn't Polly help me find supplies and show me a shortcut or two?

■■■■

"Where's your book?" Barbara demanded.

"Left it at home." I unpacked my lunch bag: the usual sandwich, apple, and juice.

"Want some goulash?"[5] Polly offered. "I made it last night." She waved her steaming fork in front of my face.

"It smells good," I said, but I couldn't stand to eat anything hot in eighty-eight-degree weather.

Barbara continued to watch me. "How come you didn't bring your book?"

"I didn't feel like it." Each day, I had been able to concentrate less and less on the words on the page. After working alone on the machine for hours, I wanted to talk—any kind of talk. And human companionship. "It was boring," I added.

Barbara stared at me suspiciously for a moment, then slapped her knee with an enormous hand and burst out laughing.

I smiled back at her.

"Sure you don't want any goulash?" Polly said again.

I shook my head.

"Want to see a picture of my boyfriend?" She pulled a wallet out of her pocket and rifled through the plastic flaps. "There he is," she said, showing me a picture of a pale scowling man with his arms folded across his chest.

---

5 **goulash:** stew made with meat and vegetables

Anne Mazer

"And here I am." She showed me another picture. She wore a black lace nightgown and was smiling with her lips pressed tightly together. There was a faint dark circle around one eye.

Polly snapped the wallet shut and stood up. "Anyone want a soda? I'm going downstairs to the machine."

Barbara tossed a few quarters across the table. "Get me a root beer."

I finished my sandwich and drank my juice. Looking out the window, Barbara slurped the remaining soda in her cup. Then she turned to me.

"Don't be like her," she said. "Or me." She wiped her forehead with a crumpled napkin. "I wanted to go to school once. I like horses. I wanted to be a veterinarian."

I imagined those massive hands smoothing the **flanks** of a horse, carrying buckets of feed, administering medicine.

flanks
sides

"Why didn't you?" I asked.

"Not everyone's a smart girl like you. Don't argue with me!" She glared at me. "Wet behind the ears! Do your job, save your money, then get out of here. Don't come back!"

■■■■

A few days later, Violet came to work on the glue machine.

"Show her everything," Barbara ordered. "You're going to train her."

Violet sat down on the chair across from me and folded her hands in front of her. Her gray hair was in a bun, she was wearing a flowered dress with a high frill around the neck, and she looked as though she were going to a Sunday school picnic, not to a factory.

"Have you ever worked a glue machine before?" I asked Violet.

"This is my first job," she quavered.[6]

■■■■

"There's nothing to it," I said several hours later for the hundredth time. "You can do it."

Violet pulled the label off the bottle with trembling hands. "I'm not much good at anything," she whispered.

I sighed. "It just takes practice. Don't give up."

"Thank you, Meredith," she said humbly.

---

6 **quavered:** trembled

She fumbled with the pile of labels, then slowly tried to insert one into the machine.

"The other way," I said quickly. She had glued quite a few on the wrong side.

"Oh, dear!" She stared at the label a moment, as if trying to figure out what it was for.

"Put it in the machine," I reminded her.

Her hands shook as she put the label through, then centered it over the bottle.

"Is this good enough, Meredith?"

The label wasn't straight and there was a large air pocket at the side. "Do it over," I said. As she watched me, I thrust another label into the machine, pressed it down hard over the bottle, and then, without stopping, did another and another and another. I felt like a star athlete showing off my moves.

Violet's pale eyes filled with tears. "I'm not suited for any kind of work."

"You'll be fine," I said. I took a breath. "You're doing a good job. It just takes time."

"Thank you, Meredith. You're so very kind."

■ ■ ■

I expected her to be fired by the end of the week, but Violet stayed on. She worked with almost painful slowness, filling less than half the boxes that I did. But no one seemed to notice, except me. I wondered if she was related to the owner in some way. How ever had she gotten the job? I couldn't even imagine her filling out an application form.

It was strange. Polly and I discussed it, wondering why she had never worked before. I wondered if she had a family, though somehow I knew the answer to that, and not just from her bare, ringless hands. Day after day, she wore her old-fashioned dresses with their frilly white collars. In spite of the heat, she always wore stockings and narrow lace-up shoes. She ate her lunch by herself; if anyone spoke to her, she raised watery, red-rimmed eyes, and answered in a tremulous[7] whisper. Barbara mostly ignored her. Mr. Kredler didn't know she existed. And Polly, who had been so kind to me, was impatient with her.

---

7 **tremulous:** timid

Anne Mazer

"Get it yourself!" she snapped when Violet asked her to take down a box of empty bottles. Or, "That's none of my business," when Violet spilled vitamins all over the floor and went to her for help.

When Violet continued to put her time card in upside down, Polly cried, "How can anyone be so dumb!"

Violet stared at her. Then she burst into deep wrenching sobs. I had never heard an adult cry that way and I was terrified. My heart was pounding. I couldn't breathe right. I grabbed the time card from Violet's hand and punched it in.

"It's okay, it's okay," I said. "Everything's all right, Violet. I fixed it."

She raised her mottled,[8] tear-streaked face. "Thank you, Meredith. You're so very kind."

"It's nothing," I muttered. I handed her a tissue. "Really, it's nothing."

■ ■ ■ ■

From then on, Violet turned to me for everything.

"Meredith, can you help me? Meredith, what should I do? The label is ripped. Meredith, is it all right if I get a drink of water?"

Suddenly I was the person in the know. And I liked it. I wasn't the baby anymore. I felt tough, almost as tough as Barbara. But little by little, Violet began to get on my nerves. For one thing, her repetition of my name began to wear me down.

"Meredith," she cried all day long. "Meredith, I can't do this. Meredith . . ."

"Don't call me that," I snapped one hot afternoon. It was pure irrationality; what else was she supposed to call me?

Her eyes filled with tears. "I'm sorry, Meredith."

I took a deep breath and spoke slowly. "It's all right. You're fine. You're doing fine."

"I'm no good," she whispered. "I'm just no good."

"Don't say that!"

"You're so very kind, Meredith."

I didn't know whether to laugh, cry, or scream.

She looked down at her hands. "Meredith, is it all right if I go to the little girl's room?"

---

8 **mottled:** spotted; blotchy

I began to hide from her. At lunch time, instead of eating with Barbara and Polly, with Violet sitting a few feet away, I crept to the back of the warehouse, where the long rows of metal shelves ended and where there were stacks of boxes thrown haphazardly on top of each other. There I sat on the floor and read until the bell called me back.

"Where were you, Meredith?" Violet asked me timidly as we sat at our table, labeling bottles.

"I needed some quiet."

"Oh." Her lip trembled. "Am I too noisy for you?"

Once again, I found myself reassuring her. "It's not you, Violet. You're all right."

■ ■ ■ ■

One day I came back from lunch and found her sitting at the table, pale and unmoving.

"Violet?"

She didn't answer me.

"What is it?" I asked. "What's wrong?"

Violet hid her face in her hands and rocked slowly from side to side.

Then I understood. "They fired you, didn't they?"

She raised her head to look at me. "No," she said. "I quit."

I stared at her in shocked silence. My mouth opened as if to speak, then closed.

She looked at me calmly. "I don't like it here."

■ ■ ■ ■

Violet left a few minutes later. "Thank you, Meredith," she said in her quiet voice. "You were so kind."

She picked up her purse and adjusted the lace collar of her dress. Then she walked to the elevator and pressed the button. She did not look at the clock. She did not punch her time card. She did not glance at Barbara, who was unloading boxes of pills from a ramp, or at Polly, who stared at her briefly, then went back to filling glass bottles. She didn't even look back at me.

I imagined her going back to a single room in a building where no one knew her. I imagined her making herself tea, sitting very straight in a hard wooden chair. I imagined her making the rounds of stores, factories, and agencies, looking for another comfortless job.

It came to me, with the force of a blow, that she was brave.

Suddenly I wanted to be just like her, to say, "I quit!" to Barbara, to forget about the time clock and the bell and the glue machine. I wanted to ride the freight elevator down to the ground floor and take my bike out into traffic. And then I would ride and ride until I had left the city entirely behind me, until my eyes were blinded by sweat and my muscles shook from exhaustion. Then I would throw myself down in the long fragrant grass of some quiet meadow and spend the rest of the day on my back, staring at the sky, only the sky.

But I stayed. Day after day I rode my bike through the city traffic, cursing drivers and pedestrians, slamming on my breaks, and pedaling harder than I needed. Week after week I picked up my paycheck and put it in the bank. And each time I punched my card into the machine was a triumph of will, of persistence, of strength. I had a job. I could do it. I was proud. I was tough. I was a gluer on the glue machine.

LITERARY LENS

What descriptions of the people or environment in "The Pill Factory" did you find particularly vivid?

Amir

Paul Fleischman

*I*n India we have many vast cities, just as in America. There, too, you are one among millions. But there at least you know your neighbors. Here, one cannot say that. The object in America is to avoid contact, to treat all as foes unless they're known to be friends. Here you have a million crabs living in a million **crevices**.

When I saw the garden for the first time, so green among the dark brick buildings, I thought back to my parents' Persian rug. It showed climbing vines, rivers and waterfalls, grapes, flower beds, singing birds, everything a desert dweller might dream of. Those rugs were indeed portable gardens. In the summers in Delhi, so very hot, my sisters and I would lie upon it and try to press ourselves into its world. The garden's green was as soothing to the eye as the deep blue of that rug. I'm aware of color—I manage a fabric store. But the garden's greatest benefit, I feel, was not relief to the eyes, but to make the eyes see our neighbors.

I grew eggplants, onions, carrots, and cauliflower. When the eggplants appeared in August they were pale purple, a strange and **eerie** shade. When my wife would bring our little son, he was forever wanting to pick them. There was nothing else in the garden with that color. Very many people came over to ask about them and talk to me. I recognized a few from the neighborhood. Not one had spoken to me before—and now how friendly they turned out to be. The eggplants gave them an excuse for breaking the rules and starting a conversation. How happy they seemed to have found this excuse, to let their natural friendliness out.

Those conversations tied us together. In the middle of summer someone dumped a load of tires on the garden at night, as if it were still filled with trash. A man's four rows of young corn were crushed. In an hour, we had all the tires by the curb. We were used to helping each other by then. A few weeks later, early in the evening a woman screamed, down the block from the garden. A man with a knife had taken her purse. Three men from the garden ran after him. I was surprised that I was one of them. Even more surprising, we caught him. Royce held the man to a wall with his pitchfork until the police arrived. I asked the others. Not one of us had ever chased a criminal before. And most likely we wouldn't have except near the garden. There, you felt part of a community.

crevices
cracks; hideouts

eerie
*unusual and
mysterious looking*

LITERARY LENS

Think about the role the garden plays in both the story and the poem as you read.

I came to the United States in 1980. Cleveland is a city of immigrants. The Poles are especially well known here. I'd always heard that the Polish men were tough steelworkers and that the women cooked lots of cabbage. But I'd never known one—until the garden. She was an old woman whose space bordered mine. She had a seven-block walk to the garden, the same route I took. We spoke quite often. We both planted carrots. When her hundreds of seedlings came up in a row, I was very surprised that she did not thin them—pulling out all but one healthy-looking plant each few inches, to give them room to grow. I asked her. She looked down at them and said she knew she ought to do it, but that this task reminded her too closely of her concentration camp, where the prisoners were inspected each morning and divided into two lines—the healthy to live and the others to die. Her father, an orchestra violinist, had spoken out against the Germans, which had caused her family's arrest. When I heard her words, I realized how useless was all that I'd heard about Poles, how much richness it hid, like the worthless shell around an almond. I still do not know, or care, whether she cooks cabbage.

The garden found this out with Royce. He was young and black. He looked rather dangerous. People watched him and seemed to be relieved when he left the garden. Then he began spending more time there. We found out that he had a stutter. Then that he had two sisters, that he liked the cats that roamed the garden, and that he worked very well with his hands. Soon all the mothers were trying to feed him. How very strange it was to watch people who would have crossed the street if they'd seen him coming a few weeks before, now giving him vegetables, more than he could eat. In return, he watered for people who were sick and fixed fences and made other repairs. He might weed your garden or use the bricks from the building that was torn down up the block to make you a brick path between your rows. He always pretended he hadn't done it. It was always a surprise. One felt honored to be chosen. He was trusted and liked—and famous, after his **exploit** with the pitchfork. He was not a black teenage boy. He was Royce.

In September he and a Mexican man collected many bricks from up the street and built a big barbecue. I was in the garden on Saturday when the Mexican family drove up in a truck with a dead

exploit
heroic deed

pig in the back. They built a fire, put a heavy metal spit through the pig, and began to roast it. A bit later their friends began arriving. One brought a guitar, another played violin. They filled a folding table with food. Perhaps it was one of their birthdays, or perhaps no reason was needed for the party. It was beautiful weather, sunny but not hot. Fall was just beginning and the garden was changing from green to brown. Those of us who had come to work felt the party's spirit enter us. The smell of the roasting pig drifted out and called to everyone, gardeners or not. Soon the entire garden was filled.

It was a harvest festival, like those in India, though no one had planned it to be. People brought food and drinks and drums. I went home to get my wife and son. Watermelons from the garden were sliced open. The gardeners proudly showed off what they'd grown. We traded harvests, as we often did. And we gave food away, as we often did also—even I, a businessman, trained to give away nothing, to always make a profit. The garden provided many excuses for breaking that particular rule.

Many people spoke to me that day. Several asked where I was from. I wondered if they knew as little about Indians as I had known about Poles. One old woman, Italian I believe, said she'd admired my eggplants for weeks and told me how happy she was to meet me. She praised them and told me how to cook them and asked all about my family. But something bothered me. Then I remembered. A year before she'd claimed that she'd received the wrong change in my store. I was called out to the register. She'd gotten quite angry and called me—despite her own accent—a dirty foreigner. Now that we were so friendly with each other I dared to remind her of this. Her eyes became huge. She apologized to me over and over again. She kept saying, "Back then, I didn't know it was *you* . . ."

Post Humus

Patti Tana

Scatter my ashes in my garden
so I can be near my loves.
Say a few honest words, sing a gentle song,
join hands in a circle of flesh.
Please tell some stories about me
making you laugh. I love to make you laugh.
When I've had time to settle, and green
gathers into buds, remember I love blossoms
bursting in spring. As the season ripens
remember my persistent passion.
And if you come in my garden
on an August afternoon
pluck a bright red globe,
let juice run down your chin and the seeds
stick to your cheek. When I'm dead
I want folks to smile and say *That Patti,*
she sure is some tomato!

LITERARY LENS
What do you think the
garden symbolizes in both
"Amir" and "Post Humus"?

War Game

Nancy Werlin

What I did to Lije. It might have seemed . . . okay, in some ways it *was* cruel; I'll give you that. But I had to do it. It was important. Okay?

You don't see? Fine. I'll explain.

Lije—Elijah Schooler—and I were friends, though nobody knew it except him and me. It had just kind of worked out that way over the years, with Lije being a boy and two years younger and going to the private school his father paid for. His bedroom window faced mine over three feet of alley, and he used to sleep with the light on. Sometimes at night we'd talk for hours—or rather I would—when Lije was worried and had trouble sleeping. For years we did that. And he lent me books. His school had an incredible library, and he could get me anything I wanted.

It wasn't a big secret, our friendship. It was a little secret, something pleasant, but not really important. Until last August when I was fourteen.

It'd been an almost unbearably hot summer. At first it was just the little kids who had the guns—you know, the big plastic machine guns with huge tanks for water. Super-Soakers. Water Uzis. Ricky Leone and Curt Quillian and even Curt's little sister, Janey, were jumping out from alleys and from around corners and behind cars, screaming like police sirens and soaking everybody in sight. The rest of us had to defend ourselves. Before you knew it, nearly every kid in the neighborhood between six and fourteen had a water gun. They were under fifteen dollars at the supermarket.

They were just plain fun, the guns. I'd had no idea. Though I'd seen real guns before, around the neighborhood and at school and stuff, I'd actually never had a toy gun before, even when I was little. But I felt so powerful, cradling the gun under my arm and pumping away. Every time you hit someone, they'd yowl. Run. Unless they were armed too; then they'd whip around and shoot back. It was incredible. I'm not a violent person—none of us were, really (except maybe Lina at times). We weren't gang kids; in fact, we did our best to keep away from the gangs. It was the city. It was summer. It was hot. That's all.

At first, we big kids just did like the little kids and **ambushed** each other. But then I said something, and we got more ambitious.

ambushed
attacked from a hiding place

Kevin DiFranco and Lina Oswego organized two teams—armies—and we were all assigned ranks. The little kids were privates and scouts, and the older kids were lieutenants or spies. I was a lieutenant colonel and head of the war council. "You're smart, Jo," Kevin said. "You do the strategy." Of course Kevin and Lina made themselves generals. Within a week, there were nearly thirty of us involved.

At first I just did it for something to do. And maybe also because it felt good to get the attention from Kevin. He'd never had much to do with me before. I wasn't interested in him, you understand; I wasn't interested in any real boys right then. That was the summer I had the tremendous crush on Talleyrand, and in all my fantasies I (or rather, my alter ego,[1] Anne Fourier) was deeply involved in the politics of the French Revolution. Anne generally disguised herself as Pierre-Ange Gaultier, a boy journalist and the best of Talleyrand's spies. I had worked out nine separate and extremely **elaborate** scenarios, all of them leading to the danger- and passion-filled moment in which Talleyrand would realize he was in love with Anne. But where were Anne's loyalties? With him or with the Revolution or with only herself? It depended on how I was feeling that day. Usually in the end I was on my own side, though, because in a war that's how you survive. That's how Talleyrand did it.

elaborate
worked out in detail

Kevin DiFranco was both popular and cute, but he couldn't have competed with my fantasy world if he'd tried.

But my imaginary life was private—I wouldn't even have told Lije the details, and he borrowed most of my books for me. A massive crush on a centuries-dead Machiavellian[2] priest-politician in a powdered wig wasn't the kind of thing you shared. And if I'd gone on to tell people about my mental war games, my elaborately researched historical alter ego, well, my **façade** of social respectability would have cracked right there, and I'd have been the butt of a million idiotic jokes. If you want to survive, you have to blend in.

façade
outer covering; front

Plus, even I couldn't live in the eighteenth century all the time. And our real-life war game fascinated me. I had a lot of say in it, a lot of control. I was the one who said we were the opposing

---

1 **alter ego:** a second self who is either a trusted friend or an opposite side of one's own usual personality

2 **Machiavellian:** term used to describe a person who follows the philosophy of Machiavelli, who believed conduct in politics was marked by trickery

guerrilla factions[3] of a country in the throes of civil war, a country located right on the equator, full of steaming jungles (the playground and the abandoned factory lot around the corner on Eastern Avenue). The jungles, I said, entirely surrounded the bombed-out capital city (our street and its alleys). I was the one who set up the POW camp behind the brick wall in the truck yard, and I wrote up the rules surrounding[4] capture, punishment, and death. Kevin and Lina were the generals, okay, and they planned the raids and battles and took care of the daily details. But I was the one who designed the game. You could even say it was *my* game.

It was amazing, when you thought about it, when you saw how well it worked. I mean, it had never happened before—all the kids in the neighborhood hanging out and doing something together. We were all different ages, of course, and on top of that there were cliques. But it worked. For a few weeks, it worked. And we had such fun.

Only Lije wasn't playing. He didn't have the summer off from school; he was in some special enrichment program and came trotting home every afternoon at around three o'clock and let himself into his apartment with his key. He'd be there alone until after eight o'clock, because his mother worked as a secretary for some big downtown law firm, and she didn't get home until late. And of course his father was, as the social workers say, not in the picture. Actually, Lije had never met him. But he did pay the tuition for Lije's private school, and, hey, I've heard of worse absentee-father deals. Mine, for instance. Lije hated it, though. Hated *him*. It was a funny thing. Lije was a fat, scared mess with a runny nose, and he couldn't sleep without the light on. But underneath that he was okay. Because he could hate.

truce
a temporary end to fighting; cease-fire

We were on the second day of a two-day **truce** (really an excuse to concentrate on covert ops[5] and training) on the afternoon we all noticed Lije. He had just come out of the convenience store on the corner of Eastern Avenue and Tenth Street. He looked dorky, especially considering the heat, in his long pants and cheap dress shirt and school tie and with his backpack dragging his shoulders down. He was holding a wrapped ice-cream sandwich that he'd obviously

---

3 **guerrilla factions:** groups of people involved in aggressive, unconventional warfare
4 **surrounding:** concerning
5 **covert ops:** secret operations

just bought, and he was completely absorbed in trying to pick open the wrapping.

He was a perfect target, and Lina pounced. "Ambush!" she yelled, and in seconds her SWAT team had him surrounded. Lije looked up, blinking, at the four Super-Soakers leveled at his head.

"Hand over the ice cream," Lina said, "or you're dead."

Lije shot a glance at me, where I was lounging on a stoop with Kevin and a couple of the little kids. But then his eyes skimmed on past. Right then it hit me that we had never talked to each other in public, only from our windows across the alley. Out here on the street, that relationship was nonexistent. It didn't even need saying. So I grinned at Lije but didn't move or speak.

Silently, he handed over the ice cream to Lina. She laughed, made a gesture, and the SWAT team opened fire. Lije didn't move. He stood there and took it, until the tanks were empty and he was completely soaked.

We all laughed. "Feels good, huh?" Lina said. If you knew her, you'd know she was actually being friendly. For Lina.

And that was the moment I understood that Lije wasn't okay after all; that he would need help to be okay. Because he wouldn't just laugh too. Couldn't even force himself to do it; couldn't even pretend. Instead, he acted like a jerk; minded; showed he minded. Why didn't he know better than to show it? Why did he have to let his lip tremble and his face get red? Why did he run like that? Why did he let them—let us—let me—see he was scared?

It's dangerous to show your fear. It marks you as a victim. And watching Lije run away like a little kid, I was afraid for him. And right then I knew I had to do something to help him. I just didn't know what, or when.

That night, though, was completely ordinary. Lije's light came on well before the sun set, and I leaned out of my window and called his name.

"You all right?" I said.

"Yeah." His hair was wet; he'd obviously just taken a shower. Another shower.

"Sorry about today," I said casually. "You just have to laugh, you know. You can't let it get to you." I watched him carefully to see if he understood what I was saying.

Lije shrugged. "Jerks," he said. He said it like he meant it, but I saw his chin tremble and his eyes brim. So he didn't get it. I decided to leave it for now.

"Did that book I wanted come in from interlibrary loan?"

He nodded and handed over a hardback copy of J. F. Bernard's biography of Talleyrand. Inches thick, crammed full of detail, and with plates not only of the man himself, but also of his wife and some of his more famous mistresses. I was thrilled. "Thanks tons," I said to Lije. "This is great. How long can I keep it?"

"Two weeks." Now that we were back on familiar ground, he was feeling more comfortable. He leaned on the windowsill. "Jo, listen. I think the librarian is getting suspicious. She asked me if I had finished the books I already had out."

"What'd you say?"

"Oh, I just shrugged and said I was working on it. But then she started asking me what I found so interesting about France, and was I taking French, and stuff like that, so I had to get out of there fast. You know, I'm not supposed to take out books for other people."

This wasn't news to me. Why was he suddenly making such a big deal out of it? "Look," I said, "I'd get them myself if the public library still did interlibrary loan."

"I know. I just want to be careful and not get into any trouble."

"Don't worry about it," I said. "They won't know anything you don't tell them. It's in your control. You're in charge."

"You always say that," Lije said, which was true. But I'd always thought before that he heard me. I looked at him and saw that he had that rabbity look that he got when he was tense, brooding about his father, or about his mother and money, or something. Life was rougher for Lije than it should have been, just because he took everything so hard, so seriously. He didn't know how to protect himself at all. I wondered how I'd missed that before.

So I said, "Okay. I'll tell you some stuff you can dazzle the librarian with." And even though I wanted nothing more than to be alone with the new book, instead I climbed up onto the sill and leaned against the window frame, while Lije pulled up a chair to his window and propped his chin on his hands. I told him about the bread riots and how they guillotined[6] the rich creeps and how, for the greater

---

6 **guillotined:** killed by a machine with a blade that severs the head from the body

274   Nancy Werlin

good, Charlotte Corday—what a woman, huh?—stabbed Marat to death[7] in his bath. And as I talked, softly as I always did when I told Lije stories, the sun set, and if it hadn't been for the smog and the city lights, there might have been stars.

"You tired enough to sleep now, Lije?" I asked finally, long after midnight. It never got quiet in our neighborhood, not exactly, but most people were sleeping.

He didn't answer, and for a moment I thought he was already asleep. Then he said, "Jo?"

"Yeah?"

"You like me, Jo, don't you? You're my friend?"

He'd never asked me anything like that before. I said, "Is this about today?" Lije didn't answer, but he did look at me, his cheeks all pudgy and his eyes, well . . . suspicious. I said, "I already told you I was sorry that happened. But Lije, you took it too seriously, you know what I mean?" But he was still staring at me with that odd look on his face, *needing*, and so finally I said, "Yeah. Yes, Lije. I like you. I am your friend. I've always been your friend." Which was the truth.

"Good," Lije said. "I'm your friend too, Jo. Always."

And then he stood up and leaned out the window and reached his hand across the alley. He held out his arm, suspended, for a few moments before I realized he wanted me to take it and shake hands. I did that. I think . . . now I think it may have been the only time we ever touched.

Then he went to bed, and I read about Talleyrand until dawn, when my mother came home from her night shift and made me get some sleep.

The next day it was nearly noon by the time I finally got outside, and Kevin was ticked at me for missing morning council. Worse, our planned morning kidnapping of Lina's best sniper,[8] Ricky Leone, hadn't worked; instead Ricky had shot two of our guys, and by our rules—my rules—they were dead for the rest of the day. An hour later Janey got caught spying and ended up in the POW camp. Lina was triumphant, Kevin furious. There were about fifteen of us engaged in a huge argument about the rules, with me trying to cool

---

7 **Charlotte Corday . . . to death:** Corday killed Jean Paul Marat in 1793 because he criticized the Girondists, representatives of the educated middle class, of whom she was a supporter

8 **sniper:** a hidden gunman whose job it is to kill the enemy

them off and Lina nearly purple with rage.

And that was when Lije came down the street again, looking dorkier than ever. I saw him see us standing there, armed of course; saw his eyes dart around as if looking for a hole to dive into. But then—because he really did have something underneath, like I said before—he squared his shoulders and came on anyway, marching like a windup toy soldier, looking neither left nor right. **Hostility**, fear, anger—they were almost visible, pulsing in the air around him as he tried to push his way right through us.

Kevin stuck out his foot and tripped him. Lije fell onto his hands and knees. A few of the littler kids snickered. Lina laughed, and it wasn't the friendly (for Lina) laugh of yesterday. She'd picked up on Lije's hostility, of course, and taken it as disrespect. "You looking for trouble?" she said to Lije's back. Two of her kids stepped forward and leveled their guns at Lije, grinning. "Soak him?" one said.

It was addressed to Lina, but Kevin answered: "Go ahead." Kevin hadn't even finished talking when Lina's kids opened fire on Lije.

First just those two. But then more of them, in a circle around Lije, shooting down first at Lije's back. Then somebody—Lina?—kicked Lije viciously, forcing him over. And the rest of the water reservoirs pummeled down on his face and chest. He was pinned to concrete by the force of the water.

Talleyrand—master strategist and supreme survivor—always knew how to **improvise** on the moment. He would have been proud of me, because I knew immediately that this was the moment to help Lije. I didn't even have to think how to do it. I knew.

I waited until everyone else was done. Waited until Lije got up, slowly. His palms were scraped and bleeding. He didn't say anything. He looked at me. And it was that look, the one I'd seen on his face last night. *Help me*, it said. *Protect me. Be my friend. I can't do it alone.* But he didn't say anything, he just watched me. Waited.

I emptied my own gun into his face. Then I said, "Run on home, kid. You don't belong out here. You might get hurt."

After a few more **excruciating** seconds, Lije left, dripping.

That night, I lay alone in bed watching the light in Lije's window and reliving those minutes. I waited until after it was full dark. Then I went to the open window and called his name. I didn't really think he would come, but he did. He looked terrible.

Nancy Werlin

"Give me back my books," he said. It was what I was expecting. It still hurt, though. Inside, I felt the way he looked. But I didn't show it. I handed him the Talleyrand biography—at least I'd had one night with it—and the others he'd got me before. I wondered how I'd get books now. Somehow. I'd figure something out.

"You're going to be okay, Lije," I said evenly.

Lije shook his head. He was standing awkwardly, arms tense, hands dangling out of sight below the windowsill. "You lied to me," he said.

I shrugged. Stared right back at him as his arms bent and lifted. I saw with pride that he had his own Super-Soaker now. He aimed it at me. His aim was lousy because he was crying, shaking, and so most of the water missed me, but I stood there and took it, as he had, until his reservoir was as empty as mine.

"I hate you, Jo," Lije said. "You're not my friend."

He went back into his room. I went and got a towel and dried myself. Then I waited. And after a while Lije put his light out and, to show me that he could, for the first time slept—if he did sleep that night—in the dark.

Okay, *yes*, I was sorry to hurt him. But the French have a saying about things like this. *C'est la guerre.* Literally it means "that's war," but really it means "that's life." And . . . Lije doesn't understand. Not now. But *you* can. He was wrong about my not being his friend.

I am the best friend he will ever have.

LITERARY LENS

Is Jo the best friend Lije ever had? Explain your reasoning.

What Happened During the Ice Storm

Jim Heynen

One winter there was a freezing rain. How beautiful people said when things outside started to shine with ice. But the freezing rain kept coming. Tree branches glistened like glass. Then broke like glass. Ice thickened on the windows until everything outside blurred. Farmers moved their livestock into the barns, and most animals were safe. But not the pheasants. Their eyes froze shut.

Some farmers went ice-skating down the gravel roads with clubs to harvest pheasants that sat helplessly in the roadside ditches. The boys went out into the freezing rain to find pheasants too. They saw dark spots along a fence. Pheasants, all right. Five or six of them. The boys slid their feet along slowly, trying not to break the ice that covered the snow. They slid up close to the pheasants. The pheasants pulled their heads down between their wings. They couldn't tell how easy it was to see them huddled there.

The boys stood still in the icy rain. Their breath came out in slow puffs of steam. The pheasants' breath came out in quick little white puffs. One lifted its head and turned it from side to side, but the pheasant was blindfolded with ice and didn't **flush**.

The boys had not brought clubs, or sacks, or anything but themselves. They stood over the pheasants, turning their own heads, looking at each other, each expecting the other to do something. To pounce on a pheasant, or to yell Bang! Things around them were shining and dripping with icy rain. The barbed-wire fence. The fence posts. The broken stems of grass. Even the grass seeds. The grass seeds looked like little yokes inside gelatin whites.[1] And the pheasants looked like unborn birds **glazed** in egg white. Ice was hardening on the boy's caps and coats. Soon they would be covered with ice too.

Then one of the boys said, Shh. He was taking off his coat, the thin layer of ice **splintering** in flakes as he pulled his arms from the sleeves. But the inside of the coat was dry and warm. He covered two of the crouching pheasants with his coat, rounding the back of it over them like a shell. The other boys did the same. They covered all the helpless pheasants. The small gray hens and the larger brown

flush
come out of hiding

glazed
covered with a shiny coating

splintering
breaking into many pieces

---

1 **gelatin whites:** the white part of an egg

cocks. Now the boys felt the rain soaking through their shirts and freezing. They ran across the slippery fields, unsure of their footing, the ice clinging to their skin as they made their way toward the blurry lights of the house.

 THE POET'S PERSPECTIVE

The Runaway

Robert Frost

Once when the snow of the year was beginning to fall,
We stopped by a mountain pasture to say, "Whose colt?"
A little Morgan had one forefoot on the wall,
The other curled at his breast. He dipped his head
And snorted to us. And then we saw him bolt.
We heard the miniature thunder where he fled,
And we saw him, or thought we saw him, dim and gray,
Like a shadow across instead of behind the flakes.
The little fellow's afraid of the falling snow.
He never saw it before. It isn't play
With the little fellow at all. He's running away.
He wouldn't believe when his mother told him, 'Sakes,
It's only weather.' He thought she didn't know!
So this is something he has to bear alone
And now he comes again with a clatter of stone,
He mounts the wall again with whited eyes
Dilated nostrils, and tail held straight up straight.
He shudders his coat as if to throw off flies.
"Whoever it is that leaves him out so late,
When all other creatures have gone to stall and bin,
Ought to be told to come and take him in."

LITERARY LENS

Compare and contrast the short story and the poem. How are they similar? How are they different?

Block Party—
145th Street Style

Walter Dean Myers

"He said what?" Peaches looked up from the math book we were studying from.

I've known Peaches all my life, which means for fifteen years, and I hated to see her sad. Peaches is not the kind of girl to get messed around easy but I was there when her mama told her about Big Joe.

"He asked me to set a date to marry him," Sadie Jones said, standing at the sink.

"He's got some nerve," Peaches said. She took a deep breath and shook her head.

"And I told him I would," her mama said. "Honey, it's time I got married. I'm not getting any younger and you know Joe's really sweet."

Peaches didn't say another word but in a minute I could see the tears running down her face. When her mama came over and put her arm around her shoulders Peaches shrugged her off. Later, when we were checking out the tube,[1] I asked her why she was so upset about Big Joe.

"You know your mama likes him and he's sweet for an Old School dude,"[2] I said.

"It doesn't have anything to do with Big Joe, Squeezie," Peaches said later, tagging[3] me like she always does when she's upset. "I think if she loved my daddy she wouldn't go messing around with somebody else."

I wasn't even going there. I mean, you're supposed to give people their propers[4] when they're alive but after they're gone for years all you have to do is just don't diss[5] them. I personally never diss no dead people, anyway. Okay, so Peaches was sad and walking around like she lost her best friend, which is me. The closer the wedding got the more down she was. Nothing anybody said could cheer her up. Her mama asked her up front if she wanted her to say no to Big Joe.

"Honey, I'll do it for you," Peaches' mama said.

"Do what you want," Peaches said.

---

1 **checking out the tube:** slang for "watching television"
2 **Old School dude:** slang for "traditional man"
3 **tagging:** slang for "naming"
4 **propers:** slang for "proper respect"
5 **diss:** slang for "disrespect"

Walter Dean Myers

I thought that was kind of mean but I knew my friend was hurting inside. She was only nine when her father passed but they had been real close. She always said that he had been her best friend before me. When Peaches was young he used to take her to the park and he would get right down in the sandbox and make castles and stuff with her. When we got older he would take me and Peaches to a restaurant on Saturday afternoons and make believe we were grown ladies and that was, like, super-cool. Having your father for a best friend was all right and I could see how she felt. But I could also see her mother's point of view. Big Joe had loved her mama for a long time and he did own a Bar-B-Que joint that was the serious bomb.[6] What's more, it didn't take geometry or nothing like that to see that her mama loved Big Joe, too.

When the woman who's the **borough** president announced that the city was sponsoring a street fair on 145th Street, I saw a chance to cheer Peaches up. Peaches and me are home girls and I can't stand for her to be sad all the time.

borough
one of five political areas in New York City

"So let's go on to the street fair and eat some potato salad or whatever else they got," I said.

She said okay and I said we should wear our black pants and put on some fly tops in case any boys showed and she said she wasn't in the mood for boys and she was going to wear the top she had on. Whatever.

So we're at the street fair and it looks like it could develop into something. They had hooked up some monster amps on a flatbed truck and the usual hoochie mamas were showing off their stuff. Me and Peaches, who are both on a **conservative** trip,[7] were standing in front of my crib[8] checking things out. I'm not homely but I don't have Peaches' looks so I was scopin' and hopin', if you know what I mean.

conservative
tending to support time-honored views; traditional

Leroy hooked up some jams and the dancing started. I was wishing that somebody would come over to us because I knew Peaches loved to dance and I figured that maybe a little shaking would get her out of her bad mood. That's when J.T. showed up.

J.T. was tall and dark, had pretty eyes, a thin face, and he was built nice for a sixteen-year-old. The guys on the block said he could

---

6 **bomb:** slang for "best"
7 **trip:** slang for "attitude" or "state of mind"
8 **crib:** slang for "house" or "residence"

really play ball, too. But he was always in trouble. He had even been in the Juvenile Detention Facility last Christmas for snatching a white lady's pocketbook. You knew you were going to read about him in the newspaper one day or see his picture on television with his hands behind his back.

"Hey, Squeeze, what's happening?" he said.

"Hey, J.T.," I came back.

He stood a little way from us and started eyeballing the food table. There was beans and rice, fried chicken, ribs, **plantains**, and corn on the cob.

plantains
tropical fruit related to bananas

I pointed him out to Peaches and right away she got caught up in her attitude and talking about why J.T. had to come around to mess things up.

"It's a street fair and he lives on this street," I said.

"You know he's a thief, right?" Peaches said. "And I got the money on me for the wedding gift."

Peaches and me had gone downtown earlier looking for a wedding gift for her moms and Big Joe.

"Why are you going to spend two hundred dollars if you're so messed around about the marriage?" I had asked her when we were walking out of Macy's.

"I got to get them something," she said. "And I am not messed around about the marriage!"

Whatever. Anyway, J.T. was slowly sliding over toward the eats.

"What do you want?" Peaches asked him.

"This is a free party, right?" he said.

"So you coming around to cop what you can get for free?" Peaches asked in this nasty way.

I didn't want to get into nothing with J.T., because sometimes when boys go to those youth houses they come out dangerous, so I told Peaches to cool it.

"Cool *what*?" Peaches put her hand on her hip. "I'm not scared of no J.T."

"Why don't you just chill?" J.T. said.

"Why don't you just shut up?" Peaches got right up in J.T.'s face. "You shouldn't even be talking to decent people. I know you're sleeping in the street. You ain't even got a home and you're telling somebody to chill. Leave me alone!"

Walter Dean Myers

Peaches was getting loud, flashing proud and drawing a crowd. People were turning to see what was going on. Mrs. Liburd, a little Cajun lady, came over and said we shouldn't argue.

"You're such lovely children," she said, reminding us that we didn't need to be showing ourselves out.[9]

J.T. dropped his head and walked away. He went toward where I thought he lived. You could see the hurt in his eyes. It made me feel bad for him and for Peaches, too, because that's not the way she shows when things go right.

I thought about saying something to Peaches but I figured it wasn't the right time.

Some brothers with dreads[10] started playing steel drums and that was getting us back to a good mood. The steel drums were on the money[11] and when Big Joe showed up with a portable barbecue grill everything was everything. Peaches' mom was working with Big Joe and they looked like a cool couple.

"You want to go help them serve?" I asked Peaches.

"They didn't ask me to help them," Peaches said.

"Maybe because they're afraid you're going to chump them off."[12] I said, "Like you did J.T."

"They just don't need me," Peaches said. "I usually make the potato salad at home. Now she got him I guess she wants to eat his nasty potato salad."

I have eaten girlfriend's potato salad and it's not all that but I saved that for later. I went over myself to lend a hand.

Big Joe had on his chef hat and an apron. He was slicing up the ribs and dipping them in the sauce. Peaches' mama had on an apron and she was serving up some lemonade. Every once in a while she would glance over at Big Joe and give him a little smile and he would give her a little smile right back. I like to see that in old folks.

Me and Peaches have been best friends for as long as I can remember but wrong is wrong and everybody knows what God don't like. After a while Peaches did come over but she made sure nobody thought she was having a good time.

---

9 **showing ourselves out:** slang for "showing off"
10 **dreads:** slang for "dreadlocks," long braids of hair
11 **on the money:** slang for "very good"
12 **chump them off:** slang for "fight with them"

"Hold up on the serving until we set out the trash cans," Big Joe said.

Big Joe was a real good cook and the food line was stretched halfway down the block.

"Now hear this! Now hear this!" It was Leroy on the P.A. system. "Anybody who is already fat and greasy should get on the back of the line and please save me some food if y'all want me to play some decent music!"

With the food going, the music blowing, 145th Street was like a huge rent party[13] without the door charge. Everybody was having fun. Except for Peaches, of course, but you could see she was needing to work at being miserable. Then little Debbie, wearing a dress so tight you could see everything she had, said something to the guys in the steel band and they started playing a reggae version of "Here Comes the Bride," which was corny but in an okay kind of way.

Peaches smiled and I half smiled back at her.

"You still mad at me, girlfriend?" she asked.

"No," I said, even though I was, a little.

"Look, you want to come with me and I'll take a plate up to J.T.?" she said. "I know I didn't act right."

"You don't have to do that," I said. "Just let it slide."

"Right, so now J.T.'s mad at me, and I hurt my moms, and now my main girl is hurt, too." Peaches gave me that smile she knows always gets around me.

"You know you got a fast mouth, girl," I said. "I don't know how you can be so correct and **righteous** in your heart, and still fix your mouth to say all them mean things."

"As long as I got my Squeezie to get me straight I'm all right," Peaches said. "Come on upstairs with me."

I really didn't want to go up to where J.T. was. I was just happy that girlfriend was seeing where she was at. "I'm not going up there," I said, but when she fixed a plate of chicken and greens and salad and said she was going anyway I naturally had to go with her.

We covered the plate with some aluminum foil and went into the building next to John's Fish House. The halls were kind of dim

righteous
morally right; free from guilt or wrong-doing

---

13 **rent party:** a party to which admission is charged, then the money is used to pay the party-givers' rent

Walter Dean Myers

and the tin on the stairs rattled as we went up, Peaches going first and me behind her.

"I guess I got to get used to my mama getting married, Squeezie," Peaches said.

"I think you do," I said. "Same way she got to get used to it if you get married."

"She's still wrong for marrying him so soon," Peaches said.

We went up to the top floor to where we thought J.T. lived and saw there was a padlock on the door. Peaches turned and looked at me and I looked at her.

"Maybe they moved," I said.

We went back toward the stairs and Peaches stopped. She looked up past the landing that led to the roof. Then she started up even though there wasn't much light up there. Like a good homey I followed.

"Who coming up here!" The voice sounded like a growl more than a person and I was ready for some serious stepping.

"It's me," Peaches said. "That you, J.T.?"

"Get out of here!" J.T. stepped down in front of Peaches. He had his shirt off and he spread his legs and had his fists balled up.

"We brought you a plate," Peaches said.

Wham! J.T. knocked that plate from Peaches' hand and it went up against the wall.

"What's wrong with you, fool?" Peaches was up in his face again.

"Get out of here!" he said.

I was reaching for Peaches to pull her back because I didn't want her to get hurt. Peaches came down two steps and turned back toward J.T. He was so mad the spit was flying out with his words.

Then, just when I thought we were going to go on down and get back to the block party, Peaches started back up the stairs again. J.T. put his arm in front of her and Peaches grabbed it and started wrestling with him.

"Don't you touch her!" I heard myself screaming.

J.T. slipped on the stairs and somehow Peaches pushed him down a little and ran past him up toward the roof. Something inside me just went crazy, like a heavy panic thing, and I tried to run up the stairs after her and J.T. put his hand right over my face and started pushing me back. I hit the wall and had to catch myself before I fell down the stairs. Then J.T. turned to go after Peaches. I caught his leg and he kicked me with his other leg and I had to let him go.

So by this time I'm crying and my shoulder is hurt. Then I hear J.T. cursing again, and this time it's cursing and almost the same growling noise he was making before. If it had been anybody else but Peaches, I would have been down the stairs in a heartbeat, but I couldn't leave her in no danger.

I got my teeth **clenched** up and went upstairs ready to scratch J.T.'s eyes clean out of his head if I had to. He was standing on the steps just below the door that led to the roof. He saw me and tried to push me back with one hand.

"Just get out of here! Just get out of here!" he was saying.

I looked on the landing and Peaches was down on her knees and there was somebody else there, too. It was J.T.'s mama. She was sitting on the landing with a blanket around her. There was an empty cracker box, old newspapers, and open cans of food scattered around the landing.

clenched
closed tightly

Walter Dean Myers

J.T.'s mama was shivering. The light coming through a crack in the door to the roof filtered through her hair to make a halo around her thin face. She looked over Peaches' shoulder to me, the big sad dark eyes looking like they were a hundred years old. Peaches was just holding her with both arms.

J.T. was still carrying on but he was slowing down and the growling noise was like him halfway crying at the same time he was talking. After a while he stopped and leaned against the **banister**. His mama brought her hand out from the blanket around her and she put it on Peaches' arm.

"Squeezie, go downstairs and tell Big Joe to come up," Peaches said, softly.

"I don't need no Big Joe up here," J.T. said.

"Tell him I need him to come up here," Peaches said. There were tears coming down her face. "Tell him that I need him real bad."

I went downstairs slow and realized that my leg was hurt, too, as well as my shoulder. The music was still going on when I reached the street and it took me a while to get though the crowd and get to where Big Joe and Peaches' mama were.

"Squeezie, what's wrong, baby?" Peaches' mama said.

I tried to say it without crying but I couldn't and I could see Mrs. Jones getting more and more upset.

"Is Peaches hurt?" Big Joe asked

"No, she just needs to help J.T.'s mama, I think," I said.

"We can take care of it," Big Joe said. He was calm as he took off his apron. "We can take care of it."

We went upstairs, and Peaches' mama wanted to run up, but Big Joe kept saying everything was all right and we went slow with him leading the way. When we got up to the top of the stairs, J.T. was sitting with his head in his hands. Big Joe told him to move and J.T. slid over.

Peaches was still sitting with J.T.'s mama, kind of rocking her in her arms. After making sure that Peaches was okay, Mrs. Jones helped J.T.'s mama to stand up and Big Joe carried her in his arms all the way downstairs and up the street to Mother Fletcher's house.

J.T. had come down and he hung back, watching. Peaches went toward him and I went over in case some fighting was going to break out but she just took his hand. She didn't say nothing, just took his hand like she was there for him.

"I couldn't even do nothing for my own mother," J.T. said. He had tears running down his cheeks. "I feel bad about, you know, fighting you and everything."

"This is 145th Street," Peaches said. "Hurt happens here just like everywhere else. Sometimes you can deal with it, sometimes you just got to get some help."

J.T. and his mama stayed with Mother Fletcher for a few days and then Big Joe got them a little place on 141st Street, across from the school. It wasn't no mansion but it was cool. Then Peaches gave them her whole two hundred dollars wedding gift money, which J.T. said he was going to pay back but I know he didn't have a job. I wouldn't have given anybody all my money. But Peaches got that kind of big heart in her. And that's how the whole block is, in a way. Yeah, you got some people who do ugly things, but I think, mostly, if they had a good chance they would be okay.

The next month was the wedding and it turned out so good! Peaches' mama had her hair done real nice, up off her neck, and she was so beautiful that I cried, which was no big thing because I always cry at weddings. Then Peaches, Big Joe, and Sadie had them a family hug which got my boo-hooing into high gear again.

"I'm still a little scared about Mama getting married," Peaches said afterward.

"But we'll deal with it, right?" I said.

"Yeah, Squeezie," she said, "we can deal with it."

"You're still number one with me," I said.

"I'm still *numero uno* with my mama, too," Peaches said. "Big Joe can't compete with me."

"Go on, girlfriend."

So that was what happened to Peaches and her mama, and to J.T. and his mama. We still see J.T. and his mama around. They're not really kicking it too tough right now but they're sliding by, you know, staying strong and being righteous. I know they're going to make it.

Oh yeah, what we gave Big Joe and the new Mrs. Big Joe for a wedding gift was a pair of boss imitation Tiffany lamps that cost sixty-three dollars. All the money came from me but that was all right because, like I always say, me and Peaches got a friendship that's all that and then some. You know what I mean?

in the inner city

Lucille Clifton

in the inner city
or
like we call it
home
we think a lot about uptown
and the silent nights
and the houses straight as
dead men
and the pastel lights
and we hang on to our no place
happy to be alive
and in the inner city
or
like we call it
home

LITERARY LENS

*Compare Peaches to
the narrator of
"in the inner city."*

RESPONDING TO UNIT FIVE
Neighborhood Panorama

REFLECTING

1. Based on your reading of the stories in this unit, what kind of neighborhood do you think would be the best one for you? Why?

2. Many of the people in this unit's selections were good friends and neighbors. Which one or ones would you give the "Good Neighbor Award," and why?

3. If you lived in the neighborhood when the war game was being played, would you have joined in the game? Give reasons for your answer.

4. Meredith, the narrator of "The Pill Factory," calls Violet brave when she quits a job they both hate. Who do you think was the brave one, Violet or Meredith? Explain.

ANALYZING

5. The people in this unit's selections relate to those around them in many different ways. Pick a character from "Block Party—145th Street Style," "Amir," or "War Game," or the speaker in the poem "Post Humus," and have that person visit the boys in "What Happened During the Ice Storm" a week after "the incident of the pheasants." Write a short dialogue between the characters.

6. Paraphrase the following sentences from "Block Party—145th Street Style."

   They had hooked up some monster amps on a flatbed truck and the usual hoochie mamas were showing off their stuff. Me and Peaches, who are both on a conservative trip, were standing in front of my crib checking things out. I'm not homely but I don't have Peaches' looks so I was scopin' and hopin', if you know what I mean.

7. Create a semantic map like the one below to gather descriptive information about "The Pill Factory." When you have completed the map, write a short description of what the workers see, feel, touch, and hear as they work.

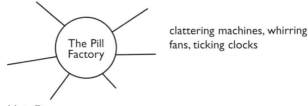

The Pill Factory

clattering machines, whirring fans, ticking clocks

8. In "War Game" Jo states that *Ces't la guerre,* which means "that's war," really means "that's life." Do you agree that war games can teach us about life?

9. Active Reading Did you stop at various points in your reading of this unit to review and **summarize** events? Did you remember to question things that confused you and to predict what might happen next?

DISCUSSING

What's the worst job or chore you ever had to do? How did you go about working through it? Did you use any techniques to make the work lighter or more enjoyable?

WRITING

Read All About It! Write a newspaper article about your community. Try to be objective as you describe the people, organizations, schools, businesses, parks, and other important elements that make where you live special.

A Feel for the Neighborhood The power of observation is essential to good writing. Being able to describe a scene, a person, or an event is what separates the good writers from the amateurs. Hone your writing skills by taking a walk around your block and jotting down anything you observe. Be sure to use a variety of senses—sight, hearing, smell, and touch. Write a short description of your walk.

WORK IN PROGRESS

Community Action Committee As a class, work together to investigate issues of concern to people in your community. Perhaps littering is a problem, or maybe kids need a place to meet and have fun on the weekends. After you gather this information, chose one issue to focus on. Try to develop solutions to the problem. When you have gathered your solutions, devise an action plan. You may want to present the plan to your city council or other appropriate community agency.

Quite a Character Pick a person in your neighborhood whom you admire, enjoy, or just think is interesting. Write a short character sketch of this person. Try to capture the person's physical and personality traits, how he or she speaks, moves, acts, and dresses. If you have time when you have finished writing, trade papers with a partner and draw a picture of the person your partner wrote about.

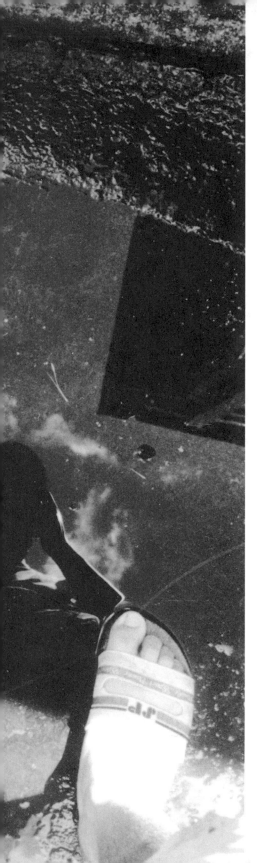

Postcards from Beyond

"Some day, kids," he said, "you're going to like having times like this to remember. A perfect frozen moment."

from *"Muffin Explains Teleology to the World at Large"* by James Alan Gardner

Active Reading Alert!

EVALUATING

As you read through the selections in this unit, make judgments about what you are reading. Use your common sense as well as the evidence in the text to arrive at sound opinions and valid conclusions about what you have read.

Black Angel

Nancy Springer

*t*imes were tough for the Jersey Devil. Hoofprints on the housetops, which were enough to win his South Devon granddaddy[1] uproar and a place in the history books back in 1855, went all but unnoticed in the Garden State in the days since the New Jersey Turnpike had replaced the supernatural as most Jerseyites' personal experience of hell. When something screamed like a woman in the pine barrens, Jersey dwellers assumed it was a woman, presumably a New Yorker, screaming in the pine barrens. Few humans, even young humans, bothered to stray into the ever-shrinking sand-and-scrub wilds of south Jersey anymore; for adventure, they preferred Nintendo. What was a weird manifestation[2] to do for attention? Not to speak of food. Few people kept chickens in their backyards anymore. What was a meat-eating equine[3] to do for blood? Hooves were not meant for hunting.

LITERARY LENS

As you read the following story and poem, think about how the horse in each is portrayed.

What a bite. Skulking in the moonlit scrub along a secondary highway, searching for a nice fresh roadkill but **affronted** by the odor of rancid opossum, the Jersey Devil indulged in **despondent** and rebellious thoughts. *Why do I even bother with the rules anymore? There's no respect for monsters left in the world. Life has lost all meaning, all mystery. How can I compete with TV? I might as well start showing myself in daylight and be done with it.*

"A horse!" whispered a breathy, youthful female voice.

In the shadow of a scrub pine the Jersey Devil froze, outraged to be caught by surprise but even more outraged to be mistaken for a common horse. *Can't you see the red fire of my eyes in the darkness? Can't you see how blackly I loom? What are you doing out here?*

The pine barrens, or what pitiful **remnants** were left of the pine barrens, belonged to creature **denizens** at night. By the rules, the human had to be frightened away. Lifting a head worthy of an equine **gargoyle**, stretching his heavy, muscular neck, and working his bulky chest like a bellows, the Jersey Devil let out his distinctive scream, a warning as chilling as a panther's screech.

affronted
insulted by; offended

despondent
very unhappy; miserable

remnants
small parts; remaining pieces

denizens
dwellers; inhabitants

gargoyle
a strange figure that projects from a church building

---

1 **South Devon granddaddy:** a reference to an historical account of horselike footprints left on rooftops in Devon, a county in southwestern England, in 1855.

2 **manifestation:** a ghost or dweller of the underworld

3 **equine:** horse

exalted
*elevated by praise;
glorified*

"What's the matter, horsie?" The girl pattered forward from the shadows. "I love horses," she said in soft, **exalted** tones. "What's the matter? Are you caught in that bush?" *The nincompoop seemed to have taken his challenge as a squall for help. Exactly what sort of brain damage was this human suffering?* "Oh!" She stopped where she stood, a preadolescent wraith[4] in the moonlight. "Oh," she breathed in tones yet more hushed, more rapt, "oh, wings! You're a Pegasus![5] Oh!"

Poised to scream again, the Jersey Devil gave an undignified grunt of surprise instead. Surprise and sneaking gratification. He had always felt, though never daring to do more than think it, that he was at least as worthy of immortalization as Pegasus. Why should a beautiful white, grass-eating horse with wings be considered a major-league mythological creature, while a not-so-beautiful black, meat-eating horse with wings—bat wings—was considered a monster, and a minor one at that? It was unfair. It was discrimination.

This girl was obviously exceptionally intelligent among humans. The Jersey Devil lowered his rawboned head to regard her with unwonted[6] interest. There she stood, fearless, a skinny child in owlish glasses, her clothing skimpy and cottony and undistinguished, her feet bare and curled in protest against the pine needles—he noticed the **pallor** of her feet in the moonlight, small fishlike surfaces even whiter than the south Jersey sand. Why did humans have such soft and inadequate feet? Dependent upon shoes. How pitiful.

pallor
sickly paleness

"I must be hungrier than I thought," the girl murmured. "I seem to be seeing things." She stepped forward until she stood directly by the Jersey Devil's shoulder, her soft feet inches from his hooves, her scrawny hand reaching for him. He shuddered at her touch yet was so fascinated by her lack of fear that he did not move either to escape or resist that fumbling contact. "No, they're real," she whispered, stroking the leather of his wings.

Her touch was as weak as her voice. Her lack of fear was perhaps due to—what? Had something driven her out here, to the darkness, the wilderness? Out of her home and out of her mind? Some extremity?[7]

---

4 **preadolescent wraith:** very young ghostlike figure
5 **Pegasus:** a winged horse of Greek mythology
6 **unwonted:** unaccustomed; unusual
7 **extremity:** an extreme danger or need

Nancy Springer

"I guess somebody heard me after all," she said. "They sent me a horse angel."

Oh, sure. Give me a break.

"What are you doing stuck in this bush?" she asked the Jersey Devil. "Are you okay?" She limped around his head to scout the other side of him, running her hand down his neck. Crouching, tense, and more than a trifle discombobulated,[8] he still stood pressed into the shelter of a scrub pine as if it could hide him from her. "Are you caught by your mane or something?" Her hand groped, trying to **ascertain** that he was not. "I don't know a thing about horses," she confided.

Noooooo, no kidding. Even an ordinary farm horse had hooves that could trample her or kick her into next week, not to speak of inch-long chisel-like teeth that could sink into her. The Jersey Devil, being a meat eater, had even nastier teeth. Customized. *Want to see my fangs?* But he did not show them to her.

"Except that I read *The Black Stallion*," the girl added. "Can I ride you, black horse?" she asked **wistfully**.

Oh, for Heaven's sake…

He was already breaking all the rules. If a human did not run from his scream, he was supposed to rampage and snarl and glare and breathe fire until the human did run, and if those tactics failed, he was supposed to traumatize the human with his hooves. But poop on all that. Poop by the scoop. He just didn't feel like it.

Fine. Whatever.

He stepped away from the pine, arched his neck, and lowered his head in a fairy-tale gesture of equine acquiescence.[9] Apparently she knew enough about fairy tales, if not about horses, to recognize the body language. She immediately grabbed his mane and scrambled on. Those soft feet had usages after all. Her monkey toes dug into his foreleg and shoulder as she climbed him. Lightweight, she settled behind his withers,[10] her knees hooked around the junctures of his wings.

---

8 **discombobulated:** confused; upset
9 **acquiescence:** consent; approval
10 **withers:** area between the shoulder bones of a horse

"Ooooh," she said, her voice worshipful and delighted, "it's high up here."

The Jersey Devil set off at a sullen, jarring walk, emerging from the pine scrub to plod down the berm[11] of the highway. So what if cars came by. So what if people saw him. His job description was ruined anyhow, and he wasn't sure what would happen to a minor monster who was doing some major messing up. His boss would have a few things to say, that was for sure.

"Oh, thank you," the girl said, though it was not clear for what she was thanking him, "thank you. Nobody else cares."

Shut up.

She did not shut up. "Nobody believes me, that's the problem," she said more softly. "Even my best girlfriend. Nobody wants to believe what's happening to me."

Like the girlfriend and the anonymous others, the Jersey Devil did not want to deal with it. *I've got my own problems.* He walked faster, slamming his heels into the ground with each step.

A mile passed, and another. Gradually his stride eased as the girl's warm presence massaged him. On his back she had gone into a trance of glory and was wordlessly singing. "I'll call you Blackie," she said suddenly. "No, that's stupid. I'll call you Black, uh, Black Angel." She said the name like an apotheosis.[12]

Up to this point the Jersey Devil had had only superficial experience of humans: Screech at them, and they ran. He had not had occasion to deal with the nearly religious fervor of a horse-besotted[13] girl. Her unquestioning adoration put him far off balance.

"Where are we going?" she asked with utter faith.

Going? The Jersey Devil had not been thinking in terms of going anywhere. She wanted a horsie ride, and he was giving her a horsie ride. But now she had called him Black Angel, and she wanted to know where they were going—she expected him to take care of her? There was a large explosion in his small brain, expressed in a snort the size of the pine barrens, the original, not the remnants. Okay. Okay, he knew where they were going. They were going to get her something to eat, and they were going to plunge him all the way

---

11 **berm:** mound of earth; here, berm refers to the mound the highway is built upon
12 **apotheosis:** glorification; adoration
13 **besotted:** infatuated

Nancy Springer

into deep manure. They were going somewhere he had never been in his entire three-hundred-year life.

They were going to McDonald's.

∎∎∎

His belly had been growling before they started, and it had become mighty in borborgymus[14] by the time they arrived at the golden arches. He saw at once that the puny doors were not large enough for him—too bad. Like a Mack truck going relentlessly into reverse, he backed up to the glass, feeling the girl grab his mane as she divined[15] his intentions; he kicked. She shrieked with glee as if on an amusement park ride. Other shrieks sounded from inside, not gleeful at all, and the Jersey Devil snorted with excitement, roused by the screams. He warmed to the sound of crashing, tinkling glass. As he continued to enlarge the entrance, the restaurant was emptying via the other doors. Cars zoomed from the parking lot, and he heard the girl on his back laughing. Such an intelligent child; she was not afraid. Not afraid at all.

He had opened almost the entire front of the establishment. There was no need for her to duck or risk her bare feet on broken glass as he carried her inside. Clear to the counter, where he stopped as if at a mounting block. She slipped down from his back to stand on the countertop, wobbling a little and hanging onto him until she got her legs back. "There's nobody to wait on us," she said, laughing.

The staff had disappeared from the kitchen area, as the Jersey Devil knew quite well; he had seen people in clownish uniforms running through the parking lot.

"I guess it's okay for me to help myself, since they ran away." She was serious now, wanting to know whether it was morally correct for her, a starving child, to take food, and she decided that since her guardian angel had brought her here, it had to be all right. "Are you hungry?" She dropped to her bony bottom and scooted down off the counter, heading for where the paper-wrapped hamburgers were ranked on the rack underneath the heat lamp. She grabbed an armload of burgers, unwrapping several and spreading them on the counter in front of the Jersey Devil before she bit into one herself.

14 **borborgymus:** intestinal noises caused by moving gas
15 **divined:** predicted; understood

Ick. Cooked meat. No better than possum cooked in the sun for three days on an asphalt highway.

Still, the Jersey Devil ate. The bread was not too bad, though squashed. The dill pickle slices were interesting. But he soon diverted his attention from the burgers on the countertop to the leavings on the tables. There was a good grease smell emanating from many small cardboard containers, and thereby he discovered fries. Salty fries, he decided, are almost as good as fresh raw chicken with the feathers on. He munched them, cardboard and all. Behind the counter, the girl had gulped down three burgers and was holding her open mouth under the Coke spigot as she pushed the button.

In french fry gestalt,[16] the Jersey Devil only gradually became aware of an annoying noise: sirens. Louder, nearer. The next moment, several police cars screeched into the McDonald's parking lot.

With her bare feet making slapping noises on the floor, the girl came out from behind the counter, stood near the side door, and looked at the Jersey Devil as if awaiting directions. He was her bat-winged equine angel. She would do whatever he said.

Go away. Let me alone. He just wanted to eat fries. He was not afraid of the cops—their bullets could not so much as dent his black, supernatural hide. His fear was of other authorities.

The police had scurried and **deployed** themselves. McDonald's seemed to have a hot line straight to the precinct. Not unlikely, what with all the Uzi wielders who liked the place. "Come out with your hands up!" a cop barked into a megaphone.

If I come out with my hooves up, you're not going to like it, fella.

"Captain," one of the other cops yelled from near a side window, "I see him. Holy cow, it's some kind of big animal." The police officer, a youngster, maybe a rookie, began to shake as if with buck fever.[17] Having just discovered Chicken McNuggets *en papier*, the Jersey Devil did not even bother to glare as the young cop leveled his gun barrel and fired. Glass flew with a soprano song. The bullet ricocheted off the Jersey Devil and shot harmlessly into a Ronald McDonald effigy[18] grinning in the corner, but the impact annoyed

---

16 **gestalt:** process whereby an individual takes in an experience as a whole rather than in isolated parts; here, euphoria; happiness

17 **buck fever:** excitement of an inexperienced hunter when confronting game for the first time

18 **effigy:** image or representation of a person

Nancy Springer

the Jersey Devil. He screeched and reared. Red lightning flashed in his eyes.

"Don't! Don't shoot at him; you'll hurt him!" The girl came running, placing her skinny body between the Jersey Devil and the offending cop.

Too late the Jersey Devil realized that although bullets could not kill him, they might very well kill her. He had to get her out of there.

It was a thought that upset the order of his universe, throwing a three-century lifetime's worth of assumptions into confusion. Not that confusion would not have existed anyway. There were shouts, another gunshot, yells—"Don't, idiot, you'll hit the kid!" He clattered across vinyl flooring and knocked tables cockeyed in his haste to stand by her, and she seemed to comprehend; she scrambled onto him. Her hand felt firm on his mane. She was okay so far.

He wheeled and leaped through the wide-open front entry. Instinctively, as whenever his adrenaline got going, his wings spread and beat the air. With his softly furred patagia[19] vibrating like drumheads, nearly singing, he surged upward. His forehooves struck the roof of the nearest cruiser; he tucked them and rose steeply, tidily clearing the ornamental pear trees.

"Oh," the girl squealed, "we're flying!"

She was not the only one who was impressed. The manly shoutings down below were achieving new heights of frenzy.

"Black Angel," the girl said, her voice hushed now, "this is wonderful. I've always wanted to fly."

Just hang on. If you splat, I'm not going to be the vulture that eats you.

The hoarse vociferations[20] of the police and onlookers faded away behind them. Flying at about five hundred feet over the lights of town, lugging a bit under the unaccustomed weight of a passenger, the Jersey Devil wheeled sluggishly southward toward the friendly darkness of the pine barrens. Now that his belly was approximately full, all he wanted was to get home, ditch this kid, and rest.

Sirens. Blue lights flashing on the roads below. The cops were following.

"Black Angel," the girl said with a panicky catch in her voice,

---

19 **patagia:** folds of skin near the front of a bird's wings
20 **vociferations:** yells; screams

discerned
seen; noticed

"don't let them get me. Please don't. They'll send me back home…"

It was the first time he had **discerned** fear in her. She was not afraid of him, a grotesque denizen of the night, yet she feared— who? what? It had to be a monster beyond imagining.

The police cruisers were following easily. Despite his bat wings, the Jersey Devil did not dart like a bat. Due to the bulk of his body, his air speed was modest, and he was too unwieldy to attempt sudden directional changes. Too bad. If he could swoop, maybe he could lose this kid.

"Please," she begged, her voice thin, terrified. "I can't go back there."

Of course, there were unquestionably ways he could get rid of her. All it would take would be a midair bucking spree—but even as he rather **venomously** thought that, he knew he was not going to do it.

venomously
cruelly; spitefully

"*Please*, Angel, do something."

I could bomb their windshields. But he knew that all the poop he had in him would not help for long. *All right, okay!* He did not like it, but he knew he would have to do it sooner or later anyway. Might as well take her with him. Maybe she could help plead his case.

To the watchers on the ground, looking up at his grotesque underbelly and wings and at the frail child riding him—"Write it up as a stranger abduction," the captain was telling the cop stuck with that **unenviable** job—to the watchers looking up at the bizarre horse-bat clearly visible in moonlight and in the light pollution from below, it was as if the apparition[21] vanished in midair, rider and all.

unenviable
that no one would want; undesirable

But to the Jersey Devil, a very minor nighttime manifestation in an unlikely place at an unsympathetic time, it was not that he had vanished. It was merely that, with a sigh and a sour-tempered rolling of his eyes, he had gone to face his tribunal.[22]

■ ■ ■ ■

This was not a nighttime place. This was a place where it was always light yet never light. A place forever dimly aglow in lambent[23] rainbow mist.

---

21 **apparition:** ghost; specter
22 **tribunal:** court; forum of justice
23 **lambent:** softly bright; radiant

Nancy Springer

"Fool! Three-hundred-year upstart! A mere sprout! Who are you to dare to extemporize?"[24]

It was the World Tree who spoke, she whose crown was forever veiled in mist and mystery, she for whom "goddess" was too lowly a title. Even had the Jersey Devil not been kneeling before her, nose to the ground, even had he been standing, he would have been able to see only the very least and lowest of her mighty branches stretching far overhead. Perching on the visible branches and looking down with a certain smug satisfaction (or so the Jersey Devil sensed) were various of the lesser mythical birds: the Gillygaloo (which laid cubical eggs and wept constantly), the lop-winged Whangdoodle, the backward Smollygaster, and many others, but no manifestations of any importance. Major mythological personages such as the Phoenix or the Roc would never be seen on such lowly branches; they were far overhead and out of sight, if indeed they were present at all. And the other winged beings, such as the Pegasus—of course they were far above, swaddled and haloed and glorified in fog. If the Pegasus were flying anywhere in the neighborhood, the Jersey Devil would never see him.

"Do you understand what you have done?" the World Tree continued to scold. "This girl, what are we to do with her? Now that she has seen us, she can never return."

"I don't want to return," the girl spoke up, her piping tone so **brash** in this empyrean[25] place that the Jersey Devil winced and trembled. "I don't care what happens to me. It can't be any worse than what has happened already."

"Nonsense. What can possibly be worse than exile from your people?"

The girl told her. As she spoke, and as the Jersey Devil began to comprehend, he felt an unfamiliar burning sensation within his chest, a hot pain that heaved his ribs, surged upward, and blocked his throat, stung his eyes. Without leave from the World Tree, he arose from his knees and went to the girl. What was this punishment taking hold of him, this saltwater tide of misery? His eyes were so blurred he could barely see the child as he reached out his gargoyle

brash
*done in haste
without regard for
consequences*

---

24 **extemporize:** improvise; deviate from the plan
25 **empyrean:** heavenly; ideal

head to nuzzle her. The anguish ran out of his eyes and down his long, ugly face.

She turned to him and hugged him around his neck, hiding her face in his mane, and his tears dripped down on her back and shoulders. There was silence.

"Well . . ." the World Tree said at last, quite softly for such a presence.

The girl did not reply, but her head had lifted from the Jersey Devil's neck and behind her thick glasses her eyes were wide and shining. She gasped, "Wings!"

At the same time the Jersey Devil saw them budding, sprouting from her shoulders, pushing through the cloth of her cheap shirt—fabric wet from his tears—the way spring flowers push through last year's leaves. Wings worthy of a skylark. Airy, uplifted wings the color of raindrops.

Humbly the Jersey Devil turned to the World Tree and said it first. "Thank you, Mother."

"Nonsense. I gave her nothing. You gave them to her."

"I—I can fly?" stammered the girl. "Oh! Oh! Thank you! I've always wanted to fly." She jiggled, jumped, stood on tiptoes with arms outstretched.

"In a moment, little one. Patience. You, Black Thing, come here."

The Jersey Devil bowed his head and took a few steps forward. He sensed that it might be politic[26] to kneel again. But he did not.

"I am going to give you a change of assignment," said the World Tree. "Decide for yourself whether it is an advancement or a demotion. I'll never tell."

It was hard to know how to react to the World Tree when she got that **quirk** in her voice. One did not quite dare to joke with her. The Jersey Devil said nothing.

"The pine barrens are a lost cause since the Turnpike went through," the World Tree said in resigned and contemplative tones. "Confine yourself to them no longer. Your new task is this: You are to seek out those who hurt children. By whatever means you choose, make their lives difficult. Do I make myself clear?"

The Jersey Devil's head had come up. His upper lip wrinkled in

quirk
a certain, special way of acting or speaking

---

26 **politic**: shrewdly tactful; expedient

Nancy Springer

the equine equivalent of a smile. His fangs showed. He bowed low, then wheeled away, eager to get started.

"Little one," the World Tree concluded in bored tones, "you had better fly along with him to make sure he gets it right. He is rather stupid."

"All *right!*" The girl sprang into the timeless air. Her thin face grew rapt with the astonishment and glory of flying. Her glasses shone like the rainbow mist. "Come on, Black Angel!" she cried.

He leaped to fly beside her. When her wings grew tired, he would take her upon his back. He would soar smoothly so as not to joggle her, and perhaps she would lay her head on his neck and sleep.

My name is not Jersey Devil anymore.

Perhaps a monster, a devil, is not so far from being an angel. Perhaps the girl had named him rightly. Black Angel, Avenging Angel. What is an angel but a strange creature with wings?

■■■

The Jersey Devil *is a holdover from an earlier era when the pine barrens of southern New Jersey were thinly populated and scary enough to support a supernatural manifestation. A horselike creature that was reputed to scream horribly in the barrens, leave hoofprints on housetops, kill chickens, and occasionally fly, the Jersey Devil might be a descendant of other horse-demons such as the Irish Pooka or whatever weird thing it was that left an arrow-straight line of hoofprints in fresh snow for ninety-seven miles along the South Devon coast in 1855.*

✳ **THE POET'S PERSPECTIVE**

Horse by Moonlight

for Juan Soriano
Alberto Blanco

A horse escaped from the circus
and lodged in my daughter's eyes:
there he ran circles around the iris
raising silver dust-clouds in the pupil
and halting sometimes
to drink from the holy water of the retina.

Since then my daughter feels a longing
for meadows of grass and green hills . . .
waiting for the moon to come
and dry with its silk sleeves
the sad water that wets her cheeks.

Translated by Jennifer Clement

LITERARY LENS
*Compare the horse in
"Black Angel" to the
horse in the poem.*

The Elevator

William Sleator

*I*t was an old building with an old elevator—a very small elevator, with a maximum capacity of three people. Martin, a thin twelve-year-old, felt nervous in it from the first day he and his father moved into the apartment. Of course he was always uncomfortable in elevators, afraid that they would fall, but there was something especially unpleasant about this one. Perhaps its **baleful** atmosphere was due to the light from the single fluorescent ceiling strip, bleak and dim on the dirty brown walls. Perhaps the problem was the door, which never stayed open quite long enough, and slammed shut with such ominous, clanging finality. Perhaps it was the way the mechanism shuddered in a kind of exhaustion each time it left a floor, as though it might never reach the next one. Maybe it was simply the dimensions of the contraption that bothered him, so small that it felt uncomfortably crowded even when there was only one other person in it.

Coming home from school the day after they moved in, Martin tried the stairs. But they were almost as bad, windowless, shadowy, with several dark landings where the light bulbs had burned out. His footsteps echoed behind him like slaps on the cement, as though there was another person climbing, getting closer. By the time he reached the seventeenth floor, which seemed to take forever, he was winded and gasping.

His father, who worked at home, wanted to know why he was so out of breath. "But why didn't you take the elevator?" he asked, frowning at Martin when he explained about the stairs. Not only are you skinny and weak and bad at sports, his expression seemed to say, but you're also a coward. After that, Martin forced himself to take the elevator. He would have to get used to it, he told himself, just the way he got used to being bullied at school, and always picked last when they chose teams. The elevator was an undeniable fact of life.

He didn't get used to it. He remained tense in the trembling little box, his eyes fixed on the numbers over the door that blinked on and off so haltingly, as if at any moment they might simply give up. Sometimes he forced himself to look away from them, to the Emergency Stop button, or the red Alarm button. What would happen if he pushed one of them? Would a bell ring? Would the elevator stop between floors? And if it did, how would they get him out?

baleful
seeming deadly; sinister

LITERARY LENS
As you read this story, consider whether Martin's fear is justified.

That was what he hated about being alone on the thing—the fear of being trapped there for hours by himself. But it wasn't much better when there were other passengers. He felt too close to any other rider, too intimate. And he was always very conscious of the effort people made *not* to look at one another, staring fixedly at nothing. Being short, in this one situation, was an advantage, since his face was below the eye level of adults, and after a brief glance they ignored him.

Until the morning the elevator stopped at the fourteenth floor, and the fat lady got on. She wore a threadbare green coat that ballooned around her; her ankles bulged above dirty sneakers. As she waddled into the elevator, Martin was sure he felt it sink under her weight. She was so big that she filled the cubicle; her coat brushed against him, and he had to squeeze into the corner to make room for her—there certainly wouldn't have been room for another passenger. The door slammed quickly behind her. And then, unlike everyone else, she did not stand facing the door. She stood with her back to the door, wheezing, staring directly at Martin.

For a moment he met her gaze. Her features seemed very small, squashed together by the loose, fleshy mounds of her cheeks. She had no chin, only a great swollen mass of neck, barely contained by the collar of her coat. Her **sparse** red hair was pinned back by a plastic barrette. And her blue eyes, though tiny, were sharp and penetrating, boring into Martin's face.

Abruptly he looked away from her to the numbers over the door. She didn't turn around. Was she still looking at him? His eyes slipped back to hers, then quickly away. She *was* still watching him. He wanted to close his eyes; he wanted to turn around and stare into the corner, but how could he? The elevator creaked down to twelve, down to eleven. Martin looked at his watch; he looked at the numbers again. They weren't even down to nine yet. And then, against his will, his eyes slipped back to her face. She was still watching him. Her nose tilted up; there was a large space between her nostrils and her upper lip, giving her a piggish look. He looked away again, clenching his teeth, fighting the impulse to squeeze his eyes shut against her.

She had to be crazy. Why else would she stare at him this way? What was she going to do next?

sparse
having very little; few

audibly
that can by heard

reluctantly
*not willingly;
hesitatingly*

She did nothing. She only watched him, breathing **audibly**, until the elevator reached the first floor at last. Martin would have rushed past her to get out, but there was no room. He could only wait as she turned—**reluctantly**, it seemed to him—and moved so slowly out into the lobby. And then he ran. He didn't care what she thought. He ran past her, outside into the fresh air, and he ran almost all the way to school. He had never felt such relief in his life.

He thought about her all day. Did she live in the building? He had never seen her before, and the building wasn't very big—only four apartments on each floor. It seemed likely that she didn't live there, and had only been visiting somebody.

But if she were only visiting somebody, why was she leaving the building at seven thirty in the morning? People didn't make visits at that time of day. Did that mean she *did* live in the building? If so, it was likely—it was a certainty—that sometime he would be riding with her on the elevator again.

He was apprehensive as he approached the building after school. In the lobby, he considered the stairs. But that was ridiculous. Why should he be afraid of an old lady? If he was afraid of her, if he let it control him, then he was worse than all the names they called him at school. He pressed the button; he stepped into the empty elevator. It stopped on three.

At least it's not fourteen, he told himself; the person she was visiting lives on fourteen. He watched the door slide open—revealing a green coat, a piggish face, blue eyes already fixed on him as though she knew he'd be there.

It wasn't possible. It was like a nightmare. But there she was, massively real. "Going up!" he said, his voice a **humiliating** squeak.

humiliating
very embarrassing

She nodded, her flesh quivering, and stepped on. The door slammed. He watched her pudgy hand move toward the buttons. She pressed, not fourteen, but eighteen, the top floor, one floor above his own. The elevator trembled and began its ascent. The fat lady watched him.

He knew she had gotten on at fourteen this morning. So why was she on three, going up to eighteen now? The only floors *he* ever went to were seventeen and one. What was she doing? Had she been waiting for him? Was she riding with him on purpose?

But that was crazy. Maybe she had a lot of friends in the building.

Or else she was a cleaning lady who worked in different apartments. That had to be it. He felt her eyes on him as he stared at the numbers slowly blinking on and off—slower than usual, it seemed to him. Maybe the elevator was having trouble because of how heavy she was. It was supposed to carry three adults, but it was old. What if it got stuck between floors? What if it fell?

They were on five now. It occurred to him to press seven, get off there, and walk the rest of the way. And he would have done it, if he could have reached the buttons. But there was no room to get past her without squeezing against her, and he could not bear the thought of any physical contact with her. He concentrated on being in his room. He would be home soon, only another minute or so. He could stand anything for a minute, even this crazy lady watching him.

Unless the elevator got stuck between floors. Then what would he do? He tried to push the thought away, but it kept coming back. He looked at her. She was still staring at him, no expression at all on her squashed little features.

When the elevator stopped on his floor, she barely moved out of the way. He had to inch past her, rubbing against her horrible scratchy coat, terrified the door would close before he made it through. She quickly turned and watched him as the door slammed shut. And he thought, *Now she knows I live on seventeen.*

"Did you ever notice a strange fat lady on the elevator?" he asked his father that evening.

"Can't say as I have," he said, not looking away from the television.

He knew he was probably making a mistake, but he had to tell somebody. "Well, she was on the elevator with me twice today. And the funny thing was, she just kept staring at me, she never stopped looking at me for a minute. You think . . . you know of anybody who has a weird cleaning lady or anything?"

"What are you so worked up about now?" his father said, turning impatiently away from the television.

"I'm not worked up. It was just funny the way she kept staring at me. You know how people never look at each other in the elevator. Well, she just kept looking at me."

"What am I going to do with you, Martin?" his father said. He sighed and shook his head. "Honestly, now you're afraid of some poor old lady."

assurance
*being positive of what
is true*

"I'm not afraid."

"You're afraid," said his father, with total **assurance**. "When are you going to grow up and act like a man? Are you going to be timid all your life?"

He managed not to cry until he got to his room—but his father probably knew he was crying anyway. He slept very little.

And in the morning, when the elevator door opened, the fat lady was waiting for him.

She was expecting him. She knew he lived on seventeen. He stood there, unable to move, and then backed away. And as he did so, her expression changed. She smiled as the door slammed.

William Sleator

He ran for the stairs. Luckily, the unlit flight on which he fell was between sixteen and fifteen. He only had to drag himself up one and a half flights with the terrible pain in his leg. His father was silent on the way to the hospital, disappointed and annoyed at him for being such a coward and a fool.

It was a simple fracture. He didn't need a wheelchair, only a cast and crutches. But he was **condemned** to the elevator now. Was that why the fat lady had smiled? Had she known it would happen this way?

At least his father was with him on the elevator on the way back from the hospital. There was no room for the fat lady to get on. And even if she did, his father would see her, he would realize how peculiar she was, and then maybe he would understand. And once they got home, he could stay in the apartment for a few days—the doctor had said he should use the leg as little as possible. A week, maybe— a whole week without going on the elevator. Riding up with his father, leaning on his crutches, he looked around the little cubicle and felt a kind of triumph. He had beaten the elevator, and the fat lady, for the time being. And the end of the week was very far away.

"Oh, I almost forgot," his father reached out his hand and pressed nine.

"What are you doing? You're not getting off, are you?" he asked him, trying not to sound panicky.

"I promised Terry Ullman I'd drop in on her," his father said, looking at his watch as he stepped off.

"Let me go with you. I want to visit her, too," Martin pleaded, struggling forward on his crutches.

But the door was already closing. "Afraid to be on the elevator alone?" his father said, with a look of total scorn. "Grow up, Martin." The door slammed shut.

Martin hobbled to the buttons and pressed nine, but it didn't do any good. The elevator stopped at ten, where the fat lady was waiting for him. She moved in quickly; he was too slow, too unsteady on his crutches to work his way past her in time. The door sealed them in; the elevator started up.

"Hello, Martin," she said, and laughed, and pushed the Stop button.

LITERARY LENS

Why do you think the lady pressed the Stop button on the elevator?

Muffin Explains Teleology to the World at Large

James Alan Gardner

*J*told my kid sister Muffin this joke.

There was this orchestra, and they were playing music, and all the violins were bowing and moving their fingers, except for this one guy who just played the same note over and over again. Someone asked the guy why he wasn't playing like the others and he said, "They're all looking for the note. I've found it."

Muffin, who's only six, told me the joke wasn't funny if you understood teleology.

I never know where she gets words like that. I had to go and look it up.

teleology [teli-oloji] *n.* doctrine or theory that all things or processes were designed to fill a purpose.

"Okay," I said when I found her again, "now I understand teleology. Why isn't the joke funny?"

"You'll find out next week," she said.

■■■■

I talked to Uncle Dave that night. He's in the university and real smart, even though he's going to be a minister instead of something interesting. "What's so great about teleology?" I said. He looked at me kind of weird so I explained, "Muffin's been talking about it."

"So have my professors," he said. "It's, uhh, you know, God has a purpose for everything, even if we can't understand it. We're all heading towards some goal."

"We took that in Sunday School," I said.

"Well, Jamie, we go into it in a bit more detail."

"Yeah, I guess."

He was quiet for a bit, then asked, "What's Muffin say about it?"

"Something big is happening next week."

"Teleologically speaking?"

"That's what she says."

Muffin was in the next room with her crayons. Uncle Dave called her in to talk and she showed him what she was working on. She'd colored Big Bird black. She has all these crayons and the only ones she ever uses are black and gray.

"What's happening next week?" Uncle Dave asked.

"It's a secret," she said.

"Not even a hint?"

"No."

"Little tiny hint? Please?"

She thought about it a minute, then whispered in his ear. Then she giggled and ran upstairs.

"What did she say?" I asked.

"She said that we'd get where we were going." He shrugged and made a face. We were both pretty used to Muffin saying things we didn't understand.

■■■■

The next day, I answered the front doorbell and found three guys wearing gray robes. They'd shaved their heads too.

"We are looking for her gloriousness," one of them said with a little bow. He had an accent.

"Uh, Mom's gone down the block to get some bread," I answered.

"It's okay," Muffin said, coming from the TV room. "They're here for me."

All three of the men fell face down on the porch making a kind of high whining sound in their throats. "You know these guys?" I asked.

"They're here to talk about teleology."

"Oh. Well, take them around to the backyard. Mom doesn't like people in the house when she's not here."

"Okay." She told the guys to get up and they followed her around the side of the house, talking in some foreign language.

■■■■

When Mom got home, I told her what happened and she half-ran to the kitchen window to see what was going on. Muffin was sitting on the swing set and the guys were cross-legged on the ground in front of her, nodding their heads at every word she spoke. Mom took a deep breath, the way she does just before she's going to yell at one of us, then **stomped** out the back door. I was sure she was going to shout at Muffin, but she bent over and talked quiet enough that I couldn't hear from inside the house. Muffin talked and Mom talked and one of the bald guys said something, and finally Mom came in all pale-looking.

stomped
walked heavily and with purpose

"They want lemonade," she said. "Take them out some lemonade. And plastic glasses. I'm going to lie down." And she went upstairs.

I took them out a pitcher of lemonade. When I got there, one of the bald guys got up to meet me and asked Muffin, "Is this the boy?"

She said yes.

"Most wondrous, most wondrous!"

He put both hands on my shoulders as if he was going to hug me, but Muffin said, "You'll spill the lemonade." He let me go, but kept staring at me with his big, weepy, white eyes.

"What's going on?" I asked.

"The **culmination** of a thousand thousand years of aimless wandering," the guy said.

culmination
the highest point

"Not aimless," Muffin cut in.

"Your pardon," he answered, quickly lowering his head. "But at times it seemed so."

"You'll be in the temple when it happens," Muffin said to him.

"A million praises!" he shouted, throwing himself flat-faced on the ground. "A billion trillion praises!" And he started to cry into our lawn. The other two bowed in the direction of our garage, over and over again.

"You want to pour me a glass of that?" Muffin said to me.

■ ■ ■ ■

The next day, Muffin told me I had to take her down to the boatyards. I said, "I don't have to do anything."

"Shows how much you know," she answered. "You don't know anything about teleology or fate or anything."

"I know how to cross streets and take buses and all, which is more than I can say for some people."

"I have ten dollars," she said, pulling a bill out of the pocket of her jeans.

That surprised me. I mean, I maybe have ten dollars in my pocket twice a year, just after Christmas and just after my birthday. "Where'd you get the money?" I asked.

"The monks gave it to me."

"Those bald guys?"

"They like me."

"Geez, Muffin, don't let Mom know you took money from strangers. She'd have a fit."

"They aren't strangers. They're the Holy Order of the Imminent Eschaton[1]—the Muffin Chapter."

"Oh, go ahead, lie to me."

"You want the ten dollars or not?"

Which wasn't what I ended up with, because she expected me to pay the bus fare out of it.

■■■■

When we got to the boatyards, I thought we'd head right down to the water, but Muffin just took out a piece of paper and stood there frowning at it. I looked over her shoulder and saw it was torn from a map of the city. There was a small red X drawn in at a place about a block from where we were. "Where'd you get that? The monks?"

"Mm-hm. Is this where we are?" She pointed at a corner. I looked and moved her finger till it pointed to the right place. "You should learn to read some time, Muffin."

She shook her head. "Might wreck my **insight**. Maybe after."

I pointed down the street. "If you want to go where X marks the spot, it's that way."

We walked along the sailboats and yachts and things on one side, and warehouses on the other. The buildings looked pretty run down, with brown smears of rust dripping down from their metal roofs, and lots of broken windows covered with plywood or cardboard. It was a pretty narrow street and there was no sidewalk, but the only traffic we saw was a Shell oil truck coming out of the Marina a ways ahead and it turned off before it got to us.

When we reached the X spot, the only thing there was another warehouse. Muffin closed her eyes for a second, then said, "Around the back and up the stairs."

"I bet there are rats around the back," I said.

"I bet there aren't."

"You go first."

"Okay." She started off down an alley between the one warehouse and the next. There was a lot of broken glass lying around and grass growing up through the pavement.

insight
the ability to under-stand things that are hidden or hard to see

---

1 **Holy Order . . . Eschaton:** a belief system concerned with the events of the end of the world

James Alan Gardner

"I bet there are snakes," I said, following her.

"Shut up, Jamie," she said.

■■■■

The back was only a strip of weeds about two yards wide, stuck between the warehouse and a chain-link fence. Halfway along, there was a flight of metal steps like a fire escape leading up to the roof. They creaked a bit when you walked on them, but didn't wobble too badly.

On the roof we found a really weird looking airplane. Or boat. Or train. Or wagon. Anyway, it had wings and tail like an airplane, but its body was built like a boat, a bit like the motorboat up at the cottage, but bigger and with those super-fat padded chairs like maybe astronauts sit in. The whole thing sat on a cart, but the cart's wheels were on the near end of a train track that ran the length of the roof and off the front into the street.

"What is this thing?" I asked.

"The monks made it for me," Muffin said, which didn't answer my question. She climbed up a short metal ladder into the plane and rummaged about in a cupboard in the rear wall. I followed her and watched her going through stuff inside. "Peanut butter. Bread. Kool-Aid. Water. Cheese. Diet Coke. What's this?" she said, handing me back a roll of something in gold plastic wrapping.

I opened one end and sniffed. "Liverwurst," I said.

"Is that like liver?" She made a face.

"No, it's sort of like peanut butter, but made from bologna."

"Weird. Do you see any hot dogs?"

I looked in the cupboard. "Nope."

"I should phone the monks. We need hot dogs."

"What for?"

She ignored me. "Is there anything else you'd want if you knew you were going to be away from home for a few days?"

"Cheerios and bacon."

She thought about that. "Yeah, you're right."

"And Big Macs."

She gave me a look like I was a moron. "Of course, dummy, but the monks will bring them just before we leave."

"We're going on a trip?"

"We're on a trip now. We're going to *arrive*."

■■■■

physics
the science of how the universe works

Early the next morning, Dr. Hariki showed up on our doorstep all excited. He works with my dad at the university. My dad teaches **physics**; he works with lasers[2] and everything. Dr. Hariki is in charge of the big telescope on the top of the Physics building, and he takes pictures of stars.

"What's up?" Dad asked.

"You tell me," Dr. Hariki said, spreading out a bunch of photographs on the coffee table.

Dad picked up a picture and looked at it. Turned it over to check out the date and time written on the back. Sorted through the stack of photos till he found whatever he was looking for and compared the two. Held the two together side by side. Held one above the other. Put them side by side again. Closed his right eye, then quick closed his left and opened his right. Did that a couple of times. Picked up another pair of photos and did the same.

Muffin came into the room with a glass of orange juice in her hand. "Looks more like a dipper now, doesn't it?" she said without looking at the pictures.

Dad and Dr. Hariki stared at her. "Well, it was a bit too spread out before, wasn't it?" she asked. "Don't you think it looks better now?"

"Muffin," Dad said, "we're talking about stars . . . suns. They don't just move about to make a nicer pattern."

"No, but if they're going to stop moving, you might as well make sure they look like a dipper in the end. Anything else is just sloppy. I mean, really."

She walked off into the TV room and a moment later we heard the *Sesame Street* theme song.

After a long silence, Dr. Hariki picked up one of the photographs and asked, all quiet, "Something to do with entropy?"[3]

"I think it's teleology," I said.

■ ■ ■

That night Uncle Dave was over for Sunday supper. Mom figures that Uncle Dave doesn't eat so good in residence,[4] so she feeds him a roast of something every Sunday. I think this is a great idea, except

---

2 **lasers:** high-powered beams of light
3 **entropy:** the belief that everything naturally tends toward disorder and chaos
4 **in residence:** on campus at the university

that every so often she serves squash because she thinks it's a delicacy. Lucky for us, it was corn season so we had corn on the cob instead.

After supper we all played Monopoly and I won. Uncle Dave said it made a nice family picture, us all sitting around the table playing a game. "Some day, kids," he said, "you're going to like having times like this to remember. A perfect frozen moment."

"There are all kinds of perfect frozen moments," Muffin said, and she had that tone in her voice like she was eleventy-seven years old instead of six. "Right now, people all over the world are doing all kinds of things. Like in China, it's day now, right Dad?"

"Right, Muffin."

"So there are kids playing tag and stuff, and that's a perfect moment. And maybe there's some bully beating up a little kid, and punching him out right now." She banged her Monopoly piece (the little metal hat) when she said 'now.' "And that's a perfect moment because that's what really happens. And bus drivers are driving their buses, and farmers are milking their cows, and mommies are kissing daddies, and maybe a ship is sinking some place. If you could take pictures of everyone right now, you'd see millions of perfect little frozen moments, wouldn't you?"

Uncle Dave patted Muffin's hand. "Out of the mouths of babes . . . I'm the one who's studying to appreciate the great wonders of Life, and you're the one who reminds me. Everything is perfect all the time, isn't it, Muffin?"

"Of course not, dummy," she answered, looking at Uncle Dave the way she did when he tried to persuade her he'd pulled a dime out of her ear. She turned around in her chair and reached over to the buffet to get the photograph they'd taken of her kindergarten class just before the summer holidays started. "See?" she said, pointing. "This is Bobby and he picks his nose all the time, and he's picking his nose here, so that's good. But this is Wendy, with her eyes closed cuz she was blinking. That's not perfect. Wendy cries every time she doesn't get a gold star in spelling, and she knows three dirty words, and she always gives Matthew the celery from her lunch, but you can't tell that from the picture, can you? She's just someone who blinked at the wrong time. If you want someone who should be blinking, it should be dozy old Peter Morgan who's fat and sweats and laughs funny."

Uncle Dave scratched his head and looked awkward for a bit, then said, "Well, Muffin, when you put it like that . . . yes, I suppose there are always some things that aren't aesthetically[5] pleasing . . . I mean, there are always some things that don't fit properly, as you say."

"Not always," she said.

"Not always? Some day things are just suddenly going to be right?" Uncle Dave asked.

Muffin handed me the dice and said, "Your turn, Jamie. Bet you're going to land in jail."

■■■■

Next morning, Muffin joggled my arm to wake me up. It was so early that the sun was just starting to rise over the lake. "Time to go down to the boatyards."

"Again?"

"Yep. This time for real." So I got up and dressed as quietly as I could. By the time I got down to the kitchen, Muffin had made some peanut butter and jam sandwiches, and was messing about with the waxed paper, trying to wrap them. She had twice as much paper as she needed and was making a botch of things.

"You're really clueless sometimes," I said, whispering so Mom and Dad wouldn't hear. I shoved her out of the way and started wrapping the sandwiches myself.

"When I rule the world, there won't be any waxed paper," she sulked.

■■■■

We were halfway down to the bus stop when Uncle Dave came running up behind us. He had been staying the night in the guest room and I suppose he heard us moving around. "Where do you think you're going?" he asked, and he was a bit mad at us.

"Down to the boatyards," Muffin said.

"No, you aren't. Get back to the house."

"Uncle Dave," Muffin said, "it's time."

"Time for what?"

"The Eschaton."

---

5 **aesthetically:** attractively

James Alan Gardner

"Where do you pick up these words, Muffin? You're talking about the end of the world."

"I know." The first bus of the day was just turning onto our street two corners down. "Come to the boatyards with us, Uncle Dave. It'll be okay."

Uncle Dave thought about it. I guess he decided it was easier to give in than fight with her. That's what I always think too. You can't win an argument with her, and if you try anything else, she bites and scratches and uses her knees. "All right," Uncle Dave said, "but we're going to phone your parents and tell them where you are, the first chance we get."

■ ■ ■ ■

"So talk to me about the Eschaton," Uncle Dave said on the bus. We were the only ones on it except for a red-haired lady wearing a Donut Queen uniform.

"Well," Muffin said, thinking things over, "you know how Daddy talks about everything moving in astronomy?[6] Like the moon goes around the sun and the sun moves with the stars in the galaxy and the galaxy is moving too?"

"Yes . . ."

"Well, where is everything going?"

Uncle Dave shrugged. "The way your father tells it, everything just moves, that's all. It's not going anywhere in particular."

"That's stupid. Daddy doesn't understand teleology. Everything's heading for where it's supposed to end up."

"And what happens when things reach the place where they're supposed to end up?"

Muffin made an exasperated face. "They *end up* there."

"They stop?"

"What else would they do?"

"All the planets and the stars and all?"

"Mm-hm."

"People too?"

"Sure."

Uncle Dave leaned his head against the window like he was tired

---

6 **astronomy:** the study of objects outside of Earth's atmosphere, such as the stars and other planets

and sad. Maybe he was. The sun was coming up over the housetops now. "Bus drivers driving their buses," he said softly, "and farmers milking their cows . . . the whole world like a coffee table book."

"I think you'd like to be in a church, Uncle Dave," Muffin said. "Or maybe walking alone along the lakeshore."

"Maybe," he smiled, all sad. Then he looked my sister right in the eye and asked, "Who are you, Muffin?"

"I'm me, dummy," she answered, throwing her arms around his neck and giving him a kiss.

■■■■

He left us in front of the warehouse by the lake. "I'm going to walk down to the Rowing Club and back." He laughed a little. "If I get back, Muffin, you are going to get such a spanking . . ."

"Bye, Uncle Dave," she said, hugging him.

I hugged him too. "Bye, Uncle Dave."

"Don't let her do anything stupid," he said to me before heading down the street. We watched for a while, but he didn't turn back.

■■■■

Up on the warehouse roof, there was a monk waiting with a McDonald's bag under his arm. He handed it to Muffin, then kneeled. "Bless me, Holy One."

"You're blessed," she said after looking in the bag. "Now get going to the temple or the airport or something. There's only about ten minutes left."

The monk hurried off, singing what I think was a hymn. We got into the plane-boat and I helped Muffin strap herself into one of the big padded seats. "The thing is," she said, "when the earth stops turning, we're going to keep on going."

"Hey, I know about **momentum**," I answered. I mean, Dad *is* a physicist.

"And it's going to be real fast, so we have to be sure we don't run into any buildings."

"We're going to shoot out over the lake?"

"We're high enough to clear the tops of the sailboats, then we just fly over the lake until we're slow enough to splash down. The monks got scientists to figure everything out."

momentum
the tendency of an object to keep moving in the same way

James Alan Gardner

I strapped myself in and thought about things for a while. "If we go shooting off real fast, isn't it going to hurt? I mean, the astronauts get all pressed down when they lift off . . ."

"Geez!" Muffin groaned. "Don't you know the difference between momentum and **acceleration**? Nothing's happening to us, it's everything else that's doing weird stuff. We don't feel a thing."

"Not even the wind?"

"The air has the same momentum we do, dummy."

I thought about it some more. "Aren't the buildings going to get wrecked when the earth stops?"

"They're going to stop too. Everything's just going to freeze except us."

"The air and the water are going to freeze too?"

"In spots. But not where we're going."

"We're special?"

"We're special."

acceleration
gathering speed; going faster

■■■■

Suddenly there was a roar like roller coaster wheels underneath us and for a moment I was pressed up against the straps holding me down on the seat. Then the pressure stopped and there was nothing but the sound of the wind a long way off. Over the side of the boat I could see water rushing by beneath us. We were climbing.

"Muffin," I asked. "Should one of us maybe be piloting this thing?"

"It's got a gyroscope[7] or something. The monks worked absolutely everything out, okay?"

"Okay."

A long way off to the right, I could see a lake freighter with a curl of smoke coming out of its stack. The smoke didn't move. It looked neat. "Nice warm day," I said.

After a while, we started playing car games to pass the time.

■■■■

The sun shone but didn't move. "If the sun stays there forever," I asked, "Won't it get really hot after a while?"

"Nah," Muffin answered. "It's some kind of special deal. I mean,

---

7 **gyroscope:** an object with spinning wheels that create a force capable of strong movement

it's not the same if you set up a nice picture of a park full of kids and then it gets hot as Mercury."

"Who's going to know?"

"It's not the same," she insisted.

■■■■

"How can we see?"

"What do you mean?"

"Well, is the light moving or what?"

"It's another special deal."

That made sense. From the way Dad talked about physics, light was always getting special deals.

■■■■

The water below us gradually stopped racing away so fast and we could sometimes see frozen whitecaps on the peaks of frozen waves. "Suppose we land on frozen water," I said.

"We won't."

"Oh. Your turn."

"I spy with my little eye something that begins with B." Right away I knew she meant the Big Macs, but I had to pretend it was a toughie. You have to humor little kids.

■■■■

We splashed down within sight of a city on the far side of the lake. It was a really good splash, like the one on the Zoomba Flume ride when you get to the bottom of the big, long, water chute. Both of us got drenched. I was kind of sad there was no way to do it again.

Then I thought to myself, maybe if we were getting a special deal on air and water and heat and all, maybe we'd get a special deal on the Zoomba Flume too.

We unstrapped ourselves and searched around a bit. Finally, we found a lid that slid back to open up a control panel with a little steering wheel and all. We pushed buttons until an inboard motor started in the water behind us, then took turns driving towards shore. Every now and then we'd see a gull frozen in the sky, wings spread out and looking great.

We put in at a public beach just outside the city. It had been early in the day and the only people in sight were a pair of joggers on a grassy ridge that ran along the edge of the sand. The man wore only track shorts and sunglasses; the woman wore red stretch pants, a T-shirt, and a headband. Both had Walkmans and were stopped in midstride. Both had deep dark tans and, as Muffin pointed out, a thin covering of sweat.

I wanted to touch one to see what they felt like, but when my finger got close, it bumped up against an invisible layer of frozen air. The air didn't feel like anything, it was just solid stuff.

Down at one end of the beach, a teenage girl was frozen in the act of unlocking the door to a snack stand. We squeezed past her and found out that we could open the freezer inside. Muffin had a couple of Popsicles, I had an ice cream sandwich, and then we went swimming.

■■■■

Lying out in the sun afterwards, I asked Muffin what was going to happen next.

"You want to go swimming again?" she asked.

"No, I mean after."

"Let's eat," she said, dragging me back towards the boat.

"You can't wiggle out of it that easy," I told her. "Are we the only ones left?"

"I think so."

"Then are we going to freeze too?"

"Nope. We got a special deal."

"But it seems pretty stupid if you ask me. Everything's kind of finished, you know? Show's over. Why are we still hanging around?"

"For a new show, dummy."

"Oh," that made sense. "Same sort of thing?"

"We'll see."

"Oh. Where do *we* fit in?"

Muffin smiled at me. "You're here to keep me company."

"And what are you here for?"

"Everything else. Get me a sandwich."

So I reached down into the basket we'd brought and pulled one out. It was inside a plastic sandwich bag. "Didn't we put these in wax paper?" I asked.

Muffin smiled.

Turn! Turn! Turn!
(To Everything There Is a Season)

adaptation and music by Pete Seeger
words from the Book of Ecclesiastes

To ev'rything
There is a season
And a time for ev'ry purpose under
    heaven.

To ev'rything (turn, turn, turn)
There is a season (turn, turn, turn)
And a time for ev'ry purpose under
    heaven.

A time to be born, a time to die;
A time to plant, a time to reap;
A time to kill, a time to heal;
A time to laugh, a time to weep.

To ev'rything (turn, turn, turn)
There is a season (turn, turn, turn)
And a time for ev'ry purpose under
    heaven.

A time to build up, a time to break
    down;
A time to dance, a time to mourn;
(There is) a time to cast away stones
A time to gather stones together.

To ev'rything
There is a season
And a time for ev'ry purpose under
    heaven.

A time to gain, a time to lose;
A time to **rend**, a time to sew;
A time to love, a time to hate;
A time for peace . . . I swear it's not
    too late.

To ev'rything
There is a season
And a time for ev'ry purpose under
    heaven.

rend
tear apart;
break

LITERARY LENS
How do Muffin's beliefs
    differ from those
presented in the song?

The Wife's Story

Ursula K. Le Guin

*H*e was a good husband, a good father. I don't understand it. I don't believe in it. I don't believe that it happened. I saw it happen but it isn't true. It can't be. He was always gentle. If you'd have seen him playing with the children, anybody who saw him with the children would have known that there wasn't any bad in him, not one mean bone. When I first met him he was still living with his mother over near Spring Lake, and I used to see them together, the mother and the sons, and think that any young fellow that was that nice with his family must be one worth knowing. Then one time when I was walking in the woods I met him by himself coming back from a hunting trip. He hadn't got any game at all, not so much as a field mouse, but he wasn't cast down about it. He was just larking[1] along enjoying the morning air. That's one of the things I first loved about him. He didn't take things hard, he didn't grouch and whine when things didn't go his way. So we got to talking that day.

And I guess things moved right along after that, because pretty soon he was over here pretty near all the time. And my sister said—see, my parents had moved out the year before and gone south, leaving us the place—my sister said, kind of teasing but serious, "Well! If he's going to be here every day and half the night, I guess there isn't room for me!" And she moved out—just down the way. We've always been real close, her and me. That's the sort of thing doesn't ever change. I couldn't ever have got through this bad time without my sis.

Well, so he came to live here. And all I can say is, it was the happy year of my life. He was just purely good to me. A hard worker and never lazy, and so big and fine-looking. Everybody looked up to him, you know, young as he was. Lodge Meeting nights, more and more often they had him to lead the singing. He had such a beautiful voice, and he'd lead off strong, and the others following and joining in, high voices and low. It brings the shivers on me now to think of it, hearing it, nights when I'd stayed home from meeting when the children was babies—the singing coming up through the trees there, and the moonlight, summer nights, the full moon shining. I'll never hear anything so beautiful. I'll never know a joy like that again.

---

1 **larking:** engaging in harmless fun

It was the moon, that's what they say. It's the moon's fault, and the blood. It was in his father's blood. I never knew his father, and now I wonder what become of him. He was from up Whitewater way, and had no kin around here. I always thought he went back there, but now I don't know. There was some talk about him, tales, that come out after what happened to my husband. It's something runs in the blood, they say, and it may never come out, but if it does, it's the change of the moon that does it. Always it happens in the dark of the moon. When everybody's home and asleep. Something comes over the one that's got the curse in his blood, they say, and he gets up because he can't sleep, and goes out into the glaring sun, and goes off all alone—drawn to find those like him.

And it may be so, because my husband would do that. I'd half rouse and say, "Where you going to?" and he'd say, "Oh, hunting, be back this evening," and it wasn't like him, even his voice was different. But I'd be so sleepy, and not wanting to wake the kids, and he was so good and responsible, it was no call of mine to go asking "Why?" and "Where?" and all like that.

So it happened that way maybe three times or four. He'd come back late, and worn out, and pretty near cross for one so sweet-tempered—not wanting to talk about it. I figured everybody got to bust out now and then, and nagging never helped anything. But it did begin to worry me. Not so much that he went, but that he come back so tired and strange. Even, he smelled strange. It made my hair stand up on end. I could not **endure** it and I said, "What is that— those smells on you? All over you!" And he said, "I don't know," real short, and made like he was sleeping. But he went down when he thought I wasn't noticing and washed and washed himself. But those smells stayed in his hair, and in our bed, for days.

And then the awful thing. I don't find it easy to tell about this. I want to cry when I have to bring it to my mind. Our youngest, the little one, my baby, she turned from her father. Just overnight. He come in and she got scared-looking, stiff, with her eyes wide, and then she begun to cry and try to hide behind me. She didn't yet talk plain but she was saying over and over, "Make it go away! Make it go away!"

The look in his eyes, just for one moment, when he heard that. That's what I don't want ever to remember. That's what I can't forget.

endure
continue to bear; tolerate

The look in his eyes looking at his own child.

I said to the child, "Shame on you, what's got into you?"—scolding, but keeping her right up close to me at the same time, because I was frightened too. Frightened to shaking.

He looked away then and said something like, "Guess she just waked up dreaming," and passed it off that way. Or tried to. And so did I. And I got real mad with my baby when she kept on acting crazy scared of her own dad. But she couldn't help it and I couldn't change it.

He kept away that whole day. Because he knew, I guess. It was just beginning dark of the moon.

It was hot and close inside, and dark, and we'd all been asleep some while, when something woke me up. He wasn't there beside me. I heard a little stir in the passage, when I listened. So I got up, because I could bear it no longer. I went out into the passage, and it was light there, hard sunlight coming in from the door. And I saw him standing just outside, in the tall grass by the entrance. His head was hanging. Presently he sat down, like he felt weary, and looked down at his feet. I held still, inside, and watched—I didn't know what for.

And I saw what he saw. I saw the changing. In his feet, it was, first. They got long, each foot got longer, stretching out, the toes stretching out and the foot getting long, and fleshy, and white. And no hair on them.

The hair begun to come away all over his body. It was like his hair fried away in the sunlight and was gone. He was white all over, then, like a worm's skin. And he turned his face. It was changing while I looked. It got flatter and flatter, the mouth flat and wide, and the teeth grinning flat and dull, and the nose just a knob of flesh with nostril holes, and the ears gone, and the eyes gone blue—blue, with white rims around the blue—staring at me out of that flat, soft, white face.

He stood up then on two legs.

I saw him, I had to see him, my own dear love, turned into the hateful one.

I couldn't move, but as I crouched there in the passage staring out into the day I was trembling and shaking with a growl that burst out into a crazy, awful howling. A grief howl and a terror howl and a calling howl. And the others heard it, even sleeping, and woke up.

It stared and peered, that thing my husband had turned into, and shoved its face up to the entrance of our house. I was still bound by mortal fear, but behind me the children had waked up, and the baby was whimpering. The mother anger come into me then, and I snarled and crept forward.

The man thing looked around. It had no gun, like the ones from the man places do. But it picked up a heavy fallen tree-branch in its long white foot, and shoved the end of that down into our house, at me. I snapped the end of it in my teeth and started to force my way out, because I knew the man would kill our children if it could. But my sister was already coming. I saw her running at the man with her head low and her mane high and her eyes yellow as the winter sun. It turned on her and raised up that branch to hit her. But I come out of the doorway, mad with the mother anger, and the others all were coming answering my call, the whole pack gathering, there in that blind glare and heat of the sun at noon.

LITERARY LENS

How would you characterize the wife's description of her husband's transformation?

The man looked round at us and yelled out loud, and brandished the branch it held. Then it broke and ran, heading for the cleared fields and plowlands, down the mountainside. It ran, on two legs, leaping and weaving, and we followed it.

I was last, because love still bound the anger and the fear in me. I was running when I saw them pull it down. My sister's teeth were in its throat. I got there and it was dead. The others were drawing back from the kill, because of the taste of the blood, and the smell. The younger ones were **cowering** and some crying, and my sister rubbed her mouth against her forelegs over and over to get rid of the taste. I went up close because I thought if the thing was dead the spell, the curse must be done, and my husband could come back— alive, or even dead, if I could only see him, my true love, in his true form, beautiful. But only the dead man lay there white and bloody. We drew back and back from it, and turned and ran, back up into the hills, back to the woods of the shadows and the twilight and the blessed dark.

cowering
cringing in fear or distress

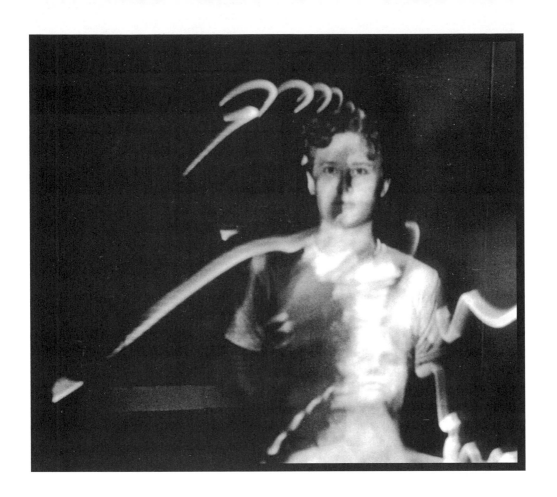

The Defender

Robert Lipsyte

*t*he Interscholastic Galactic Defender was licked awake by ice blue energy rays. Coach gently rocked his floating sleep slab. "Perfect day for the match, No. 1. Low humidity, no sunspots."

Coach tipped the slab and the Defender slid to the floor. He stepped out of his paper pajamas and onto the cleansing pedestal. A million beams refreshed his body, scraped his teeth, washed his hair, shaved his chin. The Defender then wrapped himself in a tunic of blue and gold, the school colors.

The Varsity was already at the training table. The Defender felt their admiration and envy as he took the empty seat at the head of the table.

He felt calm. His last high-school match. Across the table, his best friend, No. 2, winked. Good old No. 2, strong and steady. They had worked their way up the rankings ladder together since Basic School, rivals and teammates and buddies. It was almost over and he should have felt sad, but he didn't. One more match and he could be free to—

No. 4 caught his eye. He sensed that her feelings were the same. One more match and they wouldn't be numbers anymore, they would be Sophia and José, and they wouldn't have to guard their thoughts, or worse, turn them into darts and bombs.

Coach lifted a blue and gold competition thought helmet out of its recharging box and eased it down over the Defender's head. He fastened the chin strap, lengthened the antennae, and spun the dial to the lowest reception and projection power, just strong enough for noncompetitive thought in a small room.

For a moment, the Defender's mind was filled with a quivering crosscurrent of thought waves. There was a nasty pinprick from No. 7, only a sophomore but one of the toughest competitors in the galaxy, a star someday if he didn't burn himself out. There was a soothing velvet compress from No. 4, a hearty shoulder-banger from old No. 2.

The Defender cleared his mind for Coach, who was pacing the room. Psych talk time.

"As you know, the competition today, the Unified High School of the Barren Planets, is the first non-Earth team to ever reach the Galactic Finals. It wasn't expected and our scouting reports are incomplete."

LITERARY LENS

As you read, think about the Defender's strengths and weaknesses.

No. 7 thought a blue and gold fireball wrecking the barren planets.

"Overconfidence can beat you," snapped Coach. "These guys are tough—kids from the orphan ships, the prison planets, the pioneer systems. They've lived through things you've only screened."

The freshperson substitute, No. 8, thought, "What about their Greenie No. 1?"

"We don't use the word 'Greenie,'" said Coach. "It's a bias word."

"A Greenie?" sneered No. 7. "A hairy little round Greenie?"

"Don't judge a mind by its body," snapped No. 4, blushing when she saw the Defender's approving blinks.

No. 7 leaned back and flashed an image of himself wearing hairy green bedroom slippers. Only No. 8 laughed.

Coach said, "We respect the Challenger. It wouldn't be here if it wasn't good."

"'It'?" asked No. 2. "Male or female? Or a mixed gender?"

"We don't know anything about it," said Coach. "Except it's beaten everybody."

In silence, they drank their pregame meal—liquid fish protein and supercomplex carbs.[1]

meditation
*deep thought;
reflection*

vulnerable
*open to attack;
exposed*

Back on his slab, the Defender allowed his mind to wander. He usually spent his prematch **meditation** period reviewing the personality of his opponent—the character flaws, the gaps in understanding that would leave one **vulnerable** to a lightning thought jab, a volley of powerful images. But he knew nothing about today's opponent and little about Homo Vulgaris, mutant humans who had been treated badly ever since they began to appear after a nuclear accident. They were supposed to be stupid and unstable, one step above space ape. That one of them could actually have become No. 1 on the Power Thought Team of a major galactic high school was truly amazing. Either this one was very special, the Defender thought, or Earthlings hadn't heard the truth about these people.

He closed his eyes. He had thought he would be sentimental on the day of his last match, trying to remember every little detail. But he wished it were already over.

The wall-lights glowed yellow and he rose, dialing his helmet up to the warm-up level. He slipped into his competition robe. He began to flex his mind—logic exercises, picture bursts—as the

---

1 **carbs:** carbohydrates

elevator rose up through the Mental Athletics Department. When he waved to the chess team they stopped the clock to pound their kings on their boards in salute. The cyberspellers hand-signed cheers at him.

Officials were in the locker room running brain scans. The slightest trace of smart pills would mean instant disqualification. Everyone passed.

The Defender sat down next to No. 2. "We're almost there, Tombo." He flashed an image of the two of them lying in a meadow, smelling flowers.

Tombo laughed and bounced the image back, adding Sophia and his own girlfriend, Annie, to the meadow scene.

"Think sharp!" shouted Coach, and they lined up behind him in numerical order, keeping their minds blank as they trotted out into the roaring stadium. The Defender tipped his antennae toward his mother and father. He shook the Principal's hand.

"This is the most important moment of your life, No. 1. For the good of humanity, don't let those Unified mongrels outthink you."

The varsity teams from the Physical Athletics Department paraded by, four-hundred-pound football players and eight-foot basketball players and soccer players who moved on all fours. Some fans laughed at youngsters who needed to use their bodies to play. The Defender was always amazed at his grandfather's stories of the old days when the captain of the football team was a school hero.

It was in his father's time that cameras were invented to pick up brain waves and project them onto video screens for hundreds of thousands of fans in the arenas and millions more at home. Suddenly, kids who could think hard became more popular than kids who could hit hard.

"Let's go," roared Coach, and the first doubles team moved down into the Brain Pit.

The first match didn't last long. No. 7 and No. 4, even though they rarely spoke off the field, had been winning partners for three years. No. 7 swaggered to the midline of the court, **arrogantly** spinning his antennae, while No. 4 pressed her frail shoulders against the back wall. The Unified backcourter was a human female, but the frontcourter was a transspecies, a part-human lab creature ten feet tall and round as a cylinder.

arrogantly
showing too much pride; self-importantly

The Defender sensed the steely tension in the Unified back-courter's mind; she was set for a hellfire smash. He was proud of No. 4's first serve, a soft, curling thought of autumn smoke and hushed country lanes, an ancient thought filled with breeze-riffled lily ponds and the smell of fresh-cut hay.

Off-balance, the backcourter sent it back weakly, and No. 7 filled the lovely image with the stench of backpack rockets, war gases, and kill zone wastes and fireballed it back. The Unified brainies were still wrestling with the image when the ref tapped the screamer. Too long. One point for the home team.

As usual, No. 7 lost points for unnecessary roughness—too much death and destruction without a logical lead-up to it—but as the fans cheered wildly he and No. 4 easily won. Their minds had hardly been stretched; the Psycho-Chem Docs in the Relaxant Room would need little tranquilspray to calm them down. Good, thought the Defender; No. 4 would be out in time for his match.

Except for thinking about her, the Defender began to lose interest in the day. How many times had he waited to go down into a Pit and attack another mind? It had seemed exciting four years ago when Coach had pulled him out of a freshperson mental gym class and asked him to try out for the team. His tests had shown mental **agility**, vivid imagery, and, most important, telepathic[2] potential.

agility
alertness; quickness

It was the first thing he had ever been really good at. After he won a few matches, the popular kids began talking to him in the halls. Teachers asked him about the team. Letters began arriving at home from colleges owned by major corporations. His parents were so proud. He would be set for life.

But now it seemed like such a waste—fighting with thoughts instead of creating with them. Maybe he was just tired at the end of a long, tough season of defending his title. He thought about the meadow, with Sophia and Tombo and Annie. Instead of thoughts, they would throw an ancient toy around. It was called something like frisbill. Frisboo? Frisbee!

Coach tapped his helmet. "Pay attention."

barrage
*rapid outpouring;
bombardment*

No. 5 and No. 6 were staggering under a vicious **barrage**. They lost, and the standings at the end of the doubles were even, 1–1.

The crowd fell silent as No. 3 lost her singles match and the

---

2 **telepathic:** communication between minds without using speech

Robert Lipsyte

scoreboard blinked Visitors 2, Home 1. As No. 2 lumbered down to the Pit, the Defender sent an image of a victory wreath to him.

Good old No. 2, steady and even-tempered and sure of himself. Mentally tough. He might have been No. 1 on any other high-school team, but he never showed resentment. For a moment, the Defender almost wished that No. 2 would lose; then the score would be 3–1 and nothing No. 1 could do would be able to **salvage** the team match. No pressure—he could play the game just for himself. If he won, great, he'd be the first player in history to win the championship twice. If he lost he would only disappoint himself; he wouldn't be letting his team and his school—and humanity, according to the Principal—down.

But No. 2 won and the score was tied and it was up to him.

The No. 1 player for the Unified High School of the Barren Planets, the Interscholastic Galactic Challenger, was waiting for him in the Pit.

He (she? it?) looked like a green teddy bear. The Defender had never seen one in the flesh. He forced his mind to think of the creature only as an opponent.

The Defender served first, a probing serve to test the quickness of the Challenger. He used an image, from a poet who had written in the dying language called English, of a youth gliding over a hilltop at night to catch a star falling from a shower of milk-white light.

The Challenger slapped it right back; the star was nothing but a burnt-out children's sparkler made from fuel wastes. The youth on the hilltop was left with a sticky purple mess.

The Defender was surprised at how long he struggled with the sadness of the thought. A Judge hit the screamer. Unified led, 1–0.

Coach called time-out.

The falling-star image had been one of his best serves, a frequent ace. No one had ever handled it so well, turning the beautiful vision of humanity's **quest** for immortality into an ugly image of self-destruction.

They decided to switch tactics—to serve a fireball, No. 7 style. The Defender hurled a blazing tornado of searing gases and immeasurable heat. The Challenger's mind scooped it up like a hockey puck and plopped it into an ocean filled with icebergs.

Off-balance, the Defender tried to give himself time by thinking

salvage
save; recover

quest
search; mission to find

steaming vapors from the ocean, but the Challenger turned the vapors into great fleecy clouds that shaped themselves into mocking caricatures of famous Earthlings.

Desperately, the Defender answered with another fireball, and a Judge hit the screamer, calling it a Non Sequitur—the thought had not logically followed the Challenger's thought.

Unified led, 2–0.

The Defender served a complex image of universal peace: white-robed choruses in sweet harmony, endless vials of nutrient liquids flowing through galaxies aglow with life-giving stars, and hands—white, brown, green, orange, blue, black, red, and yellow—clasped.

dredges
earth movers; digging equipment

The Challenger slashed back with mineral **dredges** that drowned out the singing, lasers that poisoned the vials, and a dark night created by monster Earth shields that were purposely blocking the sunlight of a small planet. The clasping hands tightened until they crushed each other to bloody pulp.

The Defender was gasping at the bitter overload when he heard the screamer. He was down, 3–0. He had never lost his serve before.

The Challenger's first serve was vividly simple: black Earthling trooper boots stomping on thousands of green forms like itself.

Screamer.

The Judge called "Foul" and explained that the thought was too political—the Galactic League was still debating whether Earth colonists had trampled the rights of the hairy green offspring of the accident victims.

The Challenger's second serve was an image of black-gloved Earthling hands pulling apart Greenie families and shoving parents and children into separate cages.

Foul screamer.

The third serve was an image of Earth rocket exhausts aimed to burn down Greenie houses.

Foul screamer.

Tie score, 3–3. The Judge called an official time-out.

Coach's strong thumbs were working under the Defender's helmet. "Register a protest, right now. Don't let that little fur ball make a farce of the game."

"He's allowed to think freely," said the Defender. He wondered if the Challenger was a "he." Did it matter?

"He's using the game just to further his cause."

"Maybe he has a just cause."

"Doesn't matter," said Coach. "This is a game."

"I'll get him next period," said the Defender, trying to sound more confident than he was.

The second period was a repeat of the first. The Defender's best serves were **deflected**, twisted, sent back in bewildering patterns while the Challenger fouled on three more images of Earthling inhumanity. As the scoreboard glowed 6–6, the crowd buzzed angrily.

Coach said, "I order you to register a protest or you will never play for this high school again."

"It's my last game here."

"I'll see you don't get a college scholarship."

"I'm not sure I ever want to play this game again."

"Look, José"—Coach's voice became soft, wheedling[3]—"you are the best high-school player who ever—"

"Not anymore," said the Defender.

His helmet had never felt so tight—it was crushing his mind numb—as he trudged out for the last regulation period.

His three serves were weak, random flashes of thought that barely registered on the video screens. The Challenger easily re-created them into bursting thoughts that made the Defender's head spin. The Challenger's three serves were cluster bombs of cruelty and greed, horrible images of his people trapped in starvation and hopelessness because of Earth. They were all called foul.

It was 9–9 going into sudden-death overtime.

The Principal was waiting for No. 1 at the edge of the Pit. With him was the Chief Judge, the Superintendent of Earth High Schools, the Commissioner of the Mental Athletics Association, the Secretary-General of the Galactic League, and other important-looking faces he recognized from telepathé-news.

They all nodded as the Principal said, "You are the Defender. You have a responsibility to your school, your people, the planet. I order you to register a protest. We cannot be beaten by a foul little **malcontent** Greenie."

"It's only a game," said the Defender.

deflected
turned aside; redirected

malcontent
dissatisfied; unhappy

---

3 **wheedling:** influencing by flattery

"Maybe to you," snapped the Superintendent.

He strode back into the Pit.

The Challenger had never left; the Defender suddenly realized the little creature had no coach or friends. He had come up alone to stand and fight for himself and his people.

The warning buzzer sounded. Seconds to serve. Sudden death. The Defender would go first. He thought of his all-time best serves, the ones he saved for desperate situations, because coming up with them was so exhausting, so mind-bending that if they failed he was lost. He thought of the end of the world, of sucking black holes, of nightmares beyond hope.

Suddenly he knew what to do.

Robert Lipsyte

He served an image of a dry and dusty field on a lonely colony planet. The land was scarred and barren, filled with thousands of round green creatures standing hopelessly beyond barbed wire as a harsh wind ruffled their dry fur.

For the first time, the Challenger took the full five seconds to return serve. He was obviously puzzled. His return was his weakest so far, merely widening the image to include a ring of Earthlings, healthy and happy, pointing and laughing at the Greenies. It was just what the Defender had expected.

He took his full five, then sent a soft, slow image of two Earthlings leaving the circle to walk among the Greenies until they picked one whose hands they held.

They led it skipping into a golden meadow under a sunny blue sky. The Earthlings were José and Sophia, and the Greenie who danced and sang with them was the Challenger.

In the shocked silence of the arena, the Challenger took the thought as if it were a knockout punch, his mind wobbling.

He was unable to deal with the thought, the kindness in it, the fellowship.

He can't handle love, thought the Defender. What a way to win.

The Challenger was still struggling to answer when the screamer sounded.

The match was over, 10–9. The crowd was roaring, the Principal was dancing on his chair, the video screens were filled with the face of José Nuñez, the first ever to win the galactic championship twice.

They swarmed around him now, the important faces, calling his name, slapping at his helmet, but he pushed through, shutting out their congratulations, the screams of the crowd, the exploding scoreboard.

He made his way through to the Challenger, alone and quivering in the middle of the Pit. I don't even know its name, thought the Defender. "It"?

Sophia and Tombo were running toward them. They knew what José was thinking.

It was only a game.

But it might be a start.

LITERARY LENS

Why do you think the Defender was able to win?

RESPONDING TO UNIT SIX

Postcards from Beyond

REFLECTING

1. Did you enjoy the stories in this unit? Which one did you find the most interesting? Why?

2. In "Black Angel," the girl gives the Jersey Devil a new name and he becomes a new creature. In "The Elevator," Martin's fear increases with his father's scorn. To what extent do you think names and labels influence how people think about themselves?

3. The creatures in "Black Angel," "The Wife's Story," and "The Defender," have a rather low opinion of humans. If you were to have a cross-species conversation with one of them, how would you explain human behavior?

4. Many of the selections in this unit recount impossible circumstances or events. How can fantasy and science fiction apply to real life?

ANALYZING

5. All of the stories in this unit contain a good deal of fantasy along with healthy doses of reality. Choose two selections and compare them in terms of characters and events you never see in everyday life as well as characters and events that you do see.

6. Create a chart of mystery like the one below. Enter in the chart the titles of each of the five short stories in this unit. Identify mysteries that were unmasked as well as mysteries that remain in each selection.

Selection	Mystery Unmasked	Mystery Remaining
Black Angel		
The Elevator		
Muffin Explains Teleology to the World at Large	the reasons for Muffin's plans	what will take place next
The Wife's Story		
The Defender		

7. Authority figures in "Black Angel," "The Elevator," and "The Defender," all value something different than the main characters in those stories. What do each of these authority figures value?

8. The main characters in "Black Angel," "Muffin Explains Teleology to the World at Large," and "The Defender" all manage to expand their understanding beyond their ordinary lives. What events help them to expand their understanding?

9. **Active Reading** Did you stop at various points in this unit to **evaluate** what you were reading? Did you remember to stop once in a while to review and predict? How did using these Active Reading strategies help you?

DISCUSSING

People in different cultures (not to mention different worlds!) often have different perspectives on life. In some cases, they may come to view people outside their culture as wrong—or "the enemy." How can people build bridges to others without weakening ties to their own culture?

WRITING

Turn the World Upside Down A person's view of the world is influenced by many circumstances. Challenge your worldview by turning it upside down. What if cows raised you and your family for food? What if you could only breathe underwater? What if you could read from infancy, but you had to go to school to learn to crawl, sit, and walk? Write a fictional account of life in such an upside-down world.

Wish Upon a Star Many of the events depicted in this unit are impossible, so far as we know. If the impossible could be true, what kind of world would you imagine into being? Write about a universe you wish would exist. Include as many details as possible showing how people would live in your wonderful imaginary universe.

WORK IN PROGRESS

Perform Your Own Ending The ending of "The Elevator" is not clear. No one knows for sure what the lady is going to do—or even whether she is evil, as Martin fears. With friends, invent a series of possible endings to the story. Then perform them for the class.

Set It to Music "Turn! Turn! Turn!" sets to music a philosophy of life. Think about your own philosophy of life and jot down some of the details. Then put it to music by using a known tune or by creating a tune of your own.

Author Biographies

Arnold Adoff A celebrated biographer, anthologist, and poet, Adoff lives with his wife, Virginia Hamilton, also a writer, in Yellow Springs, Ohio. Throughout the year, Adoff travels around the country reading his poems to young audiences. He writes for young adults because he wants to "effect a change in American society. By the time we reach adulthood, we are closed and set in our attitudes." Adoff was awarded the 1988 National Council of Teachers of English Award for Excellence in Poetry for Children for his body of work. He is also recognized as one of the first cultivators of multiculturalism in American literature for young people. "Writing a poem," he says, "is making music with words and space." His most recent books are *Slow Dance Heartbreak Blues*, *Street Music*, and *Love Letters*.

Judie Angell If you can't find a book by Judie Angell, you may also want to search under the names Fran Arrick and Maggie Twohill. Born in 1937 in New York City, Angell's high school novels are written under the pen name "Fran Arrick." Her lighter, middle school books are under "Maggie Twohill." Her young adult novels are often based on experiences from her own life. *In Summertime It's Tuffy* relies on Angell's 15 years of being a camper and camp counselor. *One-Way to Ansonia*, a novel about a Jewish immigrant living in the U.S., is inspired by her grandmother's life. Angell is praised for her ability to combine serious emotions with humorous circumstances, and she has received several citations for Best Books for Young Adults.

Kathi Appelt When Kathi Appelt was in first grade, her teacher told her that she could see writing in Appelt's future. And it was! Her award-winning book *Just People & Paper/Pen/Poem: A Young Writer's Way to Begin* began as a "happy accident." Flattered by a gift of poems and stories from a class of ninth graders, Appelt wrote back, sending along more of her poems as a thank you. The correspondence went on for a year and led Appelt to write about the experience. She says that, for her, the only way to survive the solitary life of writing is to balance it with teaching, too. For beginning writers she offers this advice: "Read anything you can get your hands on and write every day—even if it's only a grocery list."

Dave Barry He believes that he'll never be funnier than dogs or the U.S. government, and the one message he'd like to send to today's teenagers is "Your hats are on backwards." A natural comedian, Barry's writing career began with short humor pieces that he wrote for his high school newspaper. Today his newspaper column is published in over 500 newspapers nationwide. Barry has written 23 books and won numerous awards, including the Pulitzer Prize for his 1988 book *Commentary*. His non-literary endeavors have included the CBS sitcom "Dave's World," based on two of his books, and playing lead guitarist in the rock band Rock Bottom Remainders, made up entirely of authors—including Stephen King and Amy Tan. Barry lives with his wife and two children in Miami, Florida.

Joan Bauer Raised in Illinois in the 1950s, Bauer grew up feeling "like a water buffalo at a tea party." She is now a graceful adult and the author of several comedic novels for young people. "I believe that humorous books teach young people to use laughter against the storms of life." Her early fascination with humor may also be attributed to her grandmother—a professional story-teller—and her mother—a high school English teacher. Bauer saw little of her father after her parents divorced, and his absence remained a source of pain into adulthood. Consequently, many of her stories contain characters that have complex, yet humorous relationships with their fathers. During a long recovery from an auto accident she was prompted to write *Squashed* in 1991. It was the humor in that story that helped her heal. "I have come to understand how deeply I need to laugh," she says. "It's like oxygen to me."

Rick Beyer The account of the war between Beyer's mother and grandmother over his eating a plate of peas was first heard as a radio broadcast in 1999. National Public Radio had extended an invitation to all listeners to send in a story that was short, true, and "sounded like fiction." Rick Beyer's story "A Plate of Peas" was chosen and read on the NPR program *All Things Considered*, and consequently included in the best-selling book *I Thought My Father Was God*. Rick Beyer lives in Lexington, Massachusetts.

Alberto Blanco Born in Mexico City, Mexico, in 1951, Blanco came to the U.S. in 1991 and taught at the University of California. In 1997 he was invited to Bellagio, Italy, to work as a translator for a theater company. Blanco has translated several books from Spanish into English, and published many of his own in both languages. Blanco's poems have been translated into English, French, German, Italian, Portuguese, Hungarian, and Russian. He has won countless awards for his work—most often his literature for children and young adults. Married with two children, he currently lives and teaches in El Paso, Texas.

Rick Book Born and raised on a wheat farm in Canada, Book didn't begin to write seriously until his forties. His first book for young adults, *Necking With Louise*, is about a 16-year old boy growing up on the prairie in the mid-1960s. "*Necking With Louise* shows how much I love where I come from," he says, though he admits he didn't always feel this way. After college, Book took a job at a small TV news station interviewing local residents about their lives. "The segments could be about some guy who caught frogs for a lab or hippies living in a mill making masks. It was the storytelling that I grew up with. . . ." Book has taught his two children to appreciate the richness of simple things. "My kids and I always look up when we go outside to see what the sky's up to, where the moon is and what stars are out. That comes with growing up on the prairies, being in touch with land and sky."

William J. Brooke Brooke wrote his first short story in second grade, and he continued to write them once he learned that it "impressed adults." In high school, Brooke learned that writing "could also impress girls." He handed out his outrageous stories to all of his crushes, until realizing that acting could impress a whole audience of girls at once. After high school, he worked for many years in the theater, doing everything from playing lead roles to writing musical scores. His first book of stories, *A Telling of the Tales*, grew from Brooke's own daydream, "I wonder what would happen if you put Paul Bunyon and Johnny Appleseed in the same room together?" The book won an American Library Association Notable Book Award. Brooke followed it up with *Untold Tales* in 1992 and *Teller of Tales* in 1994.

Rebecca Carroll Adopted as an infant, Carroll was raised by her father, an award-winning author, and her mother, an acclaimed painter. Carroll's 1997 book, *Sugar in the Raw: Voices of Young Black Girls in America*, was awarded the American Library Association's Award for Outstanding Nonfiction. "I know a lot about class issues . . . I know a lot about race, and what it's like to straddle both cultures. I write about what I know." Carroll has costarred in and written screenplays for movies, and she is a regular contributing editor to radio's *This American Life*. In 2000, she wrote a teleplay adaptation of Janet L. Waldron's memoir, *Giving Away Simone*. The book, written by her birthmother, whom she first met at age 11, tells the tale of their mother-daughter reunion and their following friendship of 20 years.

Alden R. Carter About teens, Carter says, "I find myself constantly impressed with their courage. Despite all the problems—both traditional and recently invented—that fill the teenage years, the vast majority not only survive, but triumph." Many of Carter's books focus on teens in such moments of crisis. Whether it's Carl coping with his mother's alcoholism in *Up Country* or Shar's struggle to accept her father's physical and emotional condition after a stroke in *Robodad*, Carter always creates realistic teens with realistic problems. Many of Carter's novels have been recognized by the American Library Association for their excellence.

Lucille Clifton Poet Laureate of Maryland from 1979 to 1982 as well as former Chancellor of the Academy of American Poets and two-time nominee for the Pulitzer Prize in poetry, Clifton believes that "I write about being human. If you have ever been human, I invite you to that place that we share." Clifton also writes children's books and historical nonfiction. You can find more of her work in her Everett Anderson series for children, and her volume of poems, *Good Times*. She currently serves as Distinguished Professor of Humanities at St. Mary's College of Maryland.

Judith Ortiz Cofer Born in Puerto Rico, Cofer grew up in New Jersey loving the literary works of those she calls "dead white people"—William Shakespeare, Virginia Woolf, and William Butler Yeats. Brought up as a Puerto Rican "Latina" in America, Cofer writes her poems, essays, and stories as a woman from two backgrounds. "Being both [Puerto Rican and American] makes me feel rich in cultures and languages." Cofer now lives in Georgia with her husband and daughter and teaches literature and creative writing at the University of Georgia in Athens.

Emily Dickinson Late at night, alone, Emily Dickinson wrote over 1,800 poems in her Massachusetts home. Only a handful of those poems were published in her lifetime. Born in 1830, Dickinson lived in a time when people rode in horse-drawn carriages, household duties filled a woman's days, and devotion to God and family were social mainstays. After her death in 1886, Dickinson's poetry found its place among the English-speaking world's literary treasures.

Paul Fleischman Readers of all ages can enjoy Paul Fleischman's books. His unique use of perspective (some of his poems are from the point of view of insects and birds), and the musical quality of his sentences make his books both interesting and accessible. Although Fleischman is the son of a children's book author, father Sid Fleischman, he says he had no plans to become a writer as a child. "My youth in Santa Monica, California, was spent not in libraries or curled up with a book, but at the beach, on the playground, in alleys, riding my bike." A talented pianist, he credits the lyrical sound of his writing to his interest in music. Many of his poems are written especially for reading aloud.

Robert Frost One of this country's most famous and well-respected poets, Robert Frost lived from 1874 to 1963 and won the Pulitzer Prize four times. He took as much pride in his farm as in his writing. Many of his poems revolve around country life and his deep appreciation of nature.

James Alan Gardner Gardner was one of those kids who was always writing. He helped write the script for a Star Trek parody/skit while in college and went on to write radio dramas, short stories, and novels after graduation. Gardner writes primarily science fiction and fantasy, and he has created whole new worlds (literally) of people, places, and things that come straight from his imagination. He credits Kurt Vonnegut, Jr., as having a great influence on his writing.

David Gifaldi Like many authors writing for young adults, David Gifaldi first became interested in books while a child himself. He credits his third grade teacher for introducing him to his favorite book to this day, *Tom Sawyer*. It wasn't until he was a substitute teacher that he found inspiration to write his first novel. "My father's in jail," a fifth-grade student said during sharing time, and Gifaldi used the shock and embarrassment he felt to write about a boy in similar circumstances in *One Thing for Sure*. Gifaldi says, "Growing up is hard. But it's also a time of wonder and discovery. Writing keeps me on my toes, wondering and discovering."

Stephen Gregg For the past twelve years running, Gregg's play *This Is a Test* has been the most-produced high school one-act in the country. About that play, Gregg says, "People have contacted me from all over the world to tell me about their productions." And about the Chinese that the characters speak at one point in the play, he acknowledges, "The Chinese isn't real. I made it up . . . it really embarrasses me that the Chinese isn't real. I'd change it if I could. Please feel free to make your own translations. (If you do so, send them to me, and I'll post them on the site: www.stephen-gregg.com/main.htm." Gregg received the 1994 International Thespians Founders Award for Service to Youth and Theatre.

Sara Henderson Hay Born in 1906, Hay had her first poem published as a ten-year-old. While in high school, many of her poems were published in her local newspaper, and in college she was the editor of the school magazine when she was only a freshman. By 1931, Hay was an established poet, and her poems were included in four anthologies that year. Two years later, her first full collection of poems, *Field of Honor*, was published. Over the next 20 years, she wrote two more books; her third, *The Delicate Balance*, won several prestigious prizes. In 1987 Hay died peacefully in her sleep with only one poem left unfinished at her desk.

Jim Heynen Born and raised in rural Iowa, Heynen is both proud of and fascinated by his roots. He claims that he lived in the last county in the state to get electricity, and he attended one of Iowa's last one-room schoolhouses before going away to college. A student of literature and the English Renaissance, Heynen is a writer-in-residence at colleges around the country. His best known titles include two novels, *Cosmos Coyote and William the Nice* and *Being Youngest*. His most recent project is an anthology called *Fishing for Chickens: Stories About Rural Youth*.

Langston Hughes The "Poet Laureate of Harlem" was born in Joplin, Missouri. Although he was a world traveler, Hughes considered Harlem home. Most famous for his poems, Hughes was one of the most versatile writers of the artistic movement known as the Harlem Renaissance. His writing is about "people up today and down tomorrow, working this week and fired the next, beaten and baffled, but determined not to be wholly beaten."

Angela Johnson Johnson decided in elementary school that she wanted to become a writer. "I don't believe the magic of listening to my teacher Mrs. Mitchell read stories after lunch will ever be repeated for me," she said in an interview for the African American Literature Book Club. Born in 1941, Johnson was surrounded by storytellers, especially her father and grandfather. "Book people came to life. They sat beside me in school during story time," she recounts. An enthusiastic poet during high school, she at first focused on writing books for preschool and primary grade children. Recently, however, she has successfully shifted to literature for young adults.

Jewel Kilcher Better known simply as "Jewel" to her music fans, Kilcher didn't start writing songs until she was 17. Born and raised on a farm in Homer, Alaska, Kilcher was given "workshops" in music, visual art, and writing by her mother. In the preface to her book, *A Night Without Armor: Poems*, she explains, "Long before I wrote my first song, words formed as poems in my journals; and poetry drives my song writing today." Kilcher never shies away from subjects that are difficult or painful.

Ron Koertge Ron Koertge has always been told that he "goes too far"—even in his writing. With humor that is sometimes absurd but always sharp as a knife, Koertge's work is rarely traditional or tame. He first took up a pen during graduate school, when he and a group of male friends formed a poetry group to replace their touch football team. His first novel was a success, but successive books were met with scorn. A friend suggested that he try his hand at kids' fiction. "I could write in first person and I could be a smarty pants! Who could resist an offer like that?" He currently teaches English at a city college in California.

Ursula K. Le Guin Le Guin describes her relationship with readers this way: "The writer cannot do it alone. The unread story is not a story; it is little black marks on wood pulp. The reader, reading it, makes it live." Le Guin has produced successful poetry and prose of all types: realistic fiction, fantasy, science fiction, children's books, young adult books, essays, screenplays, and verbal texts for musicians and performance artists. The author only started working on a computer in recent years, and doesn't use email or the Internet. A homebody who seldom goes on book tours, she has lived in the same Portland, Oregon, home for 40 years.

Robert Lipsyte A prizewinning author writing about a prizefighter, Robert Lipstye is the author of *The Contender*, a book based on his experiences as a sports writer following the career of boxing great Muhammad Ali. It has been required reading in many American schools for the past three decades. Praised as one of the very first realistic novels about contemporary teenagers in America, *The Contender* accomplishes what Lipsyte sets out to do when he writes. In his acceptance speech for the Margaret A. Edwards Award for Young Adult Literature in 2001, he described his goal this way: "I want to help adolescents recognize their role and importance in relationships, society, and the world."

Audre Lorde Born in 1934 to Caribbean immigrants, Audre Lorde started writing poetry at 12 and had her first poem published in *Seventeen* magazine while still in high school. Lorde's writing often reflects her struggle against social injustice. The author formed Sisterhood in Support of Sisters in South Africa in opposition to apartheid (a system that discriminated against people of color there). She also wrote many volumes of prose and poetry that speak out against the oppression of women. Late in life, Lorde was given the African name Gamba Adisa, meaning "Warrior: She Who Makes Her Meaning Clear." Lorde died of cancer in 1992. Her son, Jonathan Rollins, recalls a phrase Lorde used often—"We could lose. But we couldn't *not* fight."

Anne Mazer Anne Mazer's parents were both authors of children's books. Born in 1952, she followed in their footsteps. She learned to read at age four, and admits that she used to skip class in high school in order to walk the four miles to the library and read all day. When Mazer began writing picture books for young children, she looked to children for inspiration and new ideas. Later she expanded her work to include novels for young adults, such as the award-winning *Moose Street*. Mazer's books for older readers often showcase diverse characters that come from various economic and ethnic backgrounds.

Patrick F. McManus Humorist Patrick McManus claims that he went into writing because it was the only field for which he had all of the necessary elements: a typewriter, paper, envelopes, and postage stamps. He first began writing regularly while in college, hoping to avoid taking a "real" job. The author was already a professional writer of articles and essays before he began the humor writing for which he is now known. McManus one day decided to write something entertaining to clear his head. He submitted the result to *Field and Stream* magazine, which published it and sent him a check for $300. McManus made the calculations: $300 for an hour of leisurely and enjoyable work. It was settled. He has been a humor writer ever since.

Walter Dean Myers As a young person with a serious speech impediment, Myers discovered writing as a way to express himself. Having moved with foster parents to Harlem at age three, he grew up in a neighborhood very different from the criminal, violent Harlem now depicted on TV. Of his reading, Meyers has said, "Books took me, not so much to foreign lands and fanciful adventures, but to a place within myself that I have been exploring ever since. The public library was my most treasured place. I couldn't believe my luck in discovering that what I enjoyed most—reading—was free." His young adult novel *Scorpions* was a Newbery Honor Book.

Linda Pastan Poet Linda Pastan was born in New York in 1954. "By age 10 or 11," she says, "I knew I wanted to spend my life writing. But I don't think I knew that real people could be 'writers' until much later." Since then, she has published ten volumes of poetry, won countless prizes, and was named the poet laureate of Maryland from 1991 to 1994. Exploring the themes of family, children, the passage of time, and the beauty of nature, Pastan manages to make everyday life worth writing—and reading—about. *The San Francisco Review of Books* describes her as, "returning to the role of the poet as it served the human race for centuries: to fuel our thinking, show us our world in new ways, and to get us to feel more intensely about the ordinary."

Gary Paulsen At the age of 14, Gary Paulsen ran away from home and joined the circus. His taste for adventure led him to work as a farm hand, engineer, construction worker, truck driver, rancher, sailor, and dog trainer for the Iditarod, an Alaskan dogsled race. Some of these life experiences are reflected in the more than 175 books he has written for children and young adults. His novels *Hatchet*, *Dogsong*, and *The Winter Room* are all Newbery Honor Books. What keeps the author at his desk for up to 20 hours a day? As one biographer put it, "It is Paulsen's overwhelming belief in young people that drives him to write."

Susan Beth Pfeffer Pfeffer wrote her first story at age six—a romance between an Oreo cookie and a pair of scissors. Her first book, *Just Morgan*, was written while she was a 20-year-old college student. Since college, Pfeffer has averaged two books a year and has published over sixty books for children and young adults. She says, "For someone whose favorite subject was recess, this is professional heaven." Pfeffer's books range from humorous juvenile literature to serious young adult novels, such as *Family of Strangers*, which tells the story of a family coping with drug abuse.

Pete Seeger New York-born Pete Seeger has been a musician, songwriter, folklorist, environmentalist, labor activist, and peace advocate. Perhaps best known as an American folksinger, Seeger first came into the spotlight as a member of the band The Almanacs—a group whose songs were politically inspired and often controversial in the politically-charged 1950s. Seeger wrote some of the most beloved ballads of this era. "Where Have all the Flowers Gone?" and "Turn! Turn! Turn!" remain powerful reminders of the idealism and activism of the time. Still an outspoken advocate for social responsibility and change, Seeger continues to perform at benefit concerts for causes such as the protection of the environment.

William Sleator William Sleator, who wrote the popular novels *The Green Futures of Tycho*, *House of Stairs*, and *Interstellar Pig*, is considered one of the most original and offbeat science fiction writers for young adults. Though he is now an accomplished author, Sleator's first love was the piano. He wrote his first composition, a dark and morbid piano piece called "Guillotines in the Spring," in his early teens. He later toured with the orchestra of a ballet company in Europe after he dropped out of Harvard. When Sleator tried his hand at writing and stumbled upon science fiction, he knew he had found his perfect fit. The author divides his time between Boston and Thailand.

Gary Soto Soto grew up in a Mexican American family in Fresno, California. His novels, short stories, and poetry for both young people and adults reflect that heritage. He is one of the youngest poets to have his work appear in the *Norton Anthology of Modern Poetry*. His contribution to that volume comes from his book of autobiographical sketches, *Living Up the Street*. Soto's young adult novels include *Taking Sides* and *The Skirt*. He teaches creative writing at the University of California, Riverside, and is a member of the Royal Chicano Navy. His official Web site is www.garysoto.com.

Nancy Springer One of Nancy Springer's favorite sayings is, "Conform, go crazy, or become an artist." Born in the1950s, Springer spent her childhood working long hours at the motel her family owned. After becoming a wife and mother, she began writing as a creative outlet while suffering from depression. She says, "By becoming a writer—by becoming who I truly was—I became well and full again." Springer attracted attention for her first fantasy books, *The White Hart* and *The Silver Sun*. The author of 30 novels for young people, Springer gives this advice: "Hug a horse. Paint the porch cream and lavender. Eat Chinese food whenever possible. Put the old picture in a new frame. Take a bike ride. Go dancing. Believe in the power of dreams."

Patti Tana Tana is Professor of English and Coordinator of the Creative Writing Project at Nassau Community College (SUNY). She is also the Associate Editor of the *Long Island Quarterly* and the author of six books of poetry, most recently *Make Your Way Across This Bridge: New and Selected Writings* (Whittier Publications, Island Park, NY, 2003).

Alma Villanueva Villanueva was born and raised in the poorer parts of San Francisco, California. A woman of Spanish, Yaqui (an Indian people in Mexico), and German ancestry, Villanueva has often explored her roots in her work. She makes poetry out of ordinary life, highlighting the joys of womanhood, children, and sisterhood. Fellow author Janine Canan says of Villanueva's work, "She shows us . . . how to live every moment open to the heartbeat, the love-beat of the world." Villanueva currently lives in Santa Fe, New Mexico, and teaches in the creative writing program at Antioch University in Los Angeles, California.

Ron Wallace The author of several poetry books, including *Tunes for Bears to Dance To*, Wallace has loved poetry since childhood. As soon as he could read, he began memorizing lines of verse (many of his favorites are by Emily Dickinson). It wasn't until Wallace was "flat broke" and about to become a father, however, that his wife persuaded him to send the travel poems he had written during their yearlong journey in London to a publisher. It took eight years, but in 1982, the poems were finally published as *Plums, Stone, Kisses & Hooks*. Wallace is currently a professor of English and the Director of the Creative Writing Program at the University of Wisconsin—Madison.

Nancy Werlin A writer of suspense novels for young adults, Nancy Werlin finds it ironic that her career focuses on a stage of life that she disliked so much at the time. "I find it hilarious that I was desperate not to be a teenager, and yet, as a writer, I am forever fascinated by the teenage years," she says. As a teenager, she read more than a dozen books a week, and young adult literature is still what she enjoys reading most today. "I think suspense is the perfect form for YA novels," Werlin says. She believes that it is natural for young adults to enjoy suspense, because of the two feelings during the teen years of being "in between" and anticipating "what comes next." Werlin won an Edgar Award for her novel, *The Killer's Cousin*.

Budge Wilson Budge Wilson became an author in her early fifties, having already worked as a teacher, professional photographer, illustrator, and fitness instructor. She first turned to writing when photography became difficult for her because of vision problems. She says of writing, "I like it better than anything I've ever tried." Wilson has published over 20 books in her homeland of Canada, and her work has been translated into seven different languages. She has won countless awards, mostly for her short stories. "The Metaphor" won Second Prize in the Chatelaine Short Story contest in 1983.

Tim Wynne-Jones Born in England in 1948, Tim Wynne-Jones became a writer in a roundabout way. After studying visual arts for several years, he realized that it was the "story" of the image that truly interested him. He explains, "The word 'imagine' has the word 'image' in it, and what you want to give readers is an image in their heads." His books for young adults include *The Kinder Planets* and *The Maestro*. In addition to writing fiction, Wynne-Jones also illustrates books for other authors and takes on odd jobs for fun, such as penning the theme song for the television show "Fraggle Rock." He lives with his wife, author and calligraphy artist Amanda Lewis, and their three teenage children in Perth, Ontario.

Index of Titles and Authors

Acknowledgments

Text Credits "After the Divorce" by Jewel Kilcher from *A Night Without Armor: Poems*. Copyright © 1998 by Jewel Kilcher. Reprinted by permission of HarperCollins Publishers.

"Almost Ready:" by Arnold Adoff from *Slow Dance: Heartbreak Blues*. Copyright © 1995 by Arnold Adoff. Reprinted by permission of HarperCollins Publishers.

"Amir" by Paul Fleischman from *Seedfolks*. Copyright © 1997 by Paul Fleischman. Used by permission of HarperCollins Publishers.

"Ashes" by Susan Beth Pfeffer from *I Never Meant to Be*. Copyright © 1999 by Susan Beth Pfeffer. Reprinted by permission of the author.

"Black Angel" by Nancy Springer from *Orphans of the Night,* edited by Josepha Sherman. Copyright © 1995 by Nancy Springer. Reprinted by permission of Jean Naggar Literary Agency.

"Block Party—145th Street Style" by Walter Dean Myers from *145th Street: Short Stories*. Copyright © 2000 by Walter Dean Myers. Used by permission of Random House Children's Books, a division of Random House, Inc.

"Dawn" by Tim Wynne-Jones from *The Book of Changes*. Copyright © 1994 by Tim Wynne-Jones. Reprinted by permission of Orchard Books, an imprint of Scholastic, Inc.

"Dear Marsha" by Judie Angell from *Connections: Short Stories,* Donald R. Gallo, Editor. Copyright © 1989 by Judie Angell. Used by permission of Dell Publishing, a division of Random House, Inc.

"The Defender" by Robert Lipsyte from *Ultimate Sports,* Donald Gallo, Editor. Copyright © 1995 by Donald R. Gallo. Used by permission of Random House Children's Books, a division of Random House, Inc.

"The Dream Keeper" by Langston Hughes from *The Collected Poems of Langston Hughes*. Copyright © 1994 by The Estate of Langston Hughes. Used by permission of Alfred A. Knopf, a division of Random House, Inc.

"The Fitting of the Slipper" by William J. Brooke from *A Telling of the Tales*. Copyright © 1990 by William J. Brooke. Reprinted by permission of HarperCollins Publishers.

"Golden Glass" by Alma Luz Villanueva from *Hispanics in the United States: An Anthology of Creative Literature*. Copyright © 1982 by Alma Luz Villanueva. Reprinted by permission of Bilingual Press, Arizona State University, Tempe, AZ.

"in the inner city" by Lucille Clifton from *Good Woman: Poems and a Memoir 1960-1980*. Copyright © 1987 by Lucille Clifton. Reprinted by permission of BOA Editions, Ltd.

"Interview" by Sara Henderson Hay from *Story Hour*. Copyright © 1998 by The Board of Trustees of the University of Arkansas. Reprinted by permission of the University of Arkansas.

"Jared" by David Gifaldi from *Rearranging and Other Stories*. Copyright © 1998 by David Gifaldi. Reprinted by permission of Atheneum Books for Young Readers, an imprint of Simon & Schuster Children's Publishing Division.

"Josh" by Gary Paulsen from *My Life in Dog Years*. Copyright © 1998 by Gary Paulsen. Used by permission of Dell Publishing, a division of Random House, Inc.

"Kissing Tennessee" by Kathi Appelt from *Kissing Tennessee and Other Stories From the Stardust Dance*. Copyright © 2000 by Kathi Appelt. Reprinted by permission of Harcourt, Inc.

"A Letter from the Fringe" by Joan Bauer, copyright © 2001 by Joan Bauer, text from *On the Fringe*, edited by Donald R. Gallo. Used by permission of Dial Books for Young Readers, an imprint of Penguin Putnam Books for Young Readers, a division of Penguin Putnam Inc. All rights reserved.

"Looking for Work" by Gary Soto from *Living Up the Street* (Dell, 1993). Copyright © 1985 by Gary Soto. Reprinted by permission of the author.

"The Metaphor" by Budge Wilson from *The Leaving* (Stoddart Publishing). Copyright © 1990 by Budge Wilson. Reprinted by permission of the author.

"Mrs. Goldwasser" from the poem "Teachers: a Primer" by Ronald Wallace from *Time's Fancy*. Copyright © 1994 by Ronald Wallace. Reprinted by permission of the University of Pittsburgh Press.

"Muffin Explains Teleology to the World at Large" by James Alan Gardner from *Amazing Stories*. Copyright © 1990 by James Alan Gardner. Reprinted by permission of the author.

"The Night the Bear Ate Goombaw" by Patrick F. McManus from *The Night the Bear Ate Goombaw*. Copyright © 1989 by Patrick F. McManus. Reprinted by permission of Henry Holt & Company, LLC.

"The One Who Watches" by Judith Ortiz Cofer from *An Island Like You*. Copyright © 1995 by Judith Ortiz Cofer. Reprinted by permission of Orchard Books, an imprint of Scholastic Inc.

"Pig Brains" by Alden R. Carter. Copyright © 2000 by Alden R. Carter. Reprinted by permission of John Hawkins & Associates, Inc.